MYELINATION

Publication Number 782
AMERICAN LECTURE SERIES®

A Monograph in
The BANNERSTONE DIVISION *of*
AMERICAN LECTURES IN LIVING CHEMISTRY

Edited by

I. NEWTON KUGELMASS, M.D., Ph.D., Sc.D.
Consultant to the Departments of Health and Hospitals
New York City

MYELINATION

By

A.N. DAVISON, B.Pharm.,
Ph.D., D.Sc., F.P.S.
Professor of Biochemistry
Charing Cross Hospital Medical School
London, England

ALAN PETERS, B.Sc., Ph.D.
Chairman and Professor
Department of Anatomy
Boston University School of Medicine
Boston, Massachusetts

With Contributions by

J. McC. HOWELL
Department of Veterinary Pathology
The University of Liverpool
Liverpool, England

J.E. VAUGHN
Department of Anatomy
Boston University School of Medicine
Boston, Massachusetts

L.I. WOOLF
Division of Neurological Sciences
Faculty of Medicine
The University of British Columbia
Vancouver, Canada

CHARLES C THOMAS · PUBLISHER
Springfield · *Illinois* · *U.S.A.*

Published and Distributed Throughout the World by

CHARLES C THOMAS • PUBLISHER

BANNERSTONE HOUSE

301-327 East Lawrence Avenue, Springfield, Illinois, U.S.A.

NATCHEZ PLANTATION HOUSE

735 North Atlantic Boulevard, Fort Lauderdale, Florida, U.S.A.

With THOMAS BOOKS *careful attention is given to all details of manufacturing and design. It is the Publisher's desire to present books that are satisfactory as to their physical qualities and artistic possibilities and appropriate for their particular use.* THOMAS BOOKS *will be true to those laws of quality that assure a good name and good will.*

Printed in the United States of America
N-10

FOREWORD

OUR LIVING CHEMISTRY SERIES was conceived by Editor and Publisher to advance the newer knowledge of chemical medicine in the cause of clinical practice. The interdependence of chemistry and medicine is so great that physicians are turning to chemistry, and chemists to medicine in order to understand the underlying basis of life processes in health and disease. Once chemical truths, proofs, and convictions become foundations for clinical phenomena, key hybrid investigators clarify the bewildering panorama of biochemical progress for application in everyday practice, stimulation of experimental research, and extension of postgraduate instruction. Each of our monographs thus unravels the chemical mechanisms and clinical management of many diseases that have remained relatively static in the minds of medical men for three thousand years. Our new Series is charged with the *nisus élan* of chemical wisdom, supreme in choice of international authors, optimal in standards of chemical scholarship, provocative in imagination for experimental research, comprehensive in discussions of scientific medicine, and authoritative in chemical perspective of human disorders.

Dr. Davison of London and Dr. Peters of Boston present the newer knowledge of the formation, structure, chemistry, and metabolism of myelin and its pathology, especially in experimental demyelinating disorders. It gives us an insight into the development of the myelin sheath, the abnormalities in human metabolism, and the spectrum of myelin disorders in domestic animals. The myelin sheath is a highly organized structure with chemical building blocks regularly arranged in a definite order. It contains 22 percent protein and 78 percent lipid of equal molar ratios of cholesterol and phospholipids with about half as much galactolipid. The lipids in myelin sheath undergo little turnover once deposited at the time of its formation, but myelin remains metabolically active. It is of considerable interest since white matter

v

accounts for about a third of total cerebral oxygen consumption and the glial cells utilize two thirds of this. Peripheral nerve myelin differs chemically from central nervous tissue myelin, but the building blocks are similar in both tissues with the exception of triglycerides present in peripheral nerves, but not in cerebral white matter.

Neuropathology, founded at the beginning of this century by Nissl and Ramon y Cajal has stood the test of time despite modern technical advances. The pioneers were led on by the hope that the study of the diseased brain would lead to the interpretation of all disorders of action and conduct. Some who found this quest unrewarding were diverted to the more hopeful approach offered by psychopathology, but those who followed the older discipline have been encouraged by seeing the return of a more organic conception of many disorders of behavior. Each lobe of the brain has now its own symptomatology and the relation of hypothalamic, thalamic, and rhinencephalic centers to emotion and emotional expression is becoming better understood. The study of myelin is thus a necessary step in the march to the understanding of the ultimate physiologic responsibility of the nervous system, i.e. of behavior.

Neurons reach their maximum number in the human brain before birth, and the major increase in the mass of the brain postnatally is in the white matter accompanying myelination of the axons emanating from the nerve cells. Myelination of CNS nerve fibers begins about the fourth month of fetal life with all principal tracts showing abundant myelin by the end of the second year of life. Early myelin, composed of unchanged neuroglial plasma membrane, undergoes gradual transition to adult myelin by the incorporation of cerebroside. The myelination process provides an ideal system in which to study the molecular mechanism of lipid-protein synthesis and membrane formation. Our understanding of myelin formation and destruction was limited by the fact that preparations of the whole brain of small laboratory animals were used as the tissue for study, and little attempt was made to differentiate between truly neural activities and those due to the presence of glial tissue. Myelination inhibition can result from nutritional deficiency or hormonal imbalance. Myelin breakdown destroys body functions in demyelinating diseases with relative sparing of the axons but appears secondary in infectious, toxic, deficiency, or degenerative diseases of the nervous system. The final solution to the enigma of demyelinating disease lies merely in the resolution of unanswered questions which constitute the gaps in our full understanding of the immunologic processes. This story of myelination represents the culmination of the cooperative and intense efforts of five experts in the field whose integrated thoughts are crystallized in this work, opened with expectation and closed with profit.

A mighty maze but not without a plan.

I. NEWTON KUGELMASS, M.D., PH.D., SC.D., *Editor*

INTRODUCTION

D URING EVOLUTION THE nervous system has become increasingly intricate. The overall architecture has become more complex, and the morphology and relations between the component cells, both neurons and neuroglial cells (supporting cells), have undergone considerable modification. As a part of the increasing complexity, the cells seem to acquire more specialized functions. For example, the central nervous systems of invertebrates and of lower chordates appear to have only one type of neuroglial cell. This cell has many branching processes, and it seems to correspond to the astrocytes of higher vertebrates. Although such cells are capable of providing multilayered sheaths around axons, they do not seem able to produce compact myelin of the form which results from the spiraling of a single process around an axon. This form of ensheathment is the prerogative of a type of neuroglial cell, the oligodendrocyte, which is found only in higher vertebrates. Thus in insects, which have no oligodendrocytes, axonal sheaths composed of multiple layers of neuroglial cells are common, but the layers are not compact. A partial compaction is present in the sheaths of the nerve cord of the earthworm, but it is far from complete and is unlike the myelin sheaths of vertebrates. Moreover, there are no interruptions in the sheaths that correspond to the nodes of Ranvier. A possible exception to the lack of compact myelin in lower animals may occur in the brain of the crab. There the nerve fibers are surrounded by sheaths that appear to have all of the characteristics of vertebrate myelin, but this observation needs further confirmation.

In higher vertebrates, compact myelin is formed by two different types of cells. In the peripheral nervous system it is formed by Schwann cells, and in the central nervous system, by the oligodendrocytes. Something of the activity of these myelin-forming cells may be judged from the fact that in the fiber tracts of the central and peripheral nervous systems, the myelin, which is composed of

lipoprotein, is so abundant that it makes up as much as one half
of the dry weight of the tissue. Not all of the Schwann cells and
oligodendrocytes participate in the formation of myelin, for some
Schwann cells surround small-diameter axons which are fitted into
troughs indenting the Schwann cell surface. These are the unmyelinated axons of the peripheral nervous system. The oligodendrocytes that do not partake in the formation of myelin are mainly
found in the grey matter of the central nervous system where they
form satellite cells to neurons.

Myelin sheaths are absent in the early developmental stages
of the vertebrate nervous system, so that in this respect the nervous systems of immature vertebrates are similar to those of the
lower forms. However, in vertebrates myelin sheaths appear when
the population of neurons has been established. Presumably this
is related to the formation of connections between neurons and
the beginning of neural functioning, since the main role of the
myelin seems to be that of an insulator which facilitates the conduction of the nerve impulse along an axon. Consequently, the
study of myelin both from the point of view of its mode of formation and its biochemical composition is of great importance in
studies of all aspects of brain development. In addition, myelin is
important for other types of investigations. For example, because
it can be readily isolated, myelin provides a ready source of plasma
membranes, albeit of a rather specialized nature. Also, data from
studies of myelinogenesis may be used to indicate how membranes
are synthesized and may provide information that can be applied
to other membrane systems. Furthermore, the arrays of repeating
myelin lamellae are particularly suitable for studies utilizing
physical techniques such as low angle x-ray reflection and electron
microscopy. Indeed, it is through a study of myelin sheaths that
many of the current theories on membrane structure have been
derived.

As mentioned above, it is generally agreed that the myelin
sheath provides a strategically placed barrier to ionic current, for
it effectively diminishes the membrane capacitance between the
interruptions of the sheath that occur at the nodes of Ranvier.
However, it is not clear exactly how vital a role is played by the

myelin sheath in the activities of the nervous system. Certainly, damage to the myelin sheaths, as occurs in the demyelinating diseases and in some leukodystrophies, results in serious neurological disorders. This applies particularly to the myelin in the central nervous system in which remyelination after damage is rare. In the developing nervous system, failure to synthesize myelin may also lead to irreversible deficiencies, since central myelination is for the most part a "once and for all" process. The period of myelination may therefore be regarded as a vulnerable one during ontogeny, for a deficiency occurring at that time is difficult to repair at a later stage in development. For example, even mild undernutrition or amino acid imbalance in the brain during this critical period may result in a permanent myelin deficiency.

Some investigations have shown an impairment of intellectual development in undernourished children, and it is known that mental ability is usually adversely affected by phenylketonuria and by hypothyroidism. Whether the deficiency in myelination present in these conditions can be related to the observed low intellect has not been ascertained. In order to obtain such a correlation, we need to know more about the process of myelination, and we need additional structural and biochemical data from patients with disorders such as phenylketonuria. Such information may eventually make it possible to recognize which phases in myelin synthesis are vulnerable to different metabolic deficiencies.

In the first part of this book, the morphology of the developing and mature sheath is described. Peripheral and central myelin sheaths are compared, and the role of oligodendroglia in forming central myelin sheaths is reviewed. This is followed by an account of the biochemistry of myelin. These accounts provide a necessary framework for the studies on pathological material that are discussed in later chapters. Thus, in Chapter 3 amyelination in domestic animals is described, while in Chapter 4 an account is given of some of the disturbances in amino acid biochemistry which lead to incomplete myelination and other neurological disorders. It is hoped that these latter chapters will indicate some of the lines along which pathological research might progress. On the basis of these different approaches by the morphologist, the biochemist and the pathologist, it is hoped that it will be apparent that the acquisition of knowledge about myelin is not only of considerable fundamental interest but also of special relevance to an understanding of many neurological disorders.

CONTENTS

                                                                 Page

Foreword   v

Introduction   ix

Chapter

1. MORPHOLOGY AND DEVELOPMENT OF THE MYELIN SHEATH

   Alan Peters and James E. Vaughn   3

   Introduction   3

   The Peripheral Nervous System   7

   The Central Nervous System   37

2. THE BIOCHEMISTRY OF THE MYELIN SHEATH

   A. N. Davison   80

   The Chemical Composition of the
       Adult Myelin Sheath   80

   Developing Nervous Tissue   97

   The Metabolism of Myelin   125

   Lipid Metabolism at the Cellular Level   140

   Conclusion   143

3. MYELINATION AND DISEASES OF THE NERVOUS SYSTEM:
   ABNORMALITIES OF MYELIN COMPOSITION

   A. N. Davison   162

   Dysmyelination   163

   Damage to Myelin During Development   166

   Demyelination   173

4. MYELIN DEFICIENCIES RELATED TO INBORN ERRORS OF
   HUMAN METABOLISM

   L. I. Woolf   183

   Phenylketonuria   183

   Maple Syrup Urine Disease (Leucinosis)   190

   Conclusions   194

5. DISEASES AFFECTING MYELINATION IN DOMESTIC ANIMALS

J. McC. Howell 199
   Introduction 199
   Hypomyelinogenesis Congenita 199
   Lesions Associated with Copper Deficiency 209
   Lipid Dystrophies 215
   Conclusion 222

Postscript 229
Index 233

MYELINATION

Chapter 1

MORPHOLOGY AND DEVELOPMENT
OF THE MYELIN SHEATH

ALAN PETERS AND JAMES E. VAUGHN*

INTRODUCTION

IN THE PERIPHERAL and central nervous systems, the axons are of two types, myelinated and unmyelinated; and in the present account we shall be mainly concerned with the myelinated ones. Such axons are surrounded by segments of myelin that are termed internodes, and the periodic interruptions that occur between these segments are the nodes of Ranvier.

Light microscope investigations have provided much of the essential data on the structure of myelinated nerve fibers and their associated cells. This is especially true of the peripheral nervous system where it was possible to obtain a good deal of information from the examination of unfixed and teased preparations of nerve fibers. A recent review by Bunge (1968) provides a useful account of this era of investigation that preceded the development of chemical fixatives and stains.

The complete morphology of nerve fibers and of the nervous system in general cannot be studied in a single type of light microscope preparation. This has forced the neuroanatomist to employ a series of different techniques, each of which demonstrates a specific component of the nerve fiber — almost to the complete exclusion of all other components. Thus, the axis cylinder or axon is revealed by the silver impregnation methods largely evolved by Ramon y Cajal, Golgi, and Bielschowsky; but these techniques do not show the myelin sheath except as a halo surrounding the axon. One chemical that produces a positive image of the myelin sheath is osmic acid. This reagent may be used either directly as a fixative

*The authors wish to thank Patricia Hinds, Charmian Proskauer, and Larry McCarthy for their help in the preparation of the material and illustrations for this chapter. The work was supported by United States Public Health Service Grant No. NB-07016 and by the United Cerebral Palsy Research and Educational Foundation.

or as a stain for tissue fixed by some other means. It renders myelin black, and the myelin sheath appears as a dark cylinder that is interrupted along its length by nodes of Ranvier, the term *node* being used because of the resemblance which they bear to the nodes of a bamboo stalk. When material is treated with either osmic acid or histochemical reagents that reveal the presence of lipids (e.g. Sudan black B), axons are revealed only as central lucid areas surrounded by a tube of stained myelin.

Reticular patterns are apparent in myelin sheaths contained within preparations stained with methylene blue and to a certain extent with other common histological stains such as hematoxylin and eosin. This reticular network is called neurokeratin, and methods that reveal neurokeratin frequently stain the nuclei of the Schwann cells of the peripheral nerve fibers. These Schwann cell nuclei are elongated, and there seems to be one nucleus for each internodal length of peripheral myelin. Similar nuclei are not intimately associated with the myelin sheaths of the central nervous system, although the nuclei of neuroglial (supporting) cells can be seen interspersed between the myelinated fibers in the white matter of the brain and spinal cord.

The inadequacies of the light microscope methods have led to numerous controversies about the structure of the nerve fibers in both the peripheral and central nervous systems. It is not our intention to discuss these older disagreements in this chapter. For a comprehensive treatment of this subject, reference should be made to Causey (1960), Thomas (1963), and Bunge (1968).

Work on the detailed structure of myelin began in the 1930's. Interest in the subject was stimulated by the polarization studies of Schmidt (1936) and the early x-ray diffraction work of F. O. Schmitt and his colleagues (e.g. Schmitt and Bear, 1939; Schmitt, Bear, and Palmer, 1941), which led to the suggestion that the myelin sheath is constructed from layers, or lamellae. The lamellae are repeating units which are of the order of 170 to 180 Å (17-18 nm) thick in peripheral myelin sheaths. Changes in birefringence after nerve samples had been treated with alcohol suggested that the lipid molecules within the myelin lamellae are arranged radially and that the proteins are oriented in a tangential plane. This work was followed by that of Finean (1953a, 1953b, and 1965) who interpreted the low-angle x-ray diffraction and electron microscope data to indicate that each myelin lamella contains two bimolecular lipid layers about 55 Å thick, alternating with protein layers about 30 Å thick (Fig. 1-1). Consequently, the whole repeating unit, consisting of two of each of these layers, is about 170 to 180 Å in width, depending upon the state of hydra-

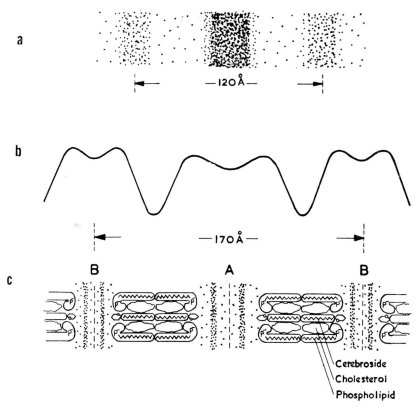

FIGURE 1-1. Molecular Organization of Myelin. The top diagram (*a*) shows the appearance of the myelin sheath in electron micrographs stained by osmium tetroxide. The dense zone in the middle represents the major dense line, and the less dense zones, the intraperiod lines. The middle diagram (*b*) shows the electron density profile, and the narrow pairs of peaks correspond to the major dense lines. The lower diagram (*c*) shows the scheme for the molecular organization proposed by Finean. (By courtesy of Dr. J. B. Finean and Elsevier Publishing Co.)

tion of the myelin. Differences have been noted in the electron density distribution curves for peripheral and central myelin of different species; the range of the periodicities is 171 to 182 Å for peripheral myelin and 153 to 159 Å for central myelin (Worthington and Blaurock, 1968). The two bimolecular lipid leaflets making up each myelin unit can be related to a center of symmetry (the intraperiod line) as would be expected if the mode of myelin formation is from two oppositely oriented thicknesses of Schwann or neuroglial cell plasma membrane (see below).

The conclusion based on polarization microscopy and x-ray diffraction analyses were directly confirmed by the electron microscope studies of Sjöstrand (1950) and Fernandéz-Morán (1950), who demonstrated that myelin is built up of multiple membrane layers. Quite soon the development of techniques such as osmium fixation and methacrylate embedding led to the availability of thin sections of material. It was then found that myelin consists of a repeating structure of alternating dark and light concentric lines: the dark electron-dense line is considered to be the polar region where lipid and protein interact, while the lighter area is thought to be the hydrophobic lipid region (Fig. 1-2). The evidence now available indicates that the repeating subunit of myelin lamellae is composed of two subunits, each one consisting of a bimolecular leaflet of lipid sandwiched between monolayers of protein. Each of these subunits is a single layer of plasma membrane of the myelin-forming cell, so that the 170 to 180 Å repeating unit which is found in x-ray diffraction studies of peripheral myelin, for example, corresponds to two thicknesses of plasma membrane. This unit is somewhat thicker than the one found in the earlier electron microscope studies of osmium-fixed tissue, namely 115 to 125 Å, and the difference between the two values may be attributed to the shrinkage that takes place when such tissue is prepared for electron microscopy. More recent studies with primary aldehyde fixation show myelin periods closer to those obtained in x-ray diffraction studies, namely 160 to 180 Å.

This chapter is primarily concerned with the formation and structure of the myelin sheath from the perspective of electron microscopy, but where appropriate, investigations utilizing other techniques have also been cited.

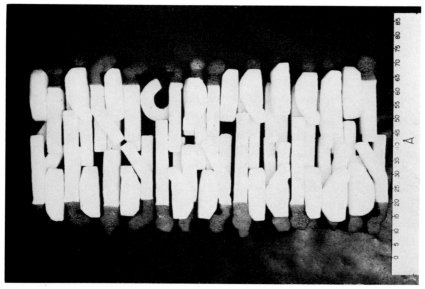

FIGURE 1-2. Molecular model of central nervous system myelin. The long lipid aceyl moieties are assembled in a bilayer with a distance of 55 to 60 Å between the polar groups (black) at their outer ends. In the middle the lipid molecules of the two layers interdigitate. The smaller and irregular shaped blocks towards the outer edges of the bilayer represent cholesterol, and the hook like configuration represents a polyunsaturated fatty acid. (By courtesy of Dr. J. S. O'Brien and the *Journal of Theoretical Biology,* vol. 15, 1967.)

THE PERIPHERAL NERVOUS SYSTEM

Schwann Cell Migration into Developing Nerves

It is generally accepted that Schwann cells migrate into developing peripheral nerves from the neural crest (Harrison, 1924), although there is still some doubt about their precise embryonic derivation (e.g. see Weston, 1963). In any case, the migration of Schwann cells lags behind the outgrowth of the axons, and Speidel (1964) has demonstrated that in the tails of living tadpoles peripheral nerve fibers develop in the following manner. A pioneer axon extends peripherally from a neuron, and its tip advances by means of an amoeboid growth cone. Soon other axons follow the path of the pioneer axon, and these are closely followed by the Schwann cells. After their initial migration into the developing peripheral nerves, the Schwann cells increase in number by mitosis (Speidel, 1964; Peters and Muir, 1959), and Asbury (1967) has shown that at least in the mouse sciatic nerve, the Schwann cell division continues until the second postnatal week. However, he points out that almost three quarters of the cells are no longer proliferating by the second postnatal day. Presumably it is these nonproliferating cells which become engaged in the formation of the myelin sheaths that are produced at a rapid rate during the first postnatal week.

Once Schwann cells begin their initial migration into peripheral nerve trunks, they soon form a complete layer surrounding the entire bundle of the young nerve fibers (Figs. 1-3 and 1-4A), which are thereby separated from the surrounding tissues. This phase of development was shown by both Kölliker (1884) and Held (1909), whose illustrations depict embryonic nerves to be

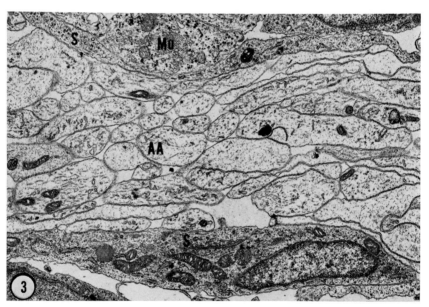

FIGURE 1-3. Small peripheral nerve bundle in the vicinity of the developing extra-ocular muscle (*Mu*) of a rat fetus, fifteenth day of gestation. The bundle is surrounded by Schwann cells (*S*). All of the axons (*AA*) are unmyelinated at this stage of development, and the Schwann cells have not yet migrated into the interior of the nerve bundle. X12,000.

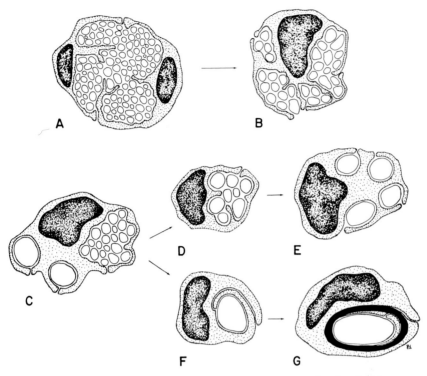

FIGURE 1-4. Diagram illustrating the sequence of stages in the development of a peripheral nerve. For further explanation see text.

composed of a tube of Schwann cells surrounding a light central region devoid of cells. More recent studies by Peters and Muir (1959) and Peters (1961a) have shown that the light central zone consists of many small axons closely packed together with no cells or cellular processes intervening between them (Fig. 1-3). Gamble and Breathnach (1965) and Gamble (1966) have confirmed this observation at a similar stage of development of human peripheral nerves.

With the formation of a complete layer of Schwann cells around the outside of a young nerve, the Schwann cells next start to invade the central core of axons, which at this stage of maturation are extremely small, each axon being only 0.2μ to 0.5μ in diameter (Peters and Muir, 1959; Peters, 1961a). As shown at the

beginning of this century by Gurwitsch (1900), these invading
Schwann cells form partitions between the axons (Fig. 1-4A and
B), and the partitioning progresses until the axons are separated
into small bundles. Local mitotic divisions provide the increase in
the number of Schwann cells that are required for this partitioning of the central mass of axons, and in the rat phrenic nerve both
the Schwann cells at the periphery and those that are invading the
axons undergo mitosis (Peters and Muir, 1959). Exact details of
the events that take place when the Schwann cells invade the
central core of axons are unknown. Electron microscope studies
have shown, however, that the partitioning effected by the invading Schwann cells leads to the formation of smaller groups of
axons and that each group is completely surrounded by Schwann
cells (Figs. 1-4C and 1-5). Although the number of axons in such
groups may vary, Gamble and Breathnach (1965) have shown
that in the ulnar nerve of a fourteen-week-old human fetus for
example, ninety or more axons may be enclosed within a single
Schwann cell. As the Schwann cells increase in number, individual
cells contain progressively smaller groups of axons; during this
process some axons, usually the largest ones present within the
nerve, gradually become individually separated from their fellows
(Fig. 1-5). Sometimes only one larger axon is related to a Schwann
cell (Fig. 1-4F), but in other cases one or two large axons may be
separately enclosed by a Schwann cell that elsewhere on its surface
also encloses a small group of axons (Figs. 1-4C and 1-5). It must
be emphasized that there is no definite sequence of events whereby
the original core of axons is first completely segregated into small
groups from which individual axons are then separated. Rather,
these two events take place simultaneously. Nevertheless, there is
a general developmental pattern that is directed toward a separation of each axon from all other axons within the nerve. The time
at which this phase of differentiation is attained varies even in
different peripheral nerves of the same animal.

    As mentioned above, certain Schwann cells enclose only one
axon (Fig. 1-4F). Such axons are generally among the largest ones
in the nerve, and these are the ones that are destined to be myelinated. It would appear that a diameter of about 2μ is the critical

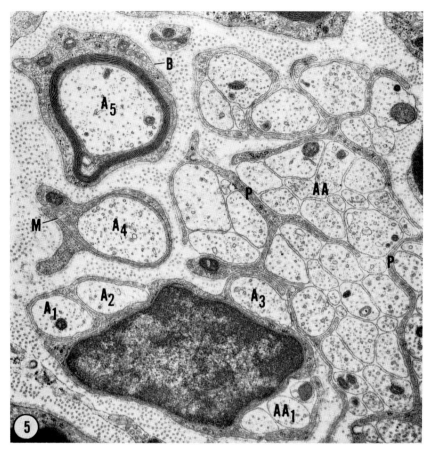

FIGURE 1-5. An electron micrograph of transversely sectioned, developing scaitic nerve from a nine-day-postnatal rat. Numerous unmyelinated axons (*AA*) are being subdivided into progressively smaller fascicles by attenuated Schwann cell processes (*P*). The Schwann cell at the bottom of this figure encloses six axons; three axons (*AA$_1$*) are in a group and the remainder (*A$_1$-A$_3$*) are enclosed in individual pockets. Another axon in this field (*A$_4$*) has been wrapped by one turn of the mesaxon (*M*). Compact myelin sheaths surround larger axons (*A$_5$*). Each Schwann cell has a basal lamina (*B*) outside of which are collagen fibers. X20,000.

size an axon must attain before it qualifies to be the only axon enclosed by a Schwann cell. The other axons, the ones not destined to myelinate, also eventually become individually enveloped by Schwann cells. But in this case the enclosure is such that in the mature animal a number of axons occupy the same Schwann cell, each axon being enclosed in its own separate pocket at a different location on the Schwann cell surface (Fig. 1-4E).

So far the description of peripheral nerve maturation has been given in terms of the events seen in transverse sections of nerves. It is obvious, however, that the same sequence of events is taking place along the whole length of a developing peripheral nerve and that over its total extent every axon has many Schwann cells related to it. The Schwann cells related to an axon are arranged in a series, and as it transverses the distance between the peripheral end organ and the bounds of the central nervous system, the axon is passed on from the territory of one Schwann cell to that of another. It is also clear from the studies carried out by Speidel (1964) that the process of maturation of a peripheral nerve follows a proximodistal gradient, so that the proximal portion of an axon may begin to myelinate while the distal portion is still extending and sending out a growth cone.

The Schwann cells that form the series along the lengths of unmyelinated axons tend to overlap and interdigitate, so that their territories are not distinct (Elfvin, 1958). On the other hand, the Schwann cells surrounding an axon which is destined to myelinate show little overlap. Instead, there are intervals between them. These intervals are the ultimate locations of the nodes of Ranvier of the mature myelinated nerve fibers, and the Schwann cells between these locations will each form an internodal myelin segment.

Before turning to the question of how the myelin sheath is formed, it is pertinent to mention that the decision about whether an axon should be unmyelinated or myelinated seems to rest with the axon itself. Thus Speidel (1964) has differentiated between myelin-emergent fibers (i.e. the unensheathed distal portions of fibers that are already myelinated more proximally) and nonmyelin-emergent fibers. He points out that there is a special affinity between myelin-emergent fibers and Schwann cells and that this affinity is greater than the one which exists between Schwann cells and nonmyelin-emergent fibers. Thus he considers Schwann cells to move preferentially towards myelin-emergent fibers. This would favor an early completion of myelin formation along these fibers or axons. The role played by the axon in determining the type of ensheathment is also shown in the experiments of Hillårp and Olivercrona (1946), who connected the severed end of the phrenic nerve of a rat to the distal stump of a postganglionic cervical sympathetic nerve. They found that when the phrenic nerve axons grew into the autonomic nerve, whose Schwann cells do not form myelin in the normal animal, they became myelinated. For a fuller account of the factors influencing the growth of peripheral nerves, reference should be made to the reviews of Weiss (1941 and 1955), Speidel (1964), and Hughes (1968).

The Formation of Peripheral Myelin

The formation of peripheral myelin sheaths was first studied with the electron microscope by Geren in 1954. She postulated that the myelin sheath consists of a greatly extended Schwann cell membrane wrapped in a spiral manner around the enclosed axon, and her postulation was soon supported by Robertson (1955), who showed the structure of the myelin sheath to be in accord with Geren's model of myelin formation. On the basis of the evidence presently available, the formation of peripheral myelin may be visualized in the following way.

During development, an axon that is destined to become myelinated lies in a furrow or groove indenting the Schwann cell in the direction of its long axis (Fig. 1-6A), and it appears that before myelination can start, this must be the only axon related to the Schwann cell. The furrow containing the axon then deepens, and its free edges extend towards each other until they come into close approximation (Fig. 1-6B). This leads to the complete envelopment of the axon by the Schwann cell, and where the edges of the furrow meet, the outer surface of their bounding plasma membranes come into apposition to form the mesaxon. At this

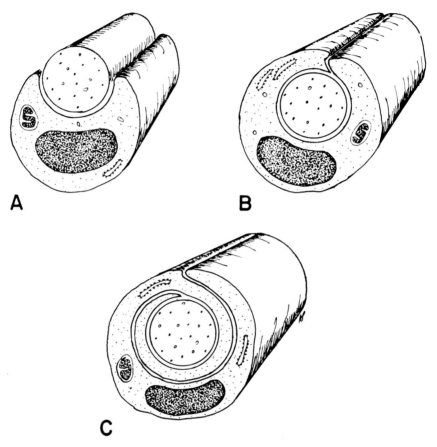

FIGURE 1-6. Diagrammatic representation of stages in the formation of a peripheral myelin sheath. In an early stage (*A*) an axon is partially surrounded by a Schwann cell whose enveloping lips come together (*B*) to form a mesaxon. The mesaxon subsequently elongates (*C*) to form a spiral around the enclosed axon.

time the relation between the enclosed axon and the Schwann cell is very similar to that existing in a mature peripheral nerve between unmyelinated axons and Schwann cells, although only one instead of many axons is enveloped by the Schwann cell prior to myelin formation. The name mesaxon was first introduced by Gasser (1952) because of the similarity between the double membrane structure "suspending" the enclosed axon and the mesentery suspending the intestine. Since an understanding of the form of the plasma membrane and the mesaxon is essential to comprehend the next steps in myelin formation, at this point it is necessary to consider the electron microscope appearance of these two structures.

In electron microscope preparations of all tissues fixed either directly with osmic acid, or secondarily with osmic acid after a primary fixation in aldehyde solutions (formaldehyde and glu-taraldehyde), it is common to stain the section with both lead salts and uranyl acetate. Then a plasma membrane appears in low-resolution electron micrographs as a dark line 70 to 75 Å thick, bounding a cell. At higher resolution, however, a plasma membrane has a three-layered structure and consists of two dark lines or leaflets each 20 to 25 Å thick, separated by a lighter interval (Figs. 1-12 and 1-28). In such preparations it is also clear that the plasma membrane is not symmetrical in form, for the dark leaflet adjacent to the cytoplasm is more dense than the leaflet on the outside.

When the edges of the furrow containing the axon come to-gether, their plasma membranes become parallel to each other, and for the most part they are separated by a gap of 130 to 165 Å (Fig. 1-6B). However, there may be one point at the outer end of the mesaxon where the plasma membranes approach closer to each other and appear to fuse.

The form of the mesaxon can often be very complex as in Figure 1-10, which shows an extreme example of complexity in which the lips of the enveloping Schwann cell interdigitate ex-tensively. But once a mesaxon is formed, it soon proceeds to elongate (Figs. 1-5 A_1 and 1-6C). The elongation of the mesaxon takes place in a basically spiral fashion, and this leads to the pro-duction of a loosely coiled mesaxon, which has cytoplasm inter-vening between successive turns (Fig. 1-7). Even this spiral may be very irregular, for various turns, usually the outer ones, may loop back on themselves for some distance before continuing into the basic spiral. Once a few, but varying number of turns have been completed, however, the cytoplasm is lost from between them. Sometimes the cytoplasm seems to be lost simultaneously

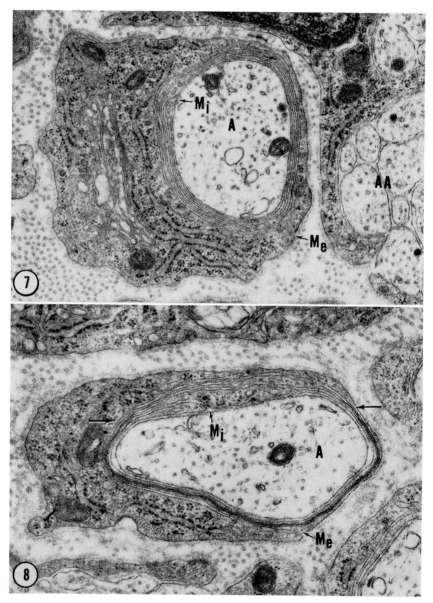

FIGURES 1-7 and 1-8. Both figures are of developing sciatic nerves of nine-day-postnatal rats. In Figure 1-7 a nerve fibre (*A*) is surrounded by a developing myelin sheath which is composed of loose turns of the mesaxon. The internal (M_i) and the external (M_e) ends of the mesaxon are indicated. The rest of the axons (*AA*) in this field are unmyelinated. X31,000. In Figure 1-8 the sheath of the nerve fibre (*A*) is formed of loose turns of the mesaxon on the side of the fiber (between arrows) where the internal mesaxon (M_i) is located. Throughout the remainder of the sheath the turns of the mesaxon have become apposed to form compact myelin. The external mesaxon (M_e) is located adjacent to compact myelin. X37,000.

throughout the entire spiral, so that the apposition of the cytoplasmic surface of the consecutive turns of the mesaxon leads to
the formation of compact myelin throughout the sheath. In other
examples, though, cytoplasm may be retained for a time in some
portions of the spiral, with the result that part of the myelin is
loose (Fig. 1-8).

From the mode of its formation it can be readily seen that
compact myelin consists of multiple layers of Schwann cell plasma
membrane, and in all sheaths a situation is ultimately attained in
which cytoplasm is retained to any extent on only the inside and
the outside of the myelin. It is in the cytoplasm that forms a
complete layer on the outside of the myelin that the Schwann-
cell nucleus lies (Fig. 1-11). It will be seen later, however, that
there are localized zones in the mature sheath where helices of
cytoplasm do intervene between the successive lamellae. These
zones are the Schmidt-Lantermann clefts or incisures (see Figs.
1-18 and 1-19). The original form of the mesaxon is still retained
at the ends of the spiral which transverse the inner and outer
layers of cytoplasm (Figs. 1-9 and 1-10), and these ends are thereafter referred to as the inner and outer mesaxons. At least in our
material the intraperiod line (see below) does not extend into
the inner and outer mesaxons. The line stops where the mesaxon
leaves the sheath, and its constituent plasma membranes become
separated by an interval of about 130 Å (Fig. 1-12). It is common,
however, for the outer leaflets of the pair of plasma membranes
of the mesaxon to become closely apposed again near the end of
the mesaxon (Fig. 1-12, *Mc*).

When the consecutive turns of the mesaxon come into contact,
the major dense line is formed, and throughout the thickness of
the myelin it alternates with the less dense intraperiod line which
results from the apposition of the outer surface of the same
Schwann cell membranes (Fig. 1-12). Presumably, the difference
in density of these two lines is a reflection of the differences in
the leaflets of the plasma membranes from which they arise. For
as pointed out above, the cytoplasmic leaflet of the plasma membrane is darker than the outer leaflet. It should be mentioned that
compared to mature sheaths, the intraperiod line is not so readily

apparent in the compact myelin of immature sheaths (Fig. 1-13).
This is true even if the same preparative procedures are employed.
While the reasons for this difference remain obscure, in some in-
stances where the intraperiod line has been clearly visualized in

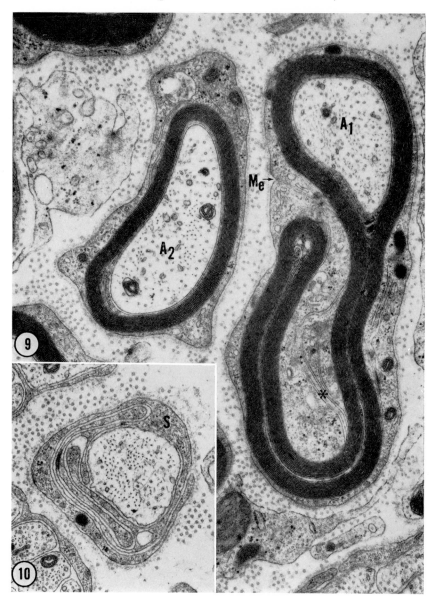

the myelin of young animals, it is apparent that the outer leaflets of the apposed plasma membranes are not fused. Instead, as in mature myelin, they are separated by a gap of 20 to 30 Å (Fig. 1-13, arrow). This suggests that a continuous gap extends from the outer mesaxon, between the myelin lamellae, to the inner mesaxon. In the mature sheath Revel and Hamilton (1969) have shown this gap to be accessible to lanthanum.

The Mechanism of Myelin Formation

Three-dimensionally, the mesaxon of the developing myelin sheath has sheetlike form, and it extends for the entire length of the Schwann cell. Precisely how the mesaxon elongates in a spiral manner around the enclosed axon is not fully understood, but in any event, it involves a tremendous elaboration of Schwann cell plasma membrane.

Various opinions have been expressed about whether the mesaxon elongates by growth at its inner or outer ends. The concept most generally favored is that the active region is associated with the outer end and that the spiral results from a rotation of the Schwann cell around the axon. This would involve one complete rotation of the nucleus for every turn of the mesaxon and hence for the addition of each myelin lamella. Movements of the Schwann cell nucleus consistent with this proposal have been observed in tissue culture by Peterson, Crain, and Murray (1958), Murray (1959, 1964), and Pomerat, Hendelman, Raiborn, and Massey (1967). But Speidel (1964) states that in his observations

←————————

FIGURES 1-9 and 1-10. Transverse sections of the developing sciatic nerve of a nine-day-postnatal rat. In Figure 1-9 a myelinated nerve fiber (A_1) is surrounded by a sheath that is many times too large. The axon (A_1) occupies only a small part of the sheath which extends into a long flap. The sheath terminates in an elongated external mesaxon (M_e), but the internal mesaxon is not apparent. The outer three lamellae of part (asterisk) of the myelin flap are loose. The other nerve fiber in this field (A_2) exhibits the more usual form of myelin sheath seen in both developing and mature peripheral nerves. X27,000. Figure 1-10 illustrates a nerve fiber that is surrounded by a Schwann cell (S), whose lips have come together to form a complex mesaxon. This complex mesaxon can not be interpreted as a spiralled elongation of a simple mesaxon. X30,000.

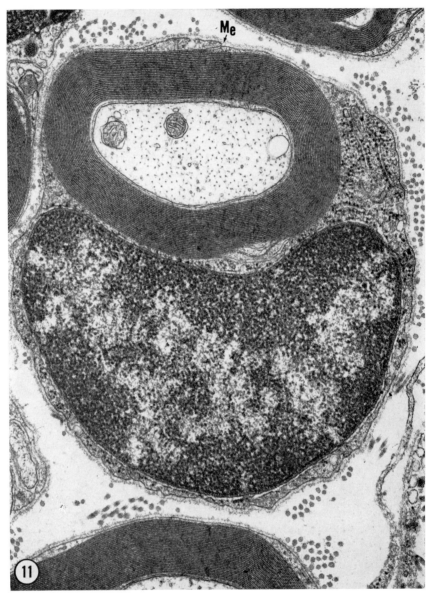

FIGURE 1-11. An adult rat trigeminal nerve fiber sectioned at the level of the Schwann cell nucleus. The external mesaxon (M_e) is clearly visible and can be seen to form the intraperiod line of the surface lamella of the myelin sheath. The intraperiod line alternates with the darker major dense line. X26,000.

on the growing nerve fibers of the tadpole tail, he has failed to observe such a rotation of the Schwann cell nuclei.

Even if the formation of the elongated mesaxon is brought about by a simple rotation of the Schwann cell as it manufactures

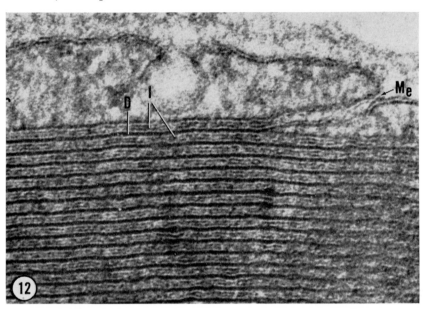

FIGURE 1-12. Enlargement of part of Figure 1-9. This sheath shows the separation of the intraperiod line (*I*) into two thinner lines that have an interval of 20 to 30 Å between them. Notice that in the external mesaxon (*M_e*), the Schwann cell membranes are separated except for a small point of contact where the mesaxon terminates. The major dense line (*D*) shows no similar separation of its components. X252,000.

more layers of plasma membrane, other factors must be involved in the later growth of the myelin. For example, as maturation proceeds, the sheath must expand in size to accommodate the growing axon which is increasing in diameter within it. Conceivably such an increase in the bore of the sheath could be achieved in a number of ways. The myelin sheath could be formed so that initially it is too large for the axon, and indeed such oversized sheaths are sometimes observed (Fig. 1-9,A₁). However, developing myelin sheaths do not always have this form, and most commonly, they fit snugly around the axon (Fig. 1-9,A₂). Then it seems that an increase in the diameter of the sheath could be brought about by either the addition of new material throughout the myelin, slippage of the lamellae over each other, or a combination of these

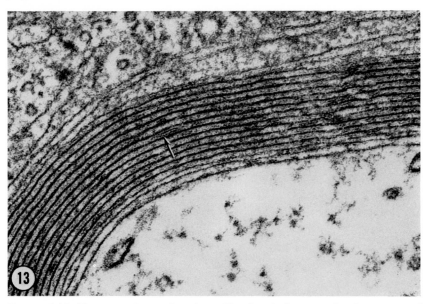

FIGURE 1-13. Transversely sectioned myelin sheath from a nine-day-postnatal rat sciatic nerve. The intraperiod line is not obvious in developing sheaths except at isolated locations (arrow) where two components are visible as in the adult. X140,000.

two. Slippage of the lamella is favored by Hirano and Dembitzer (1967), for they have found that if axons are made edematous and caused to swell, their sheaths expand to accommodate the axons.

During maturation, the myelin lamellae must also elongate in the direction parallel to the long axis of the nerve fiber because the lengths of the myelin segments increase as the animal grows. In no way can slippage account for the growth in this axis, and the only explanation seems to be the addition of new material to the already existing lamellae.

The Mature Myelin Sheath

It should be emphasized that even in mature nerves the myelin sheath is not an absolutely regular and cylindrical structure as depicted in most textbooks of histology. The phase and electron microscope studies of Webster and Spiro (1960) on the sciatic nerves of normal guinea pigs have revealed numerous variations in the contours of myelin sheaths. In general, these variations consist of outfoldings of the myelin that indent the axoplasm or protrude into the outer Schwann cell cytoplasm. Such irregularities are most common in the juxtanodal portion of a myelin segment. In transverse sections of sheaths they can lead to an appearance of isolated ovoids of myelin that are most frequent on the outside of the sheath and seem to be detached from the myelin surrounding the axon.

The basic repeating unit of the myelin sheath is a lamella, and in most preparations fixed primarily or secondarily with osmic acid and stained in section with lead and uranium salts, the periodicity of the lamellae, i.e. the distance between the centers of adjacent major dense lines, is 120 to 130 Å. In such preparations the less dense intraperiod line generally appears to be single, although Sjöstrand (1963), for example, and more recently Mizuhira and Ozawa (1967) have published electron micrographs in which it appears to be split into two thinner lines. As mentioned above, the studies undertaken by Revel and Hamilton (1969), in which the specimens were stained in the block with uranyl acetate, have consistently revealed the intraperiod line to be formed of two parallel thin lines that are separated by a gap of about 20 Å. If glutaraldehyde-fixed material is soaked in lanthanum (Revel and Karnovsky, 1967), then the lanthanum penetrates into this gap, which clearly indicates that the outer faces of the plasma membrane forming the intraperiod line are not actually fused. Rather they are in close apposition to each other. Although the results are rather less striking than those produced by Revel and Hamilton, we have also found that if the electron micrographs are taken close to focus, the splitting of the intraperiod line is also visible in preparations which have been stained with lead and uranyl salts on the section (Fig. 1-12). No similar gap appears between the cytoplasmic surfaces of membranes where they come into apposition to form the major dense line.

The observation that a gap exists within the intraperiod line could explain results like those of Robertson (1961), who found that if peripheral myelin is fixed for a short time in potassium permanganate, the intraperiod line is thin and the major dense line is thick. But if the fixation is prolonged, the intraperiod line thickens until after six hours it assumes the same thickness and intensity as the major dense line. This result could be interpreted to indicate that the gap between the plasma membrane faces at the intraperiod line has become filled with permanganate.

A further item to consider is what constituents of the myelin sheath are being stained and hence made to appear dense in electron microscope preparations. Investigations that have been carried out in the past which have utilized a variety of physical techniques (for reviews of such work see Finean, 1961; Robertson, 1961, 1966; Sjöstrand, 1963) have shown a plasma membrane consisting of a double layer, or a bimolecular leaflet of radially oriented lipid molecules. These are arranged in such a way that their nonpolar groups are directed towards the middle of the membrane. The polar end of each leaflet faces the outside of the membrane when it is covered by a monolayer of protein. Napolitano, LeBaron, and Scaletti (1967) have demonstrated that even if glutaraldehyde-fixed rat sciatic nerves are depleted of 98 percent of their lipids by extraction of the tissue with acetone-chloroform-methanol mixtures, the typical lamellar structure is still apparent after secondary fixation in osmic acid. This indicates that the dark lines apparent in electron micrographs of myelin result from a combination of the stain with the protein and not with lipid molecules.

The difference in intensity of the intraperiod and major dense lines, which is prominent in tissue prepared by conventional techniques, is still apparent after lipid extraction. This strongly suggests that the protein layers on the cytoplasmic and outer faces of the Schwann cell plasma membrane are different. Sjöstrand (1963) suggests that the difference may lie in the thickness of the two protein layers and that the one on the cytoplasmic face of the plasma membrane is thicker than the one on the outer face.

There is considerable variation in the number of myelin lamellae in the sheaths surrounding different axons of mature animals, and it is generally true that the larger the diameter of the axon, the thicker is its myelin sheath. A recent electron microscope study by Friede and Samorajski (1967) has shown that in the vagus and sciatic nerves of mice, the thinnest sheaths consist of only five lamellae, while the thickest have as many as ninety-five. According to Friede and Samorajski the thickness of the myelin sheath, or the number of lamellae that it contains, is directly related to the circumference of the enclosed axon. They chose axonal circumference as a parameter rather than axonal diameter because in their electron microscope preparations, round axonal profiles were uncommon. Most usually the axons were oval or indented. In their fixed material Friede and Samorajski found that above an initial circumferential size of 1.62μ, one lamellae is added to the sheath for each addition of 0.17μ to the circumference.

In addition to this direct relationship between axonal size and myelin thickness, it is known that the lengths of internodal segments (i.e. the length of myelin formed by one Schwann cell) also vary with the size of the axon. However, in most of the studies of internodal length, fiber diameter or the diameter across the outside of the myelin sheath has been used in preference to the thickness of the axon.

The fact that the largest nerve fibers have the greatest internodal lengths was recognized at the end of the last century by Ranvier (1875) and Key and Retzius (1876). More recently this fact has been confirmed, and quantitative data on the relationship between nerve fiber diameter and internodal length has been obtained by Hiscoe (1947), Visozo, and Young (1948), and Thomas and Young (1949). As examples of internodal lengths, Hiscoe (1947) found that in the tibial nerve of the adult rat, small fibers with diameters of 3.5μ have internodes about 350μ long, while the largest fibers of 11.5μ in diameter have internodes that are about 800μ long. Visozo and Young (1948) found similar values in the peroneal nerves of rabbits (see Fig. 1-14), but in fishes (Thomas and Young, 1949) the internodes are much longer. They have a mean value of about $7,000\mu$, which is about five times longer than the maximum length of some $1,500\mu$ for the most extensive internodes that occur in the rabbit.

It is also clear from these three studies that in the same nerve the internodal lengths are smaller in a young animal than in an older animal of greater size. Thus the ultimate lengths of internodes seem to be partially determined by the subsequent growth

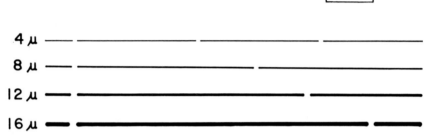

FIGURE 1-14. Scale drawing illustrating the direct relationship between nerve fiber diameters and the lengths of their internodal segments. The values at the left are the diameters of the nerve fibers which are represented by the lines. The gaps in each line represent nodes of Ranvier. The drawing is based on the data of Visozo and Young (1948).

that takes place in an animal once an axon has started to myelinate. This suggestion is supported by a good deal of evidence which indicates that once an axon has received a complement of Schwann cells at the beginning of the myelination process, no further Schwann cells are usually added to the sheath at a later time in development. In other words, the subsequent increase in length that takes place once a nerve fiber has begun to myelinate is accommodated by an increase in internodal length and not by the addition of extra internodes to the sheath. This accounts for the observation that the largest axons, which are the first ones to myelinate in development, have longer internodes than the smaller axons, which begin to myelinate later. It also explains the fact that nerve fibers in the sciatic nerve have longer internodes than the fibers in the facial nerve, for example, since after myelination commences, the linear growth of the limbs is greater than that of the face.

It is relevant to mention that the internodes which are formed when a nerve remyelinates are shorter than those existing in the same nerve prior to it being damaged. The reason for this seems to be that during remyelination, the myelin segments are being formed in a nerve of fixed length, while during normal development, once the internodes have formed, they become longer as the animal grows, and the length of the nerve increases. To illustrate this point, the results obtained by Hiscoe (1947) may be cited. Hiscoe found the average length of internodes forming in re-generating nerve fibers distal to a crush was 0.3mm. This value is similar to the one for the interval between Schwann cells (0.2mm to 0.3mm) in developing peripheral nerves just prior to the begin-ning of myelination (Speidel, 1932, 1933, 1935). It is also of the same order as the minimum length for normal internodes in a number of different animals (Thomas and Young, 1949). The ob-servations of Lascelles and Thomas (1966) also emphasize this point. They found irregularities of internodal lengths in human sural nerves from subjects over sixty-five years of age, for there is a greater number of shorter internodes than in younger subjects. Lascelles and Thomas suggest that these shorter internodes may have resulted from a remyelination of nerve fibers that had regen-erated after being damaged. Lubínska (1958, 1961) has also re-corded the presence of internodes which are much shorter and thinner than those present elsewhere on the nerve fibers and con-siders that these shorter internodes may arise through a restitution of myelin following local neuritis.

The Node of Ranvier

The interruptions or discontinuities in the myelin sheath that bear his name were first described by Ranvier in 1871. Ranvier considered them to represent transverse barriers to keep the mye-lin in position, and although he was incorrect in his interpretation of their function, the existence of the nodes in the peripheral ner-vous system has never been seriously questioned. It is now known that the nodes of Ranvier represent regions of the sheath where adjacent segments of myelin and their associated Schwann cells come together and terminate. Much of the earlier literature on the form of the node has been reviewed by Hess and Young (1952).

Clearly the distance between successive nodes of Ranvier depends upon the lengths of the segments of myelin, so that the nodes become less frequent with increasing fiber diameter. There also seems to be a correlation between the diameter of a nerve fiber and the length of the gap or node between adjacent myelin segments. Thus Hess and Young (1952) have shown that in the rabbit, the large nerve fibers with outside diameters of 18μ have nodes which are only 0.25μ long, while in smaller fibers of 5μ to 7μ in diameter, the length of the node is about 0.5μ. This observation can probably be correlated with that of Speidel (1964), who has found that initially the developing nerves in the tails of tadpoles have quite long nodes of Ranvier, which become shorter as the nerve fiber matures. Some of the decrease in the length of the node during development is undoubtedly due to the spreading out of the myelin from the region of the Schwann cell nucleus.

The detailed structure of the nodes of Ranvier was not fully appreciated until they were studied with the electron microscope (see Uzman and Nogeuira-Graf, 1957; Robertson, 1959; Elfvin, 1961; Webster, 1962; Bargmann and Lindner, 1964; Bunge, Bunge, Peterson, and Murray, 1967). These studies have confirmed that the axon is not covered by myelin at the node and have shown that the myelin lamellae terminate as they approach the node (Fig. 1-15). The region where the lamellae terminate is known as the paranode. In that part of the paranode most distant from the node, the innermost lamellae of the myelin terminate first and succeeding turns of the spiral of lamellae then overlap and project beyond the ones lying beneath. Thus the outermost lamella overlaps all of the others and terminates nearest to the node, so that the myelin sheath gradually becomes thinner as the node is approached.

As the lamellae terminate, the major dense line of the myelin sheath opens up to accommodate cytoplasm. This is the paranodal cytoplasm (Figs. 1-15 and 1-16), and since the lamellae of the sheath are arranged in a spiral whose turns successively overlap each other at the paranode, the paranodal cytoplasm lies in a helical tunnel. Through this tunnel continuity is established between the cytoplasm on the inside and the outside of the myelin.

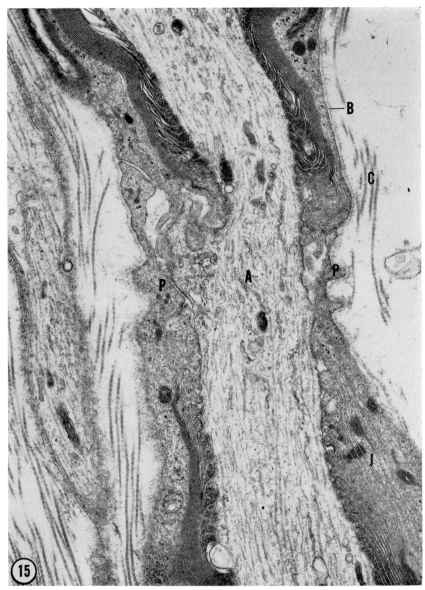

FIGURE 1-15. Longitudinal section of the node of Ranvier of a myelinated nerve fiber from a nine-day-postnatal rat sciatic nerve. Myelin does not cover the nodal axon (A) which is surrounded by interdigitating Schwann cell processes (P). In the paranodal regions the innermost lamellae open first and are successively overlapped by the more superficial ones. Notice the series of puncta adhaerentia (J) occurring between the plasma membranes bounding adjacent pockets of paranodal cytoplasm. The Schwann cells are separated from the collagen fibers (C) of the nerve by a basal lamina (B). X33,000.

In longitudinal sections through the paranodal region, the successive turns of the helix of cytoplasm are apparent as a series of pockets that lie sandwiched between the axon and the myelin lamellae (Figs. 1-15 and 1-16). In smaller nerve fibers most of these pockets extend to the surface of the axon, but in larger fibers their arrangement is usually more irregular; only some of the pockets extend as far as the axon, the remainder stop short, almost as though they cannot find a place on the axonal surface. The cytoplasm of the pockets contains microtubules, vesicles, and dense particles. The microtubules follow the path of the helical tunnel (Hendleman and Bunge, 1966) and the dense particles are aligned adjacent to the Schwann cell plasma membrane facing the axon (Elfvin, 1961; Bunge, Bunge, Peterson, and Murray, 1967). In some example of paranodes, stacks of structures resembling desmosomes are formed between the pairs of membranes separating adjacent pockets of cytoplasm (see Rosenbluth, 1962; Harkin, 1964; Bunge, Bunge, Peterson, and Murray, 1967). These desmosomelike structures closely resemble the puncta adhaerentia described by Palay (1967), for where they occur, there is a local widening of the intercellular space and an associated symmetrical density on the cytoplasmic face of each pair of plasma membranes (Figs. 1-15 and 1-16).*

Along the extent of the paranode, the pockets of cytoplasm bulge into the axon to indent the axolemma (axonal plasma membrane). These indentations occur because the plasma membranes of the axon and the pockets of Schwann cell cytoplasm are so closely apposed. At the paranode these membranes are only separated by a distance of about 30 Å, and they almost seem to be attached, for they lie parallel to each other. In low-magnification electron micrographs of longitudinal sections through the paranode, a row of periodic densities may sometimes be apparent in the interval between the axolemma and the facing Schwann cell membrane bounding the cytoplasmic pockets (Bargmann and

---

*After this manuscript was completed, our attention was drawn to the reports of Berthold and Skoglund (*Acta Soc Med Upsal, 73*:113 and 127, 1968) on the postnatal development of the paranodal region in the peripheral nerves of the cat. Berthold (*Acta Soc Med Upsal, 73*:145, 1968) has also studied the development of the node of Ranvier.

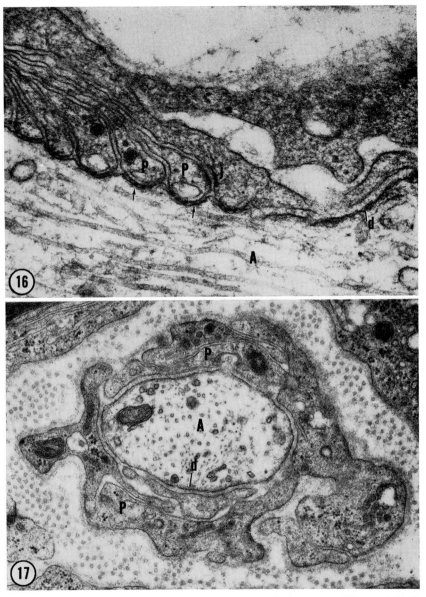

FIGURES 1-16 and 1-17. Nine-day-postnatal rat sciatic nerve. Figure 1-16 is a longitudinal section of part of the node and paranode of a peripheral nerve fiber (A). At the node, the axolemma has a dense undercoating (d). In paranodal regions, the axolemma is indented by cytoplasmic pockets (P), and the outer leaflet of the axolemma shows periodic densities (arrows). Note the punctum adhaerens (J). X74,000. Figure 1-17 is a transverse section through a node of Ranvier. The nodal axon (A) is covered externally by interdigitated Schwann cell processes (P), and its plasma membrane is undercoated by a thin layer of dense material (d). X35,000,

Lindner, 1964; Bunge, Bunge, Peterson, and Murray, 1967). The same appearance is also present in longitudinal sections of the paranodal regions of myelin sheaths of the central nervous system (Andres, 1965; Peters, 1966; Laatsch and Cowan, 1966; Hirano and Dembitzer, 1967) and in high-resolution micrographs it is clear that it is produced by a modification of the outer leaflet of the axolemma (Fig. 1-16). In more obliquely oriented longitudinal sections, these periodicities can be seen to extend into a series of regularly spaced dense bands that circumscribe the axon. Each band is about 150 Å wide and the center-to-center separation between adjacent bands is 250 to 300 Å. Whether each dense band is a complete and separate one encircling the axon or whether there is a set of six to eight separate bands that form a continuous helix which follows and is related to the helix formed by the paranodal cytoplasm is presently unknown (Hirano and Dembitzer, 1967).*

Transverse sections through the paranodal region can be readily recognized by the reduction in the extracellular space between the axolemma and the inside of the sheath as well as by the presence of the broad band of paranodal cytoplasm which lies between the axon and the myelin. In this plane of section, however, the dense bands of the outer leaflet of the axolemma are not readily apparent. Their occurrence is only indicated by discontinuities in the outer leaflet of the axolemma. The outer leaflet is visible when a band is contained within the thickness of the section and is only faintly indicated where the section passes through an interval between bands. The significance of these bands in the outer leaflet of the axolemma is unknown. It has been suggested that the close apposition between the paranodal axolemma and the plasma membrane bounding the inside of the sheath might serve to retard the passage of ions from the extracellular space around the nodal axon into the space between the myelin-forming cell and the internodal axon (Andres, 1965; Peters, 1966). A restriction upon the free flow of ions between these two compartments seems to be necessary if saltatory conduction is to occur.

---

*Hirano and Dembitzer (*J Ultrastruct Res, 28:*141, 1969) have recently shown that lanthanum, used as an electron dense tracer, penetrates the spaces between the dense bands at the paranodes of myelin sheaths in the central nervous system. The tracer also permeates into the intraperiod line of the internodal myelin.

It is relevant to note that Nageotte (1910) described a spiny bracelet in the nodal regions of myelinated axons. These bracelets are visible in light microscope preparations of nerves that are fixed in potassium permanganate and stained with acid fuchsin (Hess and Young, 1952). They appear as a ring of spines that extend outwards from the axon and point away from the node. In retrospect it now seems likely that the bracelets are produced by staining either the entire paranodal cytoplasm or some component contained within it.

Although the node of Ranvier is an interruption of the myelin sheath, the axon in this region is not bare (Figs. 1-15, 1-16, and 1-30). Instead it is covered by a number of interdigitating processes which extend from the outer cytoplasmic layers of the two adjacent Schwann cells (Robertson, 1959; Elfvin, 1961; Webster, Spiro, Waksman, and Adams, 1961; Bunge, Bunge, Peterson, and Murray, 1967). The arrangement of the interdigitating Schwann cell processes is very irregular, and their outer surfaces are covered by the basal lamina that extends over the whole surface of a Schwann cell. This halo of irregular profiles of Schwann cell processes facilitates the identification of nodes in transverse sections (Fig. 1-17), and a further aid to their recognition is the irregular outline of the nodal axolemma which has an undercoating of dense material. Since a similar undercoating of dense material is also present at the initial segment of an axon (Palay, Sotelo, Peters, and Orkand, 1968), but absent elsewhere, it might be concluded that this dense material is related to the unique functional properties of these two specific regions of the axon.

The Schmidt-Lantermann Clefts

In addition to the node of Ranvier, there are other interruptions in the myelin sheath. These are the Schmidt-Lantermann clefts which are funnel-shaped interruptions occurring in the internodal portion of the sheath. For some time these clefts or incisures were thought to be artifacts of fixation, but as shown by a number of authors (e.g. Hiscoe, 1947), the clefts are also clearly visible in living nerve fibers examined with polarizing optics. The number of clefts per internode is approximately proportional to the length of the internode, and the clefts are most commonly oriented so that the narrow or apical end points towards the nearest node of Ranvier.

The fine structure of Schmidt-Lantermann clefts has been demonstrated by Robertson (1958). He has shown that they represent areas of the myelin sheath where cytoplasm intervenes between the lamellae (Figs. 1-18 and 1-19), and essentially, the cytoplasm lies in a helical tunnel that is produced by a splitting of the major dense line (Webster, 1964). The structure of the clefts is similar to the paranodal cytoplasmic pockets, but their form may be more irregular, and in some instances the clefts do not extend across the entire width of the myelin. When they do, it is clear they provide a pathway between the cytoplasm on the inside and the outside of the sheath. It should be pointed out that faults resembling Schmidt-Lantermann clefts can sometimes occur in poorly fixed myelin, but in this case the splits do not contain cytoplasm.

The cytoplasm contained in the Schmidt-Lantermann clefts is often devoid of organelles, but Bunge, Bunge, Peterson, and Murray (1967) have shown that it may contain microtubules. Commonly, puncta adhaerentia (Palay, 1967) occur between the parts of plasma membranes that delimit the successive turns of the cytoplasmic helix (Fig. 1-19). These attachment points often form a series across the incisure, and like those at the paranode (see Fig. 1-15) they are characterized by an accumulation of dense material that extends from the attachment site into the surrounding cytoplasm. Whether these attachment points provide stablization to the clefts is not known, but their presence may be an indication that the clefts have some permanence and are not transitory structures.

Sheaths of Myelinated Ganglion Cells

In addition to the myelinated axons, the peripheral nervous systems of vertebrates also contain some myelinated ganglion cells. The most common locations for such cells are the vestibular and acoustic (spiral) ganglia, and the form of the myelin present around these neurons has been studied in the goldfish by Rosenbluth and Palay (1961) and in the rat by Rosenbluth (1962).

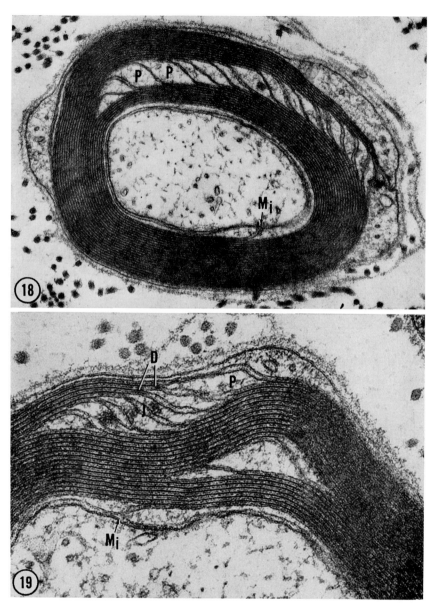

FIGURES 1-18 and 1-19. Transverse sections of adult rat trigeminal nerve fibers with Schmidt-Lantermann clefts present in their myelin sheaths. Figure 1-18 shows the entire profile of a nerve fiber, and it can be seen that the cleft is formed by the lamellae opening up to accommodate cytoplasm (P). X52,000. Figure 1-19 is a higher magnification electron micrograph of a Schmidt-Lantermann cleft. Here it is seen that the cytoplasm is contained in pockets (P) formed by a separation of the major dense line (D). Puncta adhaerentia (J) occur between adjacent cytoplasmic pockets. The internal mesaxon (M_i) is shown in both figures. X96,000.

In the goldfish the sheaths around the eighth nerve ganglion cells vary from a simple type which consists of a layer of Schwann cell cytoplasm, like that surrounding cells in dorsal root ganglia, to sheaths composed of compact myelin. Between these two extremes are the sheaths of the majority of cells. These have an intermediate form and consist of either multiple layers of Schwann cell cytoplasm, which Rosenbluth and Palay term *loose myelin,* or loose myelin and compact myelin lamellae that are in continuity with each other.

The cells that have sheaths formed of compact myelin are among the largest ones present within the ganglion, and the myelin around them is in every way comparable with that around peripheral axons. The sheaths consist of ten to ninety lamellae with a periodicity of about 115 Å. Although some of the inner lamellae may be of loose myelin that contains a thin layer of cytoplasm in place of the major dense line, all of the outer lamellae consist of compact myelin. Rosenbluth and Palay were unable to find either nodes of Ranvier, Schmidt-Lantermann clefts or other types of discontinuities in the myelin around the perikarya of ganglion cells. They state, however, that nodes are usually situated some distance away from the perikaryon, along either the neurites or the axon hillocks.

The sheaths of those smaller neurons encapsulated by loose myelin contain between two and thirty layers, and as far as Rosenbluth and Palay (1961) were able to ascertain, the number of these layers or sheets of cytoplasm appeared to be constant in all parts of a sheath surrounding any particular neuron. The thickness of individual sheets of cytoplasm usually ranges between 100 to 1,000 Å, but even in any one sheet the thickness is variable. In some places the cytoplasm may completely disappear so that the apposed plasma membranes bounding each side of the sheet come together to form a major dense line. The gap between adjacent sheets of cytoplasm ranges in width from 40 to 200 Å. But as in compact myelin, the outer faces of plasma membranes limiting adjacent sheets can sometimes come together to form an intraperiod line. In loose myelin, then, both the intervals between adjacent sheets and the thickness of the cytoplasm contained within them can vary in such a way that the plasma membranes may be separated or come together to form major dense and intraperiod lines.

It is noteworthy that sometimes the outer faces of the plasma membranes of adjacent sheets of cytoplasm may come into such close contact that even the intraperiod line, which would normally be formed by their apposition, is obliterated. Then only the cytoplasmic leaflets of the two intimately related plasma membranes are retained. The resultant structure has a form that is essentially similar to that of a single plasma membrane, although it is slightly thicker, having overall dimensions of about 100 Å. Another important point is that although each bipolar neuron in the ganglion is enclosed by a single internode of myelin, this internode may have more than one Schwann cell contributing to its formation.

In the spiral and vestibular ganglia of the rat (Rosenbluth, 1962), the sheaths of the neurons also consist of both loose and compact myelin. However, the number of sheets of cytoplasm within the loose sheaths is generally smaller than in the goldfish, for it ranges only between one and twenty. Also, in the rat the number of lamellae present within the sheath of even the same neuron may vary in different regions, for each sheath receives lamellae from more than one Schwann cell. This could account for the fact that lamellae may terminate anywhere within the sheath, but the picture is made even more complex because the lamellae may also reverse direction, bifurcate, or merge with one another. How such complex sheaths are formed is not yet known, for no developmental studies have been carried out.

Sheaths somewhat similar in form to those encapsulating neurons of the eighth nerve ganglia also occur around perikarya in the ciliary ganglion of the chick (Hess, 1965; Takahashi and Hama, 1965).

THE CENTRAL NERVOUS SYSTEM

When compared to the peripheral nervous system, information about myelin sheaths of the central nervous system has been more slowly acquired and accepted. In part this is due to a tendency to consider central myelin basically different from peripheral myelin, a tendency that has prevailed virtually since the first studies were made. For example, Ranvier described the nodes in the peripheral nervous system as early as 1871, but even he doubted their existence in the central nervous system (Ranvier, 1873, 1882). This was in spite of the fact that Tourneux and Le Goff (1875) described such nodes only three years after Ranvier's original account. Doubts about the existence of nodes in the central nervous system persisted until about fifteen years ago. For a review of the conflicting points of view in this dispute, reference should be made to the recent account of central myelin sheaths that has been given by Bunge (1968). As a more recent example of this tendency, it may be recalled that quite soon after Geren (1954) and Robertson (1955) showed the lamellae of peripheral myelin to be arranged in a spiral, Luse (1956) and De Robertis, and Gerschenfeld and Wald (1958) denied the existence of a similar spiral configuration in central myelin. It was not until 1960 that Maturana (1960) and Peters (1960a) provided evidence to indicate that the lamellae of central myelin also form a spiral.

Perhaps the most important reason for the slow acquisition of information about the myelin sheaths of the central nervous system is the absence of connective tissue in the brain and spinal cord (Fig. 1-26). Thus while single nerve fibers can be teased out of peripheral nerves, the dissection of individual nerve fibers from the central nervous system is extremely difficult, for here they are closely packed, and in addition, they are interwoven with the processes of astrocytes. This close packing of the white matter of the central nervous system also means that in light microscope preparations there is usually some overlap between the images of neighboring myelin sheaths with the result that the details of structure are difficult to resolve. Fixation of the central nervous system also presents a problem, and the first satisfactory technique for fixation of this tissue for electron microscope analysis was not published until 1962 (Palay, McGee-Russell, Gordon, and Grillo). Even today after considerable experience in the techniques of fixation has been acquired, many difficulties are still encountered in obtaining good preservation of the white matter of the brain and spinal cord.

Nevertheless, it is now clear that central and peripheral myelin sheaths do have a basically similar morphology. The two main differences between them are (1) the cytoplasm on the outside of central myelin sheaths is confined to a slender longitudinal ridge and does not form a complete cylinder around the myelin and (2) the nuclei of the cells that form the myelin of the central nervous system are not contained in the cytoplasm on the outsides of the sheaths. Instead they are located some distance away from the myelin segments which they produce.

The Formation of Central Myelin

The formation of myelin sheaths in the central nervous system has been studied in the optic nerves of early postnatal rats and mice (Peters, 1960b, 1962, 1964b), in the spinal cords of cats whose axons are being remyelinated after they have been experimentally denuded (Bunge, Bunge, and Ris, 1961), and in the corpus callosum and callosal radiations of rats remyelinating after cyanide intoxication (Hirano, Levine, and Zimmerman, 1968).

In the optic nerves of rats, myelination commences on or about the seventh postnatal day (Vaughn, 1969), but in the corpus callosum of the cat, the first myelin sheaths do not make their appearance until four weeks after birth (Fleischhauer and Wartenberg, 1967). At this time the axons that begin to myelinate are between 0.6μ and 0.7μ in diameter.

In the first stage of myelination, an axon is partially surrounded by a cell process (Figs. 1-20, 1-21, and 1-22). As in peripheral nerves the cell process then extends until it completely encircles the axon when the plasma membranes of the opposed lips of the process come together to form a mesaxon (Fig. 1-23). It should be pointed out, however, that neither in this nor the subsequent stages in myelination is it usual for the nucleus of the myelin-forming cell to be observed in the cytoplasm of the process surrounding the axon. When the process has completed the enclosure of the axon, the mesaxon becomes elongated so that it forms a loose spiral (Fig. 1-21), and at some phase in this sequence, the outer leaflets of the apposed plasma membranes of the mesaxon some closer together to form the intraperiod line. Quite soon, and

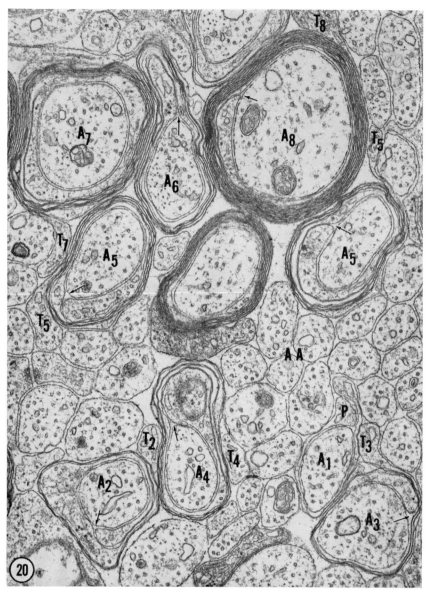

FIGURE 1-20. Transverse section of the optic nerve of a fifteen-day-postnatal rat. Most of the axons are still unmyelinated (*AA*). Others (*A₁-A₈*) have begun to myelinate and exhibit various stages in the maturation of the sheath. One axon (*A₁*) has just been enclosed by the process (*P*) of a myelin-forming cell, and around two other axons (*A₂* and *A₃*) the ensheathing process has started to form a spiral. Later stages in myelination are shown by the sheaths present around the axons labeled in the sequence of *A₄* to *A₈*. Some of the mesaxons (arrows) and external tongues of cytoplasm (*T*) related to these sheaths are indicated by corresponding subscripts. X44,000.

before many turns have been added to the spiral, the cytoplasm disappears from between the turns (Fig. 1-20). This brings about the apposition of the cytoplasmic leaflets of the plasma membranes in the spiral, the formation of the major dense line, and hence the production of compact myelin. After the loss of cytoplasm from between the turns of the mesaxon, the only cytoplasm generally retained within the sheath is confined to the layer that persists on the inside of the myelin where it lies adjacent to the axon and to a tongue process that occurs on the outside of the sheath (Figs. 1-20 and 1-23). Thus cytoplasm is only retained within the ends of the spiral (Fig. 1-26).

At this stage in myelin formation, the amount of the cytoplasm on the outside of the sheath is variable. But it is unusual for it to form a complete layer like the one present in peripheral sheaths, for when this situation does obtain, an external mesaxon is present (Peters, 1964a; Hirano, Levine and Zimmerman, 1968). Most commonly the cytoplasm is only retained in a small external tongue process (Peters, 1960a) or outer loop (Bunge, Bunge, and Ris, 1961) that occupies the terminal portion of the outer turn of the spiral. Then no external mesaxon is present, for the intraperiod line terminates where the plasma membrane bounding the external tongue turns away from the outside of the compact myelin (Fig. 1-27). Although the term *external tongue process* is used to describe the cytoplasmic process which is observed in transverse sections of myelin sheaths, it must be stressed that the tongue is a section of a cytoplasmic ridge which extends for the whole length of the myelin segment or internode. The extent of the cytoplasm retained on the inside of the myelin sheath is generally greater than that of the outer ridge, and even though it may be absent from part of the circumference, cytoplasm is usually present in the location where the spiral commences. Because of this it is common for an internal mesaxon to be evident.

Caley (1967) has recently drawn attention to the fact that central myelin does not always form in the manner outlined above. As he points out, it is common for the major dense line, rather than the intraperiod line, to form first. When the major dense line forms first, the process encircling the axon loses cytoplasm from its middle portion, so that in transverse sections it has a dumbbell shape with cytoplasm present only in each of its ends (Figs. 1-22 and 1-23) . Thus each end of the process resembles a tongue. The mesaxon may form when the two ends of the en-

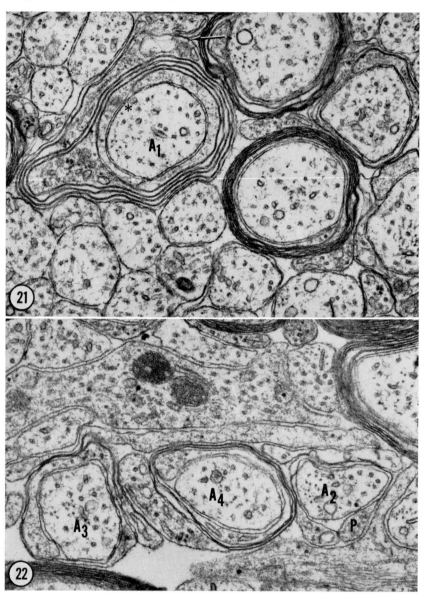

veloping process meet, but in some instances the apposition of the outer faces of the plasma membranes seems to be delayed until the process has begun to form a spiral. Consequently, when the formation of central myelin follows this pattern, the major dense line is formed first, and no cytoplasm is ever present between the turns of the spiral (Fig. 1-22), a situation which has never been encountered in the peripheral nervous system.

The later maturation of central myelin sheaths, as in the peripheral nervous system, consists of the addition of more lamellae. Central sheaths never seem to attain the thickness of peripheral ones though. In the rat optic nerve, for example, more than ten or fifteen lamellae are not commonly encountered (Fig. 1-26), whereas the sciatic and trigeminal nerve fibers of the same animal may have sheaths containing up to one hundred lamellae.

From the above account it can be appreciated that the formation of central myelin is a more irregular process than is the formation of peripheral myelin. The variations that are possible in the central nervous system may result in some very unusual forms of developing sheaths, for unlike the peripheral nervous system in which the adjacent Schwann cells are held apart by basal laminae and collagen fibers, the elements of the central nervous system are commonly separated by an intercellular space of only 120 Å. Because of a lack of intervening material, two adjacent processes of myelin-forming cells in the central nervous system can interfere in each other's activities. They may even compete to form myelin around the same axon. This can lead to the forma-

←———————— — — —

FIGURES 1-21 and 1-22. Transverse sections of fifteen-day-postnatal rat optic nerves to show the modes of myelin formation. In Figure 1-21 an axon (A_1) is surrounded by a developing sheath in which a loose spiral is formed by a mesaxon that contains cytoplasm between the turns. The mesaxon begins internally (asterisk) and spirals clockwise to complete five turns before ending (arrow). X44,000. In Figure 1-22 the spirals of the sheaths do not contain cytoplasm within the turns. One axon (A_2) is enclosed by a process (P) that has cytoplasm only at each end. Around a second axon (A_3) such a process has elongated to that the sheath has half a turn of compact myelin. In the sheath of a third axon (A_4) yet another turn has been added to the spiral. X56,000.

tion of two separate and concentric spirals around a single axon
and also result in examples in which lamellae derived from sepa-

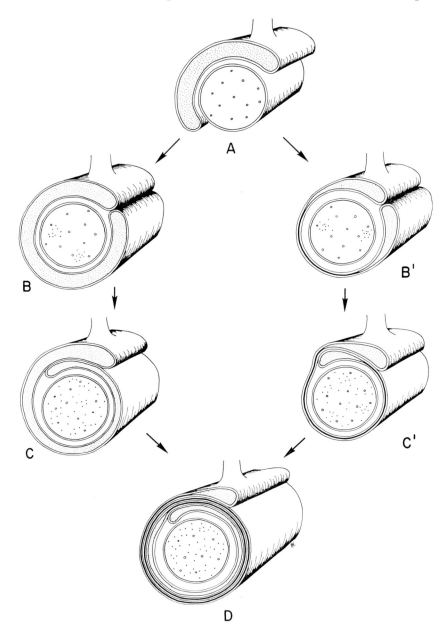

rate processes interlock and overlap (e.g. see Hirano, Levine, and Zimmerman, 1968). Unless the lamellae are distinct over their entire extent, such configurations may be very difficult to interpret.

Indeed, with all of the apparently unusual patterns that are encountered during development, it is surprising that the end result of central myelination is such a well-ordered product. Occasionally though, unusual myelin sheaths are present in the central nervous system of mature animals. For example, Hirano, Zimmerman, and Levine (1966) and Hirano and Dembitzer (1967) have described the presence of double and concentric myelin sheaths around a single axon. Sometimes the individual spirals of the lamellae of these concentric sheaths are in the same direction, but in other cases one spiral turns clockwise while the other turns counterclockwise. No doubt the precursors of these forms of sheaths are those examples in which two separate myelin-forming processes encircle the same axon. Walberg (1964) has also described unusual mature sheaths in which two or three myelinated axons are enclosed by a commonly shared outer myelin sheath. No forms parallel to these unusual patterns have been described in peripheral nerves where each Schwann cell has its territory that is delimited by the basal lamina. It is not uncommon, however, for axons in both the developing central and peripheral nervous system to have myelin sheaths that are many sizes too large for them (Figs. 1-9 and 1-24). Then the axon is usually confined to one end of a sheath that loops away into a long, flattened extension, in which the opposite sides of the sheath come together. This type of sheath has been described in the

←――――――――――

FIGURE 1-23. Diagrammatic representation of the formation of myelin in the central nervous system. The first stage (*A*) is one in which the axon is partially surrounded by the process of a myelin-forming cell. The process then completely envelops the axon and may retain cytoplasm throughout its entire extent (*B*) as it spirals (*C*) around the axon. Alternatively, the cytoplasm may be lost from the middle portion of the process (*B'*), with the result that it is a sheet of paired membranes that forms a spiral around the axon (*C'*). Irrespective of whether or not cytoplasm is retained throughout the myelin-forming process, the structure of the resulting myelin sheath (*D*) is the same in each case.

central nervous system by a number of investigators including Rosenbluth (1966) and Fleischhauer and Wartenburg (1967). Occasionally these elongated myelin sheaths are flattened around cell bodies (Rosenbluth, 1966; and Herndon, 1964), and while some contain axons (Fig. 1-24), others are empty. This type of configuration has never been encountered in the peripheral nervous system, although in some animals certain neuronal perikarya like those of the acoustic, vestibular, and ciliary ganglia may be consistently myelinated by sheaths of loose or compact myelin.

So far there appear to have been no electron microscope studies made of longitudinal sections of developing myelin sheaths. In light microscope studies of myelin that is forming in tissue cultures, however, Hild (1957, 1959) has described the first detectable myelin to be arranged as a series of short cuffs along the axon. Later these cuffs extend towards each other and eventually leave only short gaps, the nodes of Ranvier, between them.

The Myelin-forming Cells

As emphasized above, no nuclei are usually seen within the cytoplasm of the processes that form the myelin sheaths of the developing central nervous system. This led electron microscopists to conclude that the perikarya of the myelin-forming neuroglial cells must be located some distance away from the sheath. Studies were therefore undertaken to find connections between the tongue of cytoplasm on the outside of central myelin sheaths and processes emanating from neuroglial cell perikarya. Such connections were first found by Bunge, Bunge, and Pappas (1962) in the spinal cords of kittens, and they tentatively identified the myelin-forming neuroglial cell to be the oligodendrocyte. This observation has been subsequently confirmed in kittens (see Bunge and Glass, 1965; Bunge, 1968) and similar connections have also been found in the early postnatal optic nerves of rats (Peters, 1964b).

In some instances the developing myelin sheath actually indents the oligodendrocyte, which gives off a short process that is contiguous with the lamellae of the myelin sheath. Such a process becomes attenuated as the cytoplasm is lost from its inside, and the plasma membrane on opposed faces of the process come together

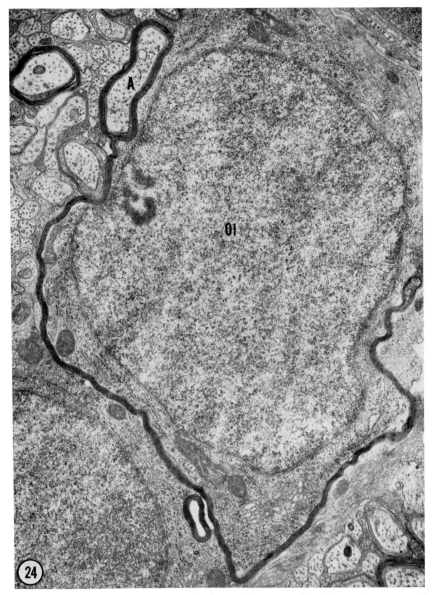

FIGURE 1-24. Transverse section of the optic nerve of a fifteen-day-postnatal rat. Most of the field is occupied by an oligodendrocyte (01) partially surrounded by myelin. This myelin belongs to an axon (*A*) that occupies only a small portion of the sheath which extends into the long tail surrounding the oligodendrocyte. X22,000.

to form the myelin lamellae (Fig. 1-25). More commonly, however, the process connecting the perikaryon to the myelin sheath is more extensive and can be as long as 12μ in the kitten (Bunge, Bunge, and Pappas, 1962) and 10μ in the rat (Peters, 1946b). Another important point is that Bunge, Bunge, and Pappas (1962), Peters (1964b), and Bunge and Glass (1965) have presented evidence that a single oligodendrocyte can be connected to two separate segments of myelin, each surrounding a different axon. Consequently, a myelin-forming cell in the central nervous system is capable of forming more than one segment of myelin. This conclusion is in agreement with the fact that although axons of the same diameter in both the peripheral and central nervous system have similar internodal lengths (see Vizoso and Young, 1948; Hess and Young, 1949), there are many fewer neuroglial cells present for a given population of myelinated nerve fibers in the central nervous system.

The conclusion that the myelin-forming cells are oligodendrocytes is based upon the morphological characteristics of the neuroglial cells forming continuities with central myelin sheaths. Briefly these characteristics are a dark cytoplasm that contains none of the filaments which are typical of the only other commonly occurring type of neuroglial cell, the astrocyte (Fig. 1-25). The conclusion is also in agreement with the observation that in the developing rat optic nerve, identifiable oligodendrocytes first appear at about seven days of postnatal life, which is the time when the initial stages in myelin formation become apparent. As other examples of electron microscope studies that implicate oligodendrocytes in myelin formation, those of Metuzals (1963), who studied the frog diencephalon, and Herndon (1964), who examined the rat cerebellum, may be cited.

Although several attempts have been made to find connections between the cytoplasm on the outside of myelin sheaths and the perikarya of oligodendrocytes in the mature, normal central nervous system, these efforts have generally met with failure. The only example of alleged continuity has been published by Kruger and Maxwell (1966), but their micrograph would seem to be open to alternative interpretations. Hirano (1968) has also re-

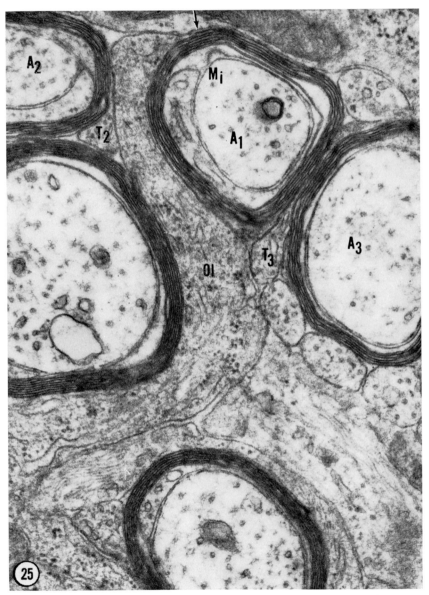

FIGURE 1-25. Transverse section of a fifteen-day-postnatal rat optic nerve. Extending across the field is an oligodendrocytic process (*ol*). This process loses its cytoplasm (arrow) so that the bounding plasma membranes come together to form the lamellae of the myelin sheath around an axon (A_1). The spiral of the lamellae of this sheath ends at the internal mesaxon (M_i). Two other axons (A_2 and A_3) have sheaths whose external tongue processes (T_2 and T_3) abut against the oligodendrocyte (*ol*). X20,000.

cently described an example of a connection between a myelin
sheath and an oligodendrocyte in a mature rat, but since an experimental lesion had been made in the brain of this animal three
weeks previously, the axon may be remyelinating. In view of the
large amount of extracellular space in the immediate vicinity of the
oligodendrocyte, it would seem likely that the brain was abnormal.
It is unlikely that the connections formed between oligodendrocytes and the cytoplasm of myelin sheaths are lost during development, and the possible reasons for the failure to find definitive
examples of connections should be examined. The most likely
reason seems to be that as the central nervous system matures and
increases in volume, the connections which are clearly defined in
early development become long and tortuous. For example, while
many of the processes of young oligodendrocytes of the rat optic
nerve are thick and stubby, in the mature nerve they are thin.
Moreover, their tortuous form is shown by the fact that it is uncommon for oligodendrocytic processes of more than a few mi-
crons in length to occur in any given electron microscope section
of the mature central nervous system.

Among the light microscopists who favored oligodendrocytes
to be responsible for myelin formation in the central nervous system were Rio Hortega (1922, 1924) and Penfield (1924). They
considered the oligodendrocytes to be the homologues of the
Schwann cell, and a discussion of their views and those of other
light microscopists is to be found in the review by Bunge (1968).
As Bunge (1968) and Bunge, Bunge, and Pappas (1962) point
out, Rio Hortega (1928) presented illustrations that show oligodendrocytes giving off processes that bifurcate into long, slender
branches which pass in opposite directions and lie parallel to the
nerve fibers. This picture can be readily interpreted in the terms
of electron microscope studies, for the long, slender processes
would represent the ridge of cytoplasm or external tongue process,
passing along the extent of the myelin segment. Thinner processes
that in Rio Hortega's illustrations (see Bunge, 1968, Figs. 1 and
2) emerge at right angles from the long and slender branches to
encircle the axon, could be taken to represent areas in which cytoplasm is retained between the lamellae of the sheath.

One important question that arises is whether the myelin sheaths of the central nervous system are always formed by oligodendrocytes. Wendell-Smith, Blunt, and Baldwin (1966) have suggested that astrocytes may partake in the formation of myelin in the optic nerves of cats. They found that thin myelin sheaths are present in the lamina cribosa, and the only neuroglial cells to occur in this region of the mature cat optic nerve are astrocytes. The nearest oligodendrocytes are several millimeters away. Observations such as this cannot be dismissed, but it may be stated that the general consensus of opinion implicates the oligodendrocyte in myelin formation. To be certain, however, examples of connections between mature sheaths and neuroglial cells must still be obtained.

The Mechanism of Myelin Formation

In common with that of the peripheral nervous system, central myelin is formed in segments, but no studies to parallel those of Spiedel (1964) on the growth of nerve fibers in the tails of living tadpoles have been possible in the spinal cord and brain. As pointed out in the previous section, it is reasonable to think that in peripheral nerves the spiral of lamellae in each myelin segment is formed by the rotation of the Schwann cell around the enclosed axon, and observations on the movements of Schwann cell nuclei in myelinating tissue cultures are consistent with this hypothesis. However, if it is accepted that a myelin-forming oligodendrocyte can be connected to two or more segments of myelin, then the rotation of the perikaryon of the oligodendrocyte around two different axons could not lead to the formation of separate spirals of lamellae. Not only would such a movement of the perikaryon lead to a hopeless tangle of lamellae, but it would be difficult to envision how the myelin-forming cell would move through the arrays of axons that make up its immediate environment. Consequently, if a rotation of any part of the myelinating process around the enclosed axon is to be assumed, then it would be logical to consider that the inner end of the spiral between the myelin and the axon is the actively growing region and not the outer end which is connected to the cell.

As pointed out by Lampert (1965), growth of the inner end of the spiral to form additional lamellae would lead to a decrease in diameter of the sheath unless the sheath can expand. A decrease in internal diameter of the sheath certainly does not occur. On the contrary, as myelination proceeds, the myelin sheath expands in order to accommodate the thickening axon. One way that the sheath could expand is by lamellar slippage, and support for this idea comes from the report of Hirano and Dembitzer (1967). They have shown that during the production of experimental edema in adult rats, the axons became severely swollen, and yet they are still surrounded by intact myelin sheaths. What is not known is whether the thickness of the expanded sheath is the same as in normal adult animals. If slippage does take place, then it would be expected that unless more material is added to the sheath, the total length of the spiral of lamellae would be the same as in the normal animal, and hence the thickness of the myelin would be reduced.

As yet there is no answer to even the basic question of whether new lamellae are added to either the inside or outside of the myelin sheath in the central and peripheral nervous systems. It may be possible to derive some information by incorporating radioactive isotopes into the newly forming portions of the sheath and then carrying out autoradiographic studies at the electron microscope level to determine the location of the label. However, because the resolution of the technique is limited, even this experiment may not provide a clear-cut result.

If the growth of the lamellae of the central myelin sheath does occur at one end, then it might be supposed that the inner and outer ends of the spiral of lamellae would be randomly disposed in respect to each other. But an analysis of transverse sections of developing sheaths has revealed that these ends, the external tongue process and the internal mesaxon, are not positioned randomly (Peters, 1964a). Instead, they show a definite tendency to be located in the same quadrant of the sheath. This suggests that if elongation of the lamellar spiral takes place at the ends, the growth must be intermittent with additional turns being formed by brief and cyclic bursts rather than by a regular and continuous activity.

The production of some of the unusual forms of myelin such as the "redundant myelin sheaths" described by Rosenbluth (1966), in which an axon has a sheath many sizes too large, is also difficult to envisage in terms of a simple mechanism by which growth occurs at only one end of the lamellar spiral. While it is possible that extensive sheaths could be formed in this manner, the relative speed at which the end of the spiral would have to grow would be considerable (see Fig. 1-24).

At the present time it is clear that we can only speculate about how the myelin sheath might be formed. To go further, more basic information is necessary; but how this information can be obtained is not readily apparent. It is unlikely, however, that it will be derived from further electron microscope studies of static phases in this dynamic process.

It must also be mentioned that problems similar to those involved in explaining the increase in thickness of the myelin sheath also obtain in accounting for the increase in length of myelin segments that take place as a nerve fiber elongates. It can only be suggested that new material is either interposed throughout the segment or at the ends of the lamellae where the paranodal cytoplasm occurs.

The Number of Myelin Segments Formed by an Oligodendrocyte

With respect to the mechanism of myelin formation, it was mentioned that the electron microscope studies of Bunge, Bunge, and Pappas (1962) and Peters (1964b) strongly suggest that an oligodendrocyte can form more than one myelin segment. Since the dissection of myelinated nerve fibers and their attached neuroglial cells is not feasible, Peters and Proskauer (1968) determined the ratio between oligodendrocytes and myelin internodes by an indirect method. The part of the central nervous system used for this study was the optic nerve of the mature rat. The optic nerve was chosen because the number of nerve fibers contained in this structure has previously been determined by Forrester and Peters (1967) to be about 117,000.

Since no account has been published previously, it will be necessary to give some details of the method used.

To determine the average length of myelin internodes, the

ratio of the number of profiles of myelin internodes to those of nodes was first counted in randomly selected electron micrographs of transverse sections of the optic nerve taken at an original magnification of X5,000. The paranodes were considered to be part of the internode (Fig. 1-26). The criteria used for the identification of a node were that the axon must be bare and show the presence of an undercoating of the plasma membrane (see Peters, 1966). Each electron micrograph contained between 150 and 200 profiles of myelinated or internodal axons and between 0 and 3 profiles of nodes. In the twenty-four micrographs that were examined, there was a total of 4,332 internodes and 31 nodes.

Next, the length of nodes were measured in twenty-four micrographs of longitudinally sectioned optic nerves, and in these the range of length was between 0.6μ to 2.2μ. The average value for the length of a node was 0.9μ.

The values obtained in this manner were then substituted in the formula:

$$\frac{\text{Average length of internode}}{\text{Average length of node}} = \frac{\text{Number of internodal profiles}}{\text{Number of nodal profiles}}$$

$$\text{The average length of an internode} = \frac{4332 \times 0.9\mu}{31}$$

$$= 125.7\mu$$

For the following calculation, however, it is necessary to add the length of the node to that of the internode so that a value of $125.7\mu + 0.9\mu = 126.6\mu$ is used.

Since the number of nerve fibers in the rat optic nerve is about 117,000, the number of internodal lengths of myelin per 1 mm length of the nerve is $1,000/126.6 \times 117,000 = 924,000$ internodes per millimeter length.

As a first step in calculating the population of oligodendrocytes, the number of their nuclei was determined in 1μ thick transverse sections of plastic embedded optic nerves stained with methylene blue and azure II (Richardson *et al.*, 1960). Between 190 and 218 oligodendrocytic nuclei were present in each of ten adjacent 1μ thick sections, and the average was 205. To find the actual numbers of these nuclei, it was necesary to know their

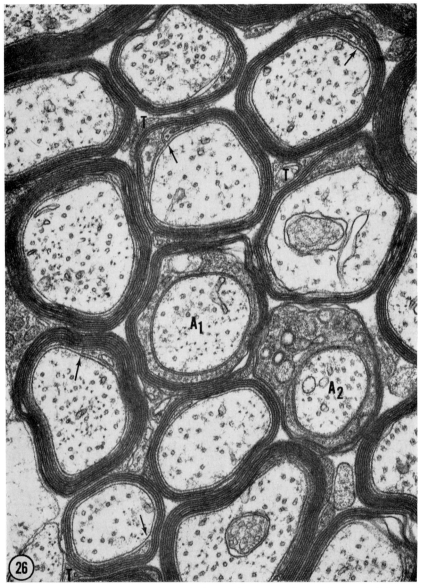

FIGURE 1-26. Transverse section of the optic nerve of an adult rat. Most of these myelin sheaths are thin. Because of the absence of connective tissue between them and the small size of the external tongue processes (*T*), adjacent sheaths come into close proximity. Some of the internal mesaxons are indicated (arrows). Included in this field are profiles of two paranodal axons (*A₁* and *A₂*). X52,000.

lengths. Consequently, in longitudinal sections of optic nerves, one hundred individual oligodendrocytic nuclei were measured. An average length of 6.0μ was obtained. Since the mean length of all the parallel chords of either a circle or an ellipse (in the direction of the selected axis) is $\pi/4 \times$ diameter, or about 79 percent of the diameter in the selected axis; the corrected average length of the oligodendrocytic nucleus is $6.0\mu/0.79\mu$ or 7.6μ. For the present purposes, this figure is a reasonable estimate regardless of the exact shape of the nucleus.

Substituting these figures in the formula derived by Abercrombie (1946) to determine the population of cells, a figure of 21.86 nuclei per micron length of optic nerve is obtained, or 21,860 oligodendrocytic nuclei per millimeter length of nerve. Therefore, the ratio of internodal lengths of myelin to the number of oligodendrocytes in the same length of optic nerve is 924,000/21,860, which is 42.3.

To be consistent with the limitations of the indirect method that was used, it seems preferable to state that there are between thirty and fifty myelin internodes for every oligodendrocyte present in the optic nerve of the mature rat. At first sight the figure seems startling high, but even if all of the cells present in the nerve — oligodendrocytes, astrocytes, and vascular wall elements — are considered to form myelin, the lowest ratio of myelin segments per cell is still about 20:1.

The only figures for internodal lengths of myelinated nerve fibers that seem to be available for comparison with the average one derived above are those of Haug (1967) and Hess and Young (1952). The modal value for the diameters of myelinated nerve fibers in the rat optic nerve is about 0.9μ (Forrester and Peters, 1967), and in the visual cortex of cats, Haug (1967) calculated the internodal length of fibers with this diameter to be 144μ, which is similar to the figure of 123μ found by Peters and Proskauer. Nerve fibers of such small diameter do not occur in the spinal cords of the rabbits examined by Hess and Young (1952), but extrapolation of their graphs show that 1μ fibers could be expected to have internodal lengths of about 150μ. It should be further added that Haug (1967) found the length of the bare axon at the node to be 0.38μ to 1.16μ in the cat, compared to the value of 0.9μ used in the above calculations.

Consequently, it is apparent that the values used by Peters and Proskauer (1968) to calculate the number of myelin internodes per unit length of the rat optic nerve are within the range of values found in other animals. However, no comparable figures for the populations of oligodendrocytes seem to be available in the literature.

In summary, it now seems clear that each oligodendrocyte in white matter can form and is responsible for a substantial number of separate segments of myelin. In the optic nerve of the rat at least, it seems that this number is in the order of thirty to fifty myelin segments per oligodendrocyte.

The Mature Myelin Sheath

The spiral form of the lamellae of the myelin sheaths was first suggested by the studies of Maturana (1960) and Peters (1960a) on the optic nerves of amphibia, and it has now been indicated in different parts of the central nervous systems of a number of animal species. These include the spinal cords of cats (Bunge, Bunge, and Ris, 1961), the optic nerves of rats and mice (Peters, 1960b, 1962), the diencephalon of frogs (Metuzals, 1960, 1963), the cerebral hemispheres of rats (Hirano, Zimmerman, and Levine, 1966; Hirano and Dembitzer, 1967), the inferior olive of cats (Walberg, 1964), and the cerebellum of rats (Herndon, 1964). Myelin sheaths with the same form also occur in tissue cultures of the cerebellum of mice, rats, and kittens (Perier and de Harven, 1961; Ross, Bornstein, and Lehrer, 1962). Furthermore, electron micrographs (see Fig. 1-27) have also been produced in which the spiral arrangement of the lamellae can be visualized directly (Peters, 1964a; Uzman, 1964; Hirano and Dembitzer, 1967).

As in peripheral nerves the intraperiod and major dense lines alternate throughout the thickness of central myelin (Fig. 1-27). The intraperiod line commences on the inside of the sheath where the outer leaflets of the pair of plasma membranes come into apposition to form the mesaxon (Figs. 1-27 and 1-28). It ends on the

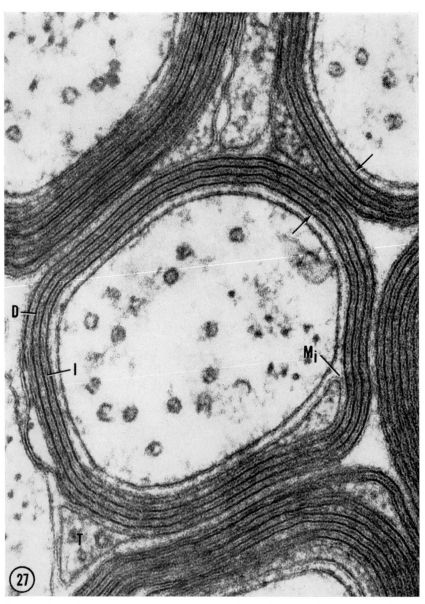

FIGURE 1-27. Transverse section of a myelinated axon from an adult rat optic nerve. The intraperiod line (*I*) of the myelin starts in the internal mesaxon (*M$_i$*) and ends on the outside of the sheath beneath the external tongue process (*T*). The major dense line (*D*) alternates with the intraperiod line. Note that where adjacent sheaths come together, an intraperiod line is formed between them, so that an uninterrupted periodicity extends across two sheaths (between arrows). X100,000.

outside of the sheath where the two membranes diverge, one to continue over the outside of the myelin and the other to extend over the cytoplasm of the external tongue process (Figs. 1-27 and 1-28). The thicker and darker major dense line takes origin on the inside of the sheath where the cytoplasm is lost from the innermost lamella, for it is produced by the apposition of the cytoplasmic faces of the plasma membrane forming the myelin. This line terminates as the membranes of the myelin diverge to accommodate the cytoplasm of the external tongue process (Figs. 1-27 and 1-28).

Because of the small extent of the external tongue process, which usually seems to occupy only between 5 to 20 percent of the outer circumference of the sheath (Peters, 1964a), the outsides of adjacent myelin sheaths frequently come into contact. Since the outer leaflet of a plasma membrane forms the outside face of the sheath, apposition of two sheaths may lead to the formation of a junction that is similar in form to the intraperiod line. In these circumstances a continuous periodicity extends across the entire thickness of the two sheaths (Fig. 1-27).

Differences Between Central and Peripheral Myelin Sheaths

Although the form of central and peripheral myelin sheaths is fundamentally similar, there are some differences between the two. The difference in the components on the outside of the sheaths has already been mentioned. This was one of the factors that delayed the correct interpretation of early electron micrographs of central myelin, for with the inferior techniques then available for the fixation, staining, and more particularly the cutting of adequate sections, it was difficult to determine the exact boundaries of adjacent sheaths. Other differences between central and peripheral myelin are the following.

Periodicity of the Myelin

X-ray diffraction studies have shown that when the myelin sheaths of the peripheral and central nervous systems are examined under identical conditions, the fundamental repeating unit of central myelin is about 10 percent less than that of periph-

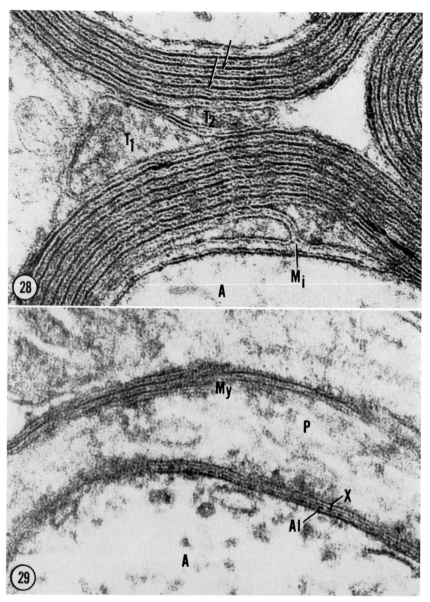

FIGURE 1-28. In this field from the optic nerve of an adult rat, there are portions of three myelin sheaths. The sheath belonging to one axon (*A*) shows the form of the internal mesaxon (M_i) and the external tongue process (T_1), which abuts against the external tongue process (T_2) of a second sheath. Note that within the myelin, the intraperiod line shows intermittent splitting (arrows). X237,000.

eral myelin (see Finean, 1961). Karlsson (1966) has also shown a difference in the thickness of lamelle in central and peripheral myelin in electron micrographs of tissue prepared in the same way. He finds that the periodicity (i.e. the thickness of lamellae measured as the distance between the centers of adjacent major dense lines) is 106 Å in central myelin and 119 Å in peripheral myelin. Part of this difference may be due to the extent of separation between the external surfaces of the plasma membrane that become apposed to form the intraperiod line. Thus in peripheral myelin (Fig. 1-12), the surfaces seem to be separated by a gap of about 20 Å that extends throughout the spiral of the lamellae (Revel and Hamilton, 1968), but a continuous gap within the intraperiod line does not seem to occur in central myelin. Instead the gap appears to be intermittent (Fig. 1-28), so that the average periodicity of the sheath as a whole would be somewhat less than in peripheral myelin. Splitting of the intraperiod line in portions of the central sheath has been shown by Hirano, Zimmerman, and Levine (1966), but whether the interval present in the intraperiod line of central myelin is open to penetration by lanthanum salts, as is that of peripheral myelin (Revel and Hamilton, 1969), has not been investigated.*

The difference in periodicity of central and peripheral myelin is also apparent in freeze-etched preparations, and Bischoff and Moor (1967a, 1967b) found the periodicity of peripheral myelin to be 185 Å, compared to a value of a 160 Å for central myelin sheaths. However, these authors seem to have misinterpreted their electron micrographs, so that they have reversed the positions of the major dense and intraperiod lines of the sheaths. This can be

←————

FIGURE 1-29. Part of a paranode from the cerebral cortex of an adult cat. The axolemma (*Al*) of the axon (*A*) and the plasma membrane (*X*) bounding the inner surface of the paranodal cytoplasm (*P*) form a seven-layered complex. The dense lines forming each side of the complex are the cytoplasmic leaflets of the two membranes. The middle two lines are their outer leaflets which are only 25 to 30 Å apart. Compare the form of the complex with that of the myelin sheath (*My*). X24,000.

————

*Hirano and Dembitzer (*J Ultrastruct Res, 28:*141, 1969) have recently shown that the intraperiod line of central myelin is open to penetration by lanthanum.

readily seen from an analysis of Figure 1 in their second paper
(Bischoff and Moor, 1967b). When this correction is made, their
pictures show that although the intraperiod line of peripheral
myelin is composed of two fine and separate lines, a similar splitting of the intraperiod line of central myelin is less distinct.

If the differences in the periodicity of central and peripheral
myelin does not reside in the extent of the gap between the plasma
membrane faces that come together to form the intraperiod line,
then we must look for a difference in the composition of the myelin from the two locations. Perhaps the lipoprotein constituents
are not the same (see Finean, Hawthorne, and Patterson, 1957;
Finean, 1960; Evans and Finean, 1965).

Korn (1966) has drawn attention to some of the difficulties in
interpreting electron micrographs of osmium-stained preparations,
and information has now become available which suggests that
biological membranes may not be continuous lamellae. Instead
they may be composed of discrete globular subunits. Electron
micrographs of sections, for example, show that chloroplast and
mitochondrial membranes have a beaded appearance, and this
corresponds to the cobblestone appearance that is clearly revealed
on surface views of membranes fractured by the method of freeze
etching (Branton, 1967).

Di Carlo (1967a) has found globular components (of about
90 Å in diameter) in both frog synaptic membrane and axonic
vesicles fixed in glutaraldehyde and postfixed with osmic acid.
However, not all membranes seem to have a consistent globular
structure. For example, nuclear membranes generally appear to
be nonglobular, and so do the lamellae of the myelin sheath. Of
special interest is the failure to detect a subunit structure in
freeze-etched myelin (Branton, 1967), and it would appear that
the x-ray diffraction data from myelin excludes the presence of
subunit structures comparable to those postulated in chloroplasts
and mitochondria. Nevertheless, there is some electron microscope
evidence to suggest that under certain conditions subunits may
occur in the myelin of amphibian and mammalian peripheral
nerve (Di Carlo, 1967b), for in high-resolution micrographs,
regular arrangements of osmiophilic granules and osmiophobic

globules may be seen. The subunits appear to form polyhedral structures, in which the central dark granules are sometimes surrounded by six osmiophobic globules. Using cryofixation techniques to minimize ice crystal formation and other artifacts, Fernandéz-Morán (1967) has shown particulate subunit structures of 60 to 80 Å. These subunits are found mainly within the plane of the intraperiod line and occur in both central and peripheral myelin. Fernandéz-Morán has also found similar units of about 50 to 60 Å in negatively stained, unfixed preparations. In addition, Gent, Gregson, Gammack, and Raper (1964) have been able to isolate globular lipoprotein subunits from myelin treated with lysolecithin, and it appears from electrophoretic and chemical criteria that there are at least two types of subunits (Gent and Gregson, 1966). A possible explanation of these apparent contradictions is that myelin might be an example of a membrane which undergoes a ready transformation (Lucy, 1968) from one form (the triple-layered structure) to another (the subunit).

Radial Component of Myelin

When transverse sections of myelin sheaths of the central nervous system are fixed with osmic acid and stained on the section with potassium permanganate, a series of dark radial lines extend across the myelin (Honjin, 1959; Peters, 1961b, 1962; Honjin, Kosaka, Takaro, and Hiramatsu, 1963; Honjin and Changus, 1964). These lines, which are usually 300 to 400 Å apart, are produced by a series of thickenings of the intraperiod line, which in these locations increases in width from 20 to 30 Å to 40 to 50 Å.

Initially it was thought that the radial component had a punctuate form, but an examination of oblique (Peters, 1964a) and longitudinal (Peters, unpublished) sections of sheaths indicates that the radial component is really formed by a series of linear thickenings that are arranged parallel to the length of the sheath. It is uncertain what produces these thickenings of the intraperiod line, but it might be speculated that if there are intermittent splits in the intraperiod line of central myelin (Fig. 1-28), then the resultant gaps might fill with the permanganate stain.

The most common location for the radial component is the

portion of the myelin sheath lying beneath the external tongue process. And since the internal mesaxon frequently lies beneath the external tongue process, the radial component seems to "bridge" across those portions of the lamellae lying between the cytoplasm on the inside and the outside of the sheath. Radial components are not confined to this part of the sheath, however, for they are frequently present where two adjacent sheaths come into apposition.

Despite the many accounts of peripheral myelin that have appeared in the literature, a similar radial component has only once been illustrated in such sheaths (see Robertson, 1960).

Schmidt-Lantermann Clefts

The final important difference between the internodal myelin of the central and peripheral nervous systems is that although Schmidt-Lantermann clefts are readily apparent in light microscope preparations of peripheral nerves, there is less certainty about their existence in the central nervous system. Ramon y Cajal (1928) claimed to have seen them, and structures resembling clefts have been illustrated by Sulzmann (1962) in silver-stained preparations. No clefts have so far been recorded in electron microscope preparations, however, so that it can probably be concluded that if they do occur in the central nervous system, they are rare. Islands of cytoplasm may sometimes be encountered between the lamellae of a central myelin sheath, but these islands are usually confined to the outer lamellae and do not seem to extend across the entire width of the sheath as do the clefts of peripheral nerves. Perhaps one reason why clefts have not been recorded by electron microscopists studying central nervous tissue is that the sheaths of the larger nerve fibers, in which clefts have most commonly been encountered by light microscopists, are not usually well fixed. Thus if the clefts exist they may have been overlooked. Consequently, the question of the existence of Schmidt-Lantermann clefts in the central nervous system is one that needs further study.

The Lengths of Myelin Segments

Because of the difficulties in preparing the material, to our knowledge only three reports have appeared in which a correlation has been made between fiber diameter and internodal length. From these reports, however, it would appear that as in peripheral nerves these two parameters are directly related to each other, so that the thickest nerve fibers have the longest internodal lengths. Hess and Young (1949, 1952) examined pieces of rabbit spinal cords stained with methylene blue. They found that in adult rabbits, the diameters of the nerve fibers are between 3μ and 15μ and that the internodal length of the myelin in such fibers is between 300μ and $1,700\mu$. In young rabbits the internodal lengths are shorter. Bodian (1951) studied the opossum brain and also found an approximately linear relationship between diameter and internodal length. He determined that the internodes range in length from below 100μ to about $1,700\mu$. In a more recent analysis employing data derived from electron micrographs of the cat visual cortex, Haug (1967) found internodal lengths of about 40μ for axons 0.4μ in diameter, and about 500μ for those of 2.5μ in diameter. The values for internodal lengths obtained by each of the above investigators are similar to those for peripheral nerve fibers of the same thickness.

The Nodes of Ranvier

There is no longer any question about the existence of nodes of Ranvier in the central nervous system, for they can be unquestioningly demonstrated in electron microscope preparations (for example, see Pease, 1955; Metuzals, 1960 and 1965; Peters, 1960b and 1966; Uzman and Villegas, 1960; Andres, 1965; Bunge, Bunge, and Ris, 1961; Bunge, 1968). The earlier debates concerning the evidence for nodes in light microscope preparations of the central nervous system need not be considered here, but for details reference should be made to the reviews by Hess and Young (1952) and by Bunge (1968).

The form of the nodes in the central nervous system is very similar to that of peripheral nerves, so there is no need to give a complete account of their structure, which is summarized in Figure 1-31. Suffice it to say that at the nodes of fibers with thin sheaths, the lamellae of the myelin terminate in such a way that each successive turn of the spiral overlaps the one lying beneath it; consequently, the myelin gradually becomes thinner (Fig. 1-30). The region where the thinning occurs is termed the paranode, and here the major dense line opens up to enclose a helix of paranodal cytoplasm. The plasma membranes of the axon and the inside of the paranodal sheath form a complex in which the two membranes are separated by an interval of only 25 to 30 Å (Fig. 1-29), and the outer layer of the axolemma is modified to form a series of bands that circumscribe the axon.

It is of interest that in the paranodal regions of large diameter fibers that have thicker sheaths, the paranodal pockets of cytoplasm may have a much more irregular configuration. Thus we have encountered sheaths in which the outer lamellae terminate on the outside of the myelin, so that there are two series of pockets. One series is on the inside while the other is outside the thinning myelin, and the pockets nearest to the node are derived from the lamellae in the middle of the myelin spiral.

The important difference between the nodes in the central and peripheral nervous system is that central nerve fibers have no interdigitating processes emanating from the cytoplasm on the outsides of the adjacent myelin segments, and the nodal axon is not covered by a basal lamina (Fig. 1-31). Therefore, the nodal axon in the brain and spinal cord is bare (Fig. 1-30). Although processes of neurons and neuroglial cells may come close to this bare nodal axon, it often seems to be surrounded by an unusually large intercellular space containing a dark matrix (Metuzals, 1965; Robertson, Bodenheimer, and Stage, 1963; Peters, Proskauer, and Kaiserman-Abramof, 1968). In electron micrographs, profiles of nodes may sometimes be confused with those of initial axon segments, since both possess a similar dark undercoating of the axolemma. At the node, however, the axon does not contain the clusters of microtubules that are so characteristic of the initial segment (see Palay, Sotelo, Peters, and Orkand, 1968; Peters, Proskauer, and Kaiserman-Abramof, 1968).

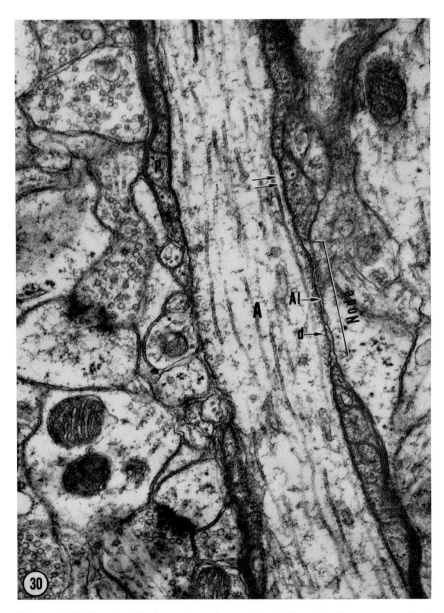

FIGURE 1-30. Longitudinal section of a node of Ranvier from rat cerebral cortex. At each of the paranodes the myelin sheath becomes thinner as the lamellae terminate in pockets (*P*) of cytoplasm. Where these pockets come close to the axolemma (*Al*), a series of periodic densities (arrows) is apparent. At the node, the axon (*A*) is bare, and the axolemma has an undercoating of dense material (*d*). X55,000.

In the central nervous system the lengths of the nodes seem to be greater than in peripheral nerves. This view was expressed by Hess and Young (1952), but insufficient information is presently available to be certain of this contention.

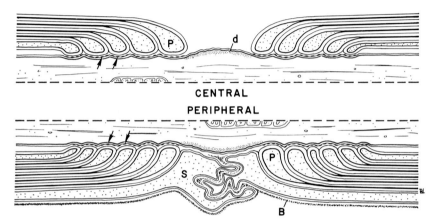

FIGURE 1-31. Diagram to compare the form of the nodal region of myelinated axons in the central (above) and peripheral (below) nervous systems. In each case, the myelin becomes thinner at the paranode as the myelin lamellae terminate to enclose pockets (P) of cytoplasm. Where these pockets indent the axolemma, the extracellular space is greatly reduced, and the outer leaflet of the axolemma forms a series of dense bands (arrows). In the central nervous system, the nodal axon is bare and the axolemma has an undercoating of dense material (d). A similar undercoating is also present at the peripheral node, but here the axon is covered by interdigitating processes that extend from the outer layer of cytoplasm (S) of the two Schwann cells. A basal lamina (B) is present on the outside of the myelin sheath in the peripheral nervous system, but absent in the central nervous system.

A few brief statements may be made to complete the picture of the node of Ranvier as well as the terminations of myelin sheaths: (1) Myelinated nerve fibers in both the central and peripheral nervous systems branch at nodes of Ranvier, and at such locations three myelin segments come together. Apart from the complication produced by the addition of one more paranode, the form of the nodal region is similar to that of the simple nodes described above. (2) In the central nervous system a nodal axon may participate in the formation of a synapse (Bodian and Taylor, 1963; Andres, 1965; Khattab, 1966). In every case so far encountered, the nodal axon is the presynaptic component and forms a protruberance that is filled with synaptic vesicles and mitochondria just like any other presynaptic element. (3) Where anterior and posterior roots leave and enter the central nervous system, there must be a node at which there is a transition between segments of peripheral and central myelin. However, no detailed accounts of this region seem to have been published. (4) A myelinated axon of the central nervous system acquires its sheath a short distance beyond the origin of the axon from the neuronal perikaryon. The short unmyelinated portion of the axon is termed the initial segment; this loses its characteristic clusters of microtubules and the undercoating of the axolemma (see Palay, Sotelo, Peters, and Orkand, 1968), where the myelin sheath commences. Where a central axon loses its sheath prior to terminating, the axon displays no unusual features and does not acquire the undercoating that characterizes both the nodal axon and the initial axon segment.

REFERENCES

ABERCROMBIE, M.: Estimation of nuclear populations from microtome sections. *Anat Rec, 94:*239, 1946.

ANDRES, K. H.: Über die Feinstruktur besonderer Einrichtungen in markhaltigen Nervenfasern des Kleinhirns der Ratte. *Z Zellforsch Mikroskop Anat, 65:*701, 1965.

ASBURY, A. K.: Schwann cell proliferation in developing mouse sciatic nerve. A radioautographic study. *J Cell Biol, 34:*735, 1967.

BARGMANN, W., and LINDNER, E.: Über den Feinbau des Nebennierenmarkes des Igels *(Erinaceus europaeus L.). Z Zellforsch Mikroskop Anat, 64:*868, 1964.

BISCHOFF, A., and MOOR, H.: Ultrastructural differences between the myelin sheaths of peripheral nerve fibers and CNS white matter. *Z Zellforsch Mikroskop Anat, 81:*303, 1967a.

BISCHOFF, A., and MOOR, H.: The ultrastructure of the "difference factor" in the myelin. *Z Zellforsch Mikroskop Anat, 81:*571, 1967b.

BODIAN, D.: Note on nodes of Ranvier in the central nervous system. *J Comp Neurol, 94:*475, 1951.

BODIAN, D., and TAYLOR, N.: Synapse arising at central node of Ranvier, and note on fixation of the central nervous system. *Science, 139:*330, 1963.

BRANTON, D.: Fracture faces of frozen myelin. *Exp Cell Res, 45:*703, 1967.

BRANTON, D.: Fracture faces of myelin. *Proc Nat Acad Sci USA, 55:* 1048, 1968.

BRANTON, D., and PARK, R. B.: Subunits in chloroplast lamellae. *J Ultrastruct Res, 19:*283, 1967.

BUNGE, R. B.: Glial cells and the central myelin sheath. *Physiol Rev, 48:*197, 1968.

BUNGE, M. B.; BUNGE, R. P., and PAPPAS, G. D.: Electron microscopic demonstration of connections between glia and myelin sheaths in the developing mammalian central nervous system. *J Cell Biol, 12:* 448, 1962.

BUNGE, M. B.; BUNGE, R. P.; PETERSON, E. R., and MURRAY, M. R.: A light and electron microscope study of long-term organized cultures of rat dorsal root ganglia. *J Cell Biol, 32:*439, 1967.

BUNGE, M. B.; BUNGE, R. P., and RIS, H.: Ultrastructural study of remyelination in an experimental lesion in adult spinal cord. *J Biophys Biochem Cytol, 10:*67, 1961.

BUNGE, R. P., and GLASS, P. M.: Some observations on myelin-glial relationships and on the etiology of the cerebrospinal fluid exchange lesion. *Ann NY Acad Sci, 122:*15, 1965.

CALEY, D. W.: Ultrastructural differences between central and peripheral myelin sheath formation in the rat. *Anat Record, 157:*223A, 1967.

CAUSEY, G.: *The Cell of Schwann.* Baltimore, Williams & Wilkins, 1960.

DE ROBERTIS, E.; GERSCHENFELD, H., and WALD, F.: Cellular mechanism of myelination in the central nervous system. *J Biophys Biochem Cytol, 4:*651, 1958.

DI CARLO, V.: Ultrastructure of the membrane of synaptic vesicles. *Nature (London), 213:*833, 1967a.

DI CARLO, V.: Electron microscopical aspects of myelin ultrastructure. *Experientia, 23:*462, 1967b.

ELFVIN, L.-G.: The ultrastructure of unmyelinated fibers in the splenic nerve of the cat. *J Ultrastruct Res, 1:*428, 1958.

ELFVIN, L.-G.: The ultrastructure of the nodes of Ranvier in cat sympathetic nerve fibers. *J Ultrastruct Res, 5:*374, 1961.

EVANS, M. J., and FINEAN, J. B.: The lipid composition of myelin from brain and peripheral nerve. *J Neurochem, 12:*729, 1965.

FERNÁNDEZ-MORÁN, H.: Electron microscope observations on the structure of the myelinated nerve fiber sheath. *Exptl Cell Res, 1:* 143, 1950.

FERNÁNDEZ-MORÁN, H.: Membrane ultrastructure in nerve cells. In Quarton, G. C.; Melnechunk, T., and Schmitt, F. O. (Eds.) : *The Neurosciences. A Study Program.* New York, Rockefeller U. P., 1967, p. 281.

FINEAN, J. B.: Further observations on the structure of myelin. *Exp Cell Res, 5:*202, 1953a.

FINEAN, J. B.: Phospholipid-cholesterol complex in the structure of myelin. *Experientia, 9:*17, 1953b.

FINEAN, J. B.: Electron microscope and x-ray diffraction studies of the effects of dehydration on the structure of nerve myelin. II. Optic nerve. *J Biophys Biochem Cytol, 8:*31, 1960.

FINEAN, J. B.: X-ray diffraction and electron microscope studies of nerve myelin. In Boyd, J. D.; Johnson, F. R., and Lever, J. D. (Eds.) : *Electron Microscopy in Anatomy.* London, Edward Arnold, 1961, p. 114.

FINEAN, J. B.: Molecular parameters in the nerve myelin sheath. *Ann NY Acad Sci, 122:*51, 1965.

FINEAN, J. B.; HAWTHORNE, H. N., and PATTERSON, J. D. E.: Structural and chemical differences between optic and sciatic nerve myelins. *J Neurochem, 1:*256, 1957.

FLEISCHHAUER, K., and WARTENBERG, H.: Elektronmikroskopische Untersuchungen über das Wachtum der Nervenfasern und über das Auftreten von Marscheiden im Corpus Callosum der Katze. *Z Zellforsch Mikroskop Anat, 83:*568, 1967.

FORRESTER, J., and PETERS, A.: Nerve fibres in optic nerve of rat. *Nature (London), 214:*245, 1967.

FRIEDE, R. L., and SAMORAJSKI, T.: Relation between the number of myelin lamellae and axon circumference in fibers of vagus and sciatic nerves of mice. *J Comp Neurol, 130:*223, 1967.

GAMBLE, H. J.: Further electron microscope studies of human foetal peripheral nerves. *J Anat (London), 100:*487, 1966.

GAMBLE, H. J., and BREATHNACH, A. S.: An electron-microscope study of human foetal peripheral nerves. *J Anat (London), 99:*573, 1965.

GASSER, H. S.: Discussion of a paper by B. Frankenhaeuser, The neuron. In Warren, K. B. (Ed.) : *Cold Spring Harbor Symposia on*

Quantitative Biology. Cold Spring Harbor, The Biological Laboratory, 1952, vol. 17, p. 32.

GENT, W. L. G., and GREGSON, N. A.: Inhomogeneity of lysolecithin-solubolized membrane systems. *Biochem J, 98*:27P, 1966.

GENT, W. L. G.; GREGSON, N. A.; GAMMACK, D. B., and RAPER, J. H.: The lipid-protein unit in myelin. *Nature, 204*:533, 1964.

GEREN, B. B.: The formation from the Schwann cell surface of myelin in the peripheral nerves of chick embryos. *Exptl Cell Res, 7*:558, 1954.

GURWITSCH, A.: Die Histogenese der Schwannscheiden Schiede, 1900. Cited from: J. Nageotte. In Penfield, W. (Ed.) : *Cytology and Cellular Pathology of the Nervous System.* New York, Hoeber, 1932, vol. 1, p. 233.

HARKIN, J. C.: A series of desmosomal attachments in the Schwann sheath of myelinated mammalian nerves. *Z Zellforsch Mirkoskop Anat, 64*:189, 1964.

HARRISON, R. G.: Neuroblast versus sheath cell in the development of peripheral nerves. *J Comp Neurol, 37*:123, 1924.

HAUG, H.: Die Länge der Internodien der Markfasern im Bereich der Sehrinde der eryachsenen Katze. *Z Zellforsch Mikroskop Anat, 83*:265, 1967.

HELD, H.: *Die Entwicklung des Nervengewebes bei den Wirbeltieren.* Leipzig, J. A. Barth, 1909.

HENDELMAN, W., and BUNGE, M. B.: Some observations on the disposition of microtubules in relation to the myelin sheath. *J Cell Biol, 31*:46A, 1966.

HERDON, R. M.: The fine structure of the rat cerebellum. II. The stellate neurons, granule cells, and glia. *J Cell Biol, 23*:277, 1964.

HESS, A.: Developmental changes in the structure of the synapse on the myelinated cell bodies of the chicken ciliary ganglion. *J Cell Biol, 25*:1, 1965.

HESS, A., and YOUNG, J. Z.: Correlation of internodal length and fibre diameter in the central nervous system. *Nature, 164*:490, 1949.

HESS, A., and YOUNG, J. Z.: The nodes of Ranvier. *Proc Roy Soc (London) Ser B, 140*:301, 1952.

HILD, W.: Myelogenesis in cultures of mammalian central nervous tissue. *Z Zellforsch Mikroskop Anat, 46*:71, 1957.

HILD, W.: Myelin formation in cultures of mammalian central nervous tissue. In Korey, S. R. (Ed.) : *The Biology of Myelin.* New York, Hoeber-Harper, 1959, p. 188.

HILLÅRP, N. A., and OLIVECRONA, H.: Role played by axons and Schwann cells in degree of myelination of peripheral nerve fibres. *Acta Anat, 2:*17, 1946.

HIRANO, A.: A confirmation of the oligodendroglial origin of myelin in the adult rat. *J Cell Biol, 38:*637, 1968.

HIRANO, A., and DEMBITZER, H. M.: A structural analysis of the myelin sheath in the central nervous system. *J Cell Biol, 34:*555, 1967.

HIRANO, A.; LEVINE, S., and ZIMMERMAN, H. M.: Remyelination in the central nervous system after cyanide intoxication. *J Neuropath Exp Neurol, 27:*234, 1968.

HIRANO, A.; ZIMMERMAN, H. M., and LEVINE, S.: Myelin in the central nervous system as observed in experimentally induced edema in the rat. *J Cell Biol, 31:*397, 1966.

HISCOE, H. B.: The distribution of nodes and incisures in normal and regenerating nerve fibers. *Anat Rec, 99:*447, 1947.

HONJIN, R.: Electron microscopic studies on the myelinated nerve fibers in the central nervous system. *Acta Anat Nipponica, 34:*43, 1959. (In Japanese).

HONJIN, R., and CHANGUS, G. W.: Electron microscopy of nerve fibers VIII. Again on the radial component in the myelin sheath. *Okajimas Folia Anat Japon, 39:*251, 1964.

HONJIN, R.; KOSAKA, T.; TAKANO, I., and HIRAMATSU, K.: Electron microscopy of nerve fibers VII. On the electron dense radial component in the laminated myelin sheath. *Okajimas Folia Anat Japon, 39:*39, 1963.

HUGHES, A. F. W.: *Aspects of Neural Ontogeny.* London and New York, Logus and Academic, 1968.

KARLSSON, U.: Comparison of the myelin period of peripheral and central origin by electron microscopy. *J Ultrastruct Res, 15:*451, 1966.

KEY, A., and RETZIUS, G.: *Studien in der Anatomie des Nervensystems und des Bindegewebes.* Stockholm, Sampson and Wallin, 1876.

KHATTAB, F. I.: Synaptic contacts at nodes of Ranvier in central nervous tissue. *Anat Record, 156:*91, 1966.

KÖLLIKER, A.: *Grundriss der Entwicklungsgeschichte des Menschen,* 1884. Cited from: J. Nageotte. In Penfield, W. (Ed.): *Cytology and Cellular Pathology of the Nervous System.* New York, Hoeber, 1932, vol. 1, p. 233.

KORN, E. D.: Structure of biological membranes. *Science, 153:*1491, 1966.

KRUGER, L., and MAXWELL, D. S.: Electron microscopy of oligodendrocytes in normal rat cerebrum. *Am J Anat, 118:*411, 1966.

LAATSCH, R. H., and COWAN, W. M.: A structural specialization at nodes of Ranvier in the central nervous system. *Nature, 210:*757, 1966.

LAMPERT, P. W.: Demyelination and remyelination in experimental allergic encephalomyelitis. Further electron microscope observations. *J Neuropathol Exptl Neurol, 24:*371, 1965.

LASCELLES, R. G., and THOMAS, P. K.: Changes due to age in internodal length in the sural nerve in man. *J Neurol Neurosurg Psychiat, 29:*40, 1966.

LUBÍNSKA, L.: 'Intercalated' internodes in nerve fibres. *Nature, 181:* 957, 1958.

LUBÍNSKA, L.: Sedentary and migratory states of Schwann cells. *Exp Cell Res Suppl, 8:*74, 1961.

LUCY, J. A.: Ultrastructure of membranes: Micellar organization. *Brit Med Bull, 24:*127, 1968.

LUSE, S. A.: Formation of myelin in the central nervous systems of mice and rats, as studied with the electron microscope. *J Biophys Biochem Cytol, 2:*777, 1956.

MATURANA, H. R.: The fine anatomy of the optic nerve of Anurans — an electron microscope study. *J Biophys Biochem Cytol, 7:*107, 1960.

METUZALS, J.: Ultrastructure of myelinated nerve fibers and nodes of Ranvier in the central nervous system of the frog. In Houwind, A. L., and Spit, B. J. (Eds.): *The Proceedings of the European Regional Conference on Electron Microscopy, Delft, 1960,* Delft, Nederlandse Vereniging voor Electronenmicroscopie, vol. 2, 1960, p. 799.

METUZALS, J.: Ultrastructure of myelinated nerve fibers in the central nervous system of the frog. *J Ultrastruct Res, 8:*30, 1963.

METUZALS, J.: Ultrastructure of the nodes of Ranvier and their surrounding structures in the central nervous system. *Z Zellforsch Mikroskop Anat, 65:*719, 1965.

MIZUHIRA, V., and OZAWA, H.: On the fine structure of nerve myelin by means of glutaraldehyde fixation. *J Electron Microscopy, 16:* 169, 1967.

MURRAY, M. R.: Factors bearing on myelin formation in vitro. In Korey, S. R. (Ed.): *The Biology of Myelin.* New York, Harper, 1959, p. 201.

MURRAY, M. R.: Myelin formation and neuron histogenesis in tissue culture. In Richter, D. (Ed.) : *Comparative Neurochemistry*. Proc. Fifth Int. Neurochem. Symp. Oxford, England, Pergamon, 1964, p. 49.

NAGEOTTE, J.: Phénomènes de sécrétion dans le protoplasma des cellules névrogliques de la substance grise. *Compt Rend Soc Biol Paris, 68:*1068, 1910.

NAPOLITANO, L.; LEBARON, F., and SCALETTI, J.: Preservation of myelin lamellar structure in the absence of lipid: A correlated chemical and morphological study. *J Cell Biol, 34:*817, 1967.

PALAY, S. L.: Principles of cellular organization in the nervous system. In Quarton, G. C.; Melnechuk, T., and Schmitt, F. O. (Eds.) : *The Neurosciences*. New York, Rockefeller U. P., 1967, p. 24.

PALAY, S. L.; McGEE-RUSSELL, S. M.; GORDON, S., and GRILLO, M. A.: Fixation of neural tissues for electron microscopy by perfusion with solutions of osmium tetroxide. *J Cell Biol, 12:*385, 1962.

PALAY, S. L.; SOTELO, C.; PETERS, A., and ORKAND, P. M.: The axon hillock and the initial segment. *J Cell Biol, 38:*193, 1968.

PEASE, D. C.: Nodes of Ranvier in the central nervous system. *J Comp Neurol, 103:*11, 1955.

PENFIELD, W.: Oligodendroglia and its relation to classical neuroglia. *Brain, 47:*430, 1924.

PERIER, O., and DE HARVEN, E.: Electron microscope observations on myelinated tissue cultures of mammalian cerebellum. In *Cytology of Nervous Tissue, Proceedings of the Anatomical Society of Great Britain and Ireland*. London, Taylor and Francis, 1961, p. 78.

PETERS, A.: The structure of myelin sheaths in the central nervous system of *Xenopus laevis* (Daudin) . *J Biophys Biochem Cytol, 7:* 121, 1960a.

PETERS, A.: The formation and structure of myelin sheaths in the central nervous system. *J Biophys Biochem Cytol, 8:*431, 1960b.

PETERS, A.: The development of peripheral nerves in *Xenopus laevis*. In Boyd, J. D.; Johnson, F. R., and Lever, J. D. (Eds.) : *Electron Microscopy in Anatomy*. London, Edward Arnold, 1961a, p. 142.

PETERS, A.: A radial component of central myelin sheaths. *J Biophys Biochem Cytol, 11:*733, 1961b.

PETERS, A.: Myelinogenesis in the central nervous system. In *Proceedings, IV. International Congress of Neuropathology* (Munich, 1961). *Electronmicroscopy and Biology*. Stuttgart, Georg Thieme Verlag, 1962, vol. 2, p. 50.

PETERS, A.: Further observations on the structure of myelin sheaths in the central nervous system. *J Cell Biol, 20:*281, 1964a.

PETERS, A.: Observations on the connexions between myelin sheaths and glial cells in the optic nerves of young rats. *J Anat (London), 98:*125, 1964b.

PETERS, A.: The node of Ranvier in the central nervous system. *Quart J Exptl Physiol, 51:*229, 1966.

PETERS, A., and MUIR, A. R.: The relationship between axons and Schwann cells during development of peripheral nerves in the rat. *Quart J Exptl Physiol, 44:*117, 1959.

PETERS, A.; PROSKAUER, C. C., and KAISERMAN-ABRAMOF, I. R.: The small pyramidal neuron of the rat cerebral cortex: the axon hillock and initial segment. *J Cell Biol, 39:*604, 1968.

PETERS, A., and PROSKAUER, C. C.: Unpublished observations, 1968.

PETERSON, E. R.; CRAIN, S. M., and MURRAY, M. R.: Activities of Schwann cells during myelin formation *in vitro. Anat Rec, 130:*357 (Abstract) , 1958.

POMERAT, C. M.; HENDELMAN, W. J.; RAIBORN, C. W., and MASSEY, J. F.: Dynamic activities of nervous tissue *in vitro.* In Hyden, H. (Ed.) : *The Neuron.* Amsterdam, Elsevier, 1967, p. 119.

RAMON Y CAJAL, S.: *Degeneration and Regeneration of the Nervous System,* (translated by R. May) . London, Oxford U. P., 1928.

RANVIER, L.: Contributions à l'histologie et à la physiologie des nerfs périphériques. *Compt Rend, 73:*1168, 1871.

RANVIER, L.: Sur les élements conjonctifs de la moelle èpiniére. *Compt Rend, 77:*1299, 1873.

RANVIER, L.: *Traité Technique d'Histologie.* Paris, F. Savy, 1875.

RANVIER, L.: Des modifications de structure qu'éprouvent les tubes nerveux en passant des racines spinales dans la moelle épinière. *Compt Rend, 95:*1066, 1882.

REVEL, J. P., and KARNOVSKY, M. J.: Hexagonal array of subunits in intercellular junctions of the mouse heart and liver. *J Cell Biol, 33:*C7, 1967.

REVEL, J. P., and HAMILTON, D. W.: The double nature of the intermediate dense line in peripheral nerve myelin. *Anat Record, 163:*7, 1969.

RICHARDSON, K. C.; JARETT, L., and FINKE, E. H.: Embedding in epoxy resins for ultrathin sectioning in electron microscopy. *Stain Technol, 35:*313, 1960.

RIO-HORTEGA, P. DEL: Son homologables la glia de escasas radiociones y la célula de Schwann? *Bol Soc Espan Biol, 10:*25, 1922.

RIO-HORTEGA, P. DEL: La glie à radiations peu nombreuses et la cellule de Schwann sont elles homologables? *Compt Rend Soc Biol, 91:* 818, 1924.

RIO-HORTEGA, P. DEL: Tercera aportación al conocimiento morfológico e interpretación functional de la oligodendroglia. *Mem Real Soc Espan Hist Nat, 14:*5, 1928.

ROBERTSON, J. D.: The ultrastructure of adult vertebrate peripheral myelinated nerve fibers in relation to myelinogenesis. *J Biophys Biochem Cytol, 1:*271, 1955.

ROBERTSON, J. D.: The ultrastructure of Schmidt-Lantermann clefts and related shearing defects of the myelin sheath. *J Biophys Biochem Cytol, 4:*39, 1958.

ROBERTSON, J. D.: Preliminary observations on the ultrastructure of nodes of Ranvier. *Z Zellforsch Mikroskop Anat, 50:*553, 1959.

ROBERTSON, J. D.: The molecular structure and contact relationships of cell membranes. *Progr Biophys, 10:*343, 1960.

ROBERTSON, J. D.: The unit membrane. In Boyd, J. D.: Johnson, F. R., and Lever, J. D. (Eds.): *Electron Microscopy in Anatomy.* London, Edward Arnold, 1961, p. 74.

ROBERTSON, J. D.: Current problems of unit membrane structure and contact relationships. In Rodahl, K., and Issekutz, B., Jr. (Eds.): *Nerve as a Tissue.* New York, Harper, 1966, p. 11.

ROBERTSON, J. D.; BODENHEIMER, T. S., and STAGE, D. E.: The ultrastructure of Mauthner cell synapses and nodes in goldfish brains. *J Cell Biol, 19:*159, 1963.

ROSENBLUTH, J.: The fine structure of acoustic ganglia in the rat. *J Cell Biol, 12:*329, 1962.

ROSENBLUTH, J.: Redundant myelin sheaths and other ultrastructure features of the toad cerebellum. *J Cell Biol, 28:*73, 1966.

ROSENBLUTH, J., and PALAY, S. L.: The fine structure of nerve cell bodies and their myelin sheaths in the eighth nerve ganglion of the goldfish. *J Biophys Biochem Cytol, 9:*853, 1961.

ROSS, L. L.; BORNSTEIN, M. B., and LEHRER, G. M.: Electron microscopic observations of rat and mouse cerebellum in tissue culture. *J Cell Biol, 14:*19, 1962.

SCHMIDT, W. J.: Doppelbrechung und Feinbau der Markscheide der Nerverfazern. *Z Zellforsch, 23:*657, 1936.

SCHMITT, F. O., and BEAR, R. S.: The ultrastructure of the nerve axon sheath. *Biol Rev, 14:*27, 1939.

SCHMITT, F. O.; BEAR, R. S., and PALMER, K. J.: X-ray diffraction studies on the structure of the nerve myelin sheath. *J Cellular Comp Physiol, 18:*31, 1941.

SJÖSTRAND, F. S.: Electron microscopic demonstration of a membrane structure isolated from nerve tissue. *Nature, 165:*482, 1950.

SJÖSTRAND, F. S.: The structure and formation of the myelin sheath. In Rose, A. S., and Pearson, C. M. (Eds.) : *Mechanisms of Demyelination.* New York, McGraw, 1963, p. 1.

SPEIDEL, C. C.: Studies on living nerves. The movements of individual sheath cells and nerve sprouts correlated with the process of myelin sheath formation in amphibian larvae. *J Exper Zool, 61:*279, 1932.

SPEIDEL, C. C.: Studies on living nerves. Activities of amoeboid growth cones, sheath cells, and myelin segments as revealed by prolonged observation of individual nerve fibers in frog tadpoles. *Amer J Anat, 52:*1, 1933.

SPEIDEL, C. C.: Studies on living nerves. Growth, regeneration and myelination of peripheral nerves in salamanders. *Biol Bull, 68:*140, 1935.

SPEIDEL, C. C.: *In vitro* studies of myelinated nerve fibers. In Bourne, G. H., and Danielli, J. F. (Eds.) : *International Review of Cytology.* New York and London, Academic, 1964, vol. 16, p. 173.

SULZMANN, R.: Die mikroskopische Morphologie der zentralen markhaltigen Nervenfaser. *Wiss Z Friedrich-Schiller-Univ Jena Math-Natur Reihe, 11:*197, 1962.

TAKAHASHI, K., and HAMA, K.: Some observations on the fine structure of the synaptic area in the ciliary ganglion of the chick. *Z Zellforsch Mikroskop Anat, 67:*174, 1965.

THOMAS, P. K.: The connective tissue of peripheral nerve: an electron microscope study. *J Anat (London), 97:*35, 1963.

THOMAS, P. K., and YOUNG, J. Z.: Internode lengths in the nerves of fishes. *J Anat (London), 83:*336, 1949.

TOURNEUX, F., and LE GOFF, R.: Note sur les étranglements des tubes nerveux de la moelle épinière. *J Anat Physiol, 11:*403, 1875.

UZMAN, B. G.: The spiral configuration of myelin lamellae. *J Ultrastruct Res, 11:*208, 1964.

UZMAN, B. G., and NOGUEIRA-GRAF, G.: Electron microscope studies of the formation of nodes of Ranvier in mouse sciatic nerves. *J Biophys Biochem Cytol, 3:*589, 1957.

UZMAN, B. G., and VILLEGAS, G. M.: A comparison of nodes of Ranvier in sciatic nerves with node-like structures in optic nerves of the mouse. *J Biophys Biochem Cytol, 7:*761, 1960.

VAUGHN, J. E.: An electron microscopic analysis of gliogenesis in rat optic nerves. *Z Zellforsch Mikroskop Anat, 94:*293, 1969.

VIZOSO, A. D., and YOUNG, J. Z.: Internode length and fibre diameter in developing and regeneration nerves. *J Anat (London), 82:*110, 1948.

WALBERG, F.: Further electron microscopical investigations of the inferior olive of the cat. In Bargmann, W., and Schade, J. P. (Eds.) : *Progress in Brain Research,* Vol. *6: Topics in Basic Neurology.* Amsterdam, Elsevier, 1964, p. 59.

WEBSTER, H. DE F.: Transient, focal accumulation of axonal mitochondria during the early stages of Wallerian degeneration. *J Cell Biol, 12:*361, 1962.

WEBSTER, H. DE F.: Some ultrastructural features of segmental demyelination and myelin regeneration in peripheral nerve. In Singer, M., and Schade, J. P. (Eds.) : *Progress in Brain Research,* Vol. *13: Mechanisms of Neural Regeneration.* Amsterdam, Elsevier, 1964, p. 151.

WEBSTER, DE F. H., and SPIRO, D.: Phase and electron microscope studies of experimental demyelination. I. Variations in myelin sheath contour in normal guinea pig sciatic nerve. *J Neuropath Exp Neurol, 19:*42, 1960.

WEBSTER, H. DE F.; SPIRO, D.; WAKSMAN, B., and ADAMS, R. D.: Phase and electron microscopic studies of experimental demyelination. II. Schwann cell changes in guinea pig sciatic nerves during experimental diphtheritic neuritis. *J Neuropathol Exptl Neurol, 20:* 5, 1961.

WEISS, P.: Nerve patterns: the mechanics of nerve growth. *Growth, 5 (Suppl.):*163, 1941.

WEISS, P.: Nervous System (Neurogenesis) . In Willer, B. H.; Weiss, P., and Hamburger, V. (Eds.) : *Analysis of Development.* Philadelphia, Saunders, 1955, p. 346.

WENDELL-SMITH, C. P.; BLUNT, M. J., and BALDWIN, F.: The ultrastructural characterization of macroglial cell types. *J Comp Neurol, 127:*219, 1966.

WESTON, J. A.: A radioautographic analysis of the migration and localization of trunk neural crest cells in the chick. *Develop Biol, 6:*279, 1963.

WORTHINGTON, C. R., and BLAUROCK, A. E.: Electron density model for nerve myelin. *Nature, 218:*87, 1968.

Chapter 2

THE BIOCHEMISTRY OF
THE MYELIN SHEATH

A. N. DAVISON

THE CHEMICAL COMPOSITION OF THE ADULT
MYELIN SHEATH

EARLY WORK ON THE CHEMICAL composition of the grey matter in comparison with the myelin-rich white matter and on the chemical content of myelinated in comparison with nonmyelinated nervous tissue led to the view that myelin was composed of both proteins and lipids. It appeared that cholesterol, galactolipids, and the phospholipids, — sphingomyelin and phosphatides of ethanolamine, choline, serine, and inositol, were the chief lipid species, and it was thought that the central nervous system protein was a chloroform-methanol soluble proteolipid protein. These conclusions were supported by the analyses of Lowry, and Robins, and their collaborators on the white matter in Ammon's horn of rabbit (Lowry *et al.*, 1954) and the monkey cerebellar cortex (Robins, Eydt, and Smith, 1956). However, axoplasm and glial cell processes were unavoidably present in the tracts analyzed, and the direct proof of the composition of myelin had to wait for the development of improved techniques for its isolation from nervous tissue.

Isolation of Myelin

The application of conventional methods of differential centrifugation to the separation of subcellular fractions from brain (Brody and Bain, 1952) led to the isolation of an unusually lipid-rich mitochondrial fraction (Schwartz, Bachelard, and McIlwain, 1962; Biran and Bartley, 1961). This subcellular fraction proved to be heterogeneous, for it contained large amounts of myelin (Petrushka and Giuditta, 1959; Aldridge, 1957; Petersen and Schou, 1955). August, Davison, and Williams (1961) adopted the methods of Korey (1957), Korey, Orchen, and Brotz (1958), and

Whittaker (1959) for the separation of myelin by centrifugation of a crude brain mitochondrial fraction suspended in 0.25M sucrose (10 ml) over a discontinuous density gradient consisting of 10 ml of 0.5M and 10 ml of 1.75M sucrose. The white material floating at the top of the centrifuge tube was then separated, diluted with water, and collected as a pellet by further centrifuging at 12,000 g for 10 minutes. This material was found by light and electron microscopy to be rich in myelin and could be conveniently freeze-dried for storage below 0°C. Laatsch, Kies, Gordon, and Alvord (1962) centrifuged brain suspensions in 0.88M layered with 0.25M sucrose and collected the myelin layer floating at the interface of the centrifuge tube.

A third method for the isolation of myelin was developed by Norton (Autilio, Norton, and Terry, 1964). In this method fresh white matter from oxen is stored on ice, and then homogenized in 0.32M sucrose solution using a Dounce homogenizer, and the strained suspension layered over 0.65M sucrose (density, 1.085). After centrifugation for 30 minutes at 40,000 g, myelin concentrates as a white, well-packed, cohesive layer at the interface. The myelin is collected and the procedure repeated. The crude myelin is subjected to osmotic shock by suspending it in distilled water and resedimentating at 40,000 g for 10 minutes. Finally the pellet is resuspended in 0.32M sucrose and layered over a continuous sucrose gradient, from 0.32M (density, 1.045) to 0.8M sucrose (density, 1.103) and centrifuged at 53,000 g for one hour. In these preparations four distinctive layers are observed: two small bands near the top of the tube and two major white bands farther down. One of these lower bands is of so-called light myelin (in the middle of the tube density equivalent to approximately 0.5M) and the other, heavy myelin (towards the bottom of the gradient density equivalent to approximately 0.7M). The myelin is collected and washed free of sucrose by repeated suspension in distilled water and centrifugation. Electron microscopy shows that this gives a myelin preparation of very high purity. Little difference was seen in the appearance and chemical composition of the light and heavy bands of bovine myelin (Norton and Autilio, 1966). It now seems probable that the appearance on separation

of the two or more subfractions (Cuzner and Davison, 1968) may
depend on the length of storage of nervous tissue before fractionation (Adams and Fox, 1968; Lumsden and colleagues, unpublished observation). Certainly, storage of nervous tissue at −10° to
20°C for longer than a few weeks produces changes in the character of myelin (O'Brien, Sampson, and Stern, 1967), so that on fractionation a fatty layer also separates at the top of the centrifuge
tube (Howell, Davison, and Oxberry, 1968). A scheme for the
preparation of purified myelin is shown in Figure 2-1.

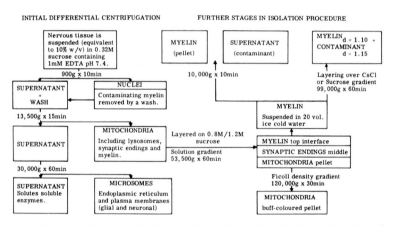

FIGURE 2-1. Method for the isolation of myelin and subcellular fractions from
nervous tissue. The following outline scheme indicates the main stages of
one such procedure developed in the author's laboratory. Reference should
be made to original papers (Cuzner and Davison, 1968), for full practical
details and the essential morphological and biochemical controls provided.
In the following scheme figures relate to centrifuge fields and length of cen-
trifigation in minutes.

Isolation of peripheral nerve myelin is generally complicated by
the presence of connective tissue and adipose tissue (Evans and
Finean, 1965). This problem is diminished by using intradural
spinal roots as a source. O'Brien *et al.* (1967) prepared peripheral
nerve myelin from fresh bovine spinal cord intradural roots, using
a modification of the method of Autilio *et al.* (1964). The nerve
was homogenized in 0.32M sucrose, using a Waring blender with
a rotorstator attachment. Horrocks (1967) used squirrel monkey

brachial plexus and found it necessary to first mince the tissue, but even after repeated homogenization, a substantial residue remained undispersed. The yield of myelin from brachial plexus was thereby reduced. A new and promising method for the isolation of peripheral nervous system myelin has been introduced by Adams, Abdulla, Turner, and Bayliss (1968). In this technique the nerve sample is cut on a freezing microtome, and collagen is dissociated by suspension in a glycine buffer pH 6; myelin is separated by layering over 0.8M sucrose solution.

Various other groups of investigators have used these or similar methods for the isolation of central nervous system myelin. More recent modifications introduced into the general procedure are the use of cesium chloride gradients (Thompson, Goodwin, and Cumings, 1967) and special methods for the isolation of myelin from the developing brain.

Purity

Electron microscopy of multiple sections of purified myelin preparations show minimal contamination of such samples by other subcellular particles and by stainable cytoplasmic contaminants. However, rigorous purification is difficult, for during preparation separated myelin lamellae tend to form vesicles, so that axoplasm and other nonmyelin materials are trapped (Whittaker, personal communication). It is also probable that myelin preparations contain axolemma as well as variable amounts of other membranes such as those derived from neuronal and glial plasma membranes.

Biochemical Criteria. Some indication of the purity of a myelin preparation may be obtained by chemical analysis during successive stages in the fractionation procedure and by assay of marker enzymes thought to be associated with other subcellular particles. Thus on purification there is a steady decrease in the chloroform-methanol (2:1, v/v) insoluble residue (finally not more than 1% and 5% of the dry weight for light and heavy myelin respectively) and a corresponding increase in lipid and proteolipid protein content (Autilio *et al.,* 1964; Norton and Autilio, 1966). The combined nucleic acid content (DNA + RNA) of myelin has been shown to be the equivalent of about $0.73\mu g$ P/mg dry weight (but see Edström, 1964). Adams, Davison, and Gregson (1963) found little enzyme activity which could be associated with subcellular contaminants in myelin isolated from whole adult rat brain, and the absence of adenosine triphosphatase (ATPase) activity has been used as a criteria of purity by Norton, Poduslo, and Suzuki (1967).

Composition of Adult Myelin

Lipid Analysis

Extraction. During the preparation of purified myelin it is possible that there may be some loss of water-soluble constituents (e.g. electrolytes, proteins, carbohydrates), but it is probable that such losses are quite small. However, there may be a systematic loss of myelin during succesive water washes. The first step in analysis is the determination of the dry weight myelin. This may be achieved either by simply weighing freeze-dried material or by taking a sample to constant weight through drying at $110°C$, but great care must be taken to ensure that sucrose and other solutes are not present. Lipids should be extracted from fresh nervous tissue or from freeze-dried samples. Where extracts are to be stored for long periods, they should be kept over nitrogen in the cold and 0.1% 2:6-di-*tert*-butyl-*p*-cresol may be included wherever possible to minimize autoxidation of lipids, glycerophosphatides and cholesterol. Determination of the lipid content may be effected by weighing the total protein-free lipid, but this procedure is not without difficulty, since proteolipid-protein is soluble in chloroform-methanol (2:1, v/v), and complete removal of the protein is both time consuming (Folch, Lees, and Sloane-Stanley, 1957) and inefficient. Probably the best procedure is to determine the weight of lipid by direct analysis and to assess the protein of the chloroform-methanol extract by calculation from the extinction coefficient (see below).

Analysis of Whole Lipid Extract. (1) Sterols. When sufficient material is available, it is possible to determine total cholesterol, galactolipid, and phospholipid content by direct analysis of the washed chloroform-methanol lower phase, although these analyses are of *limited* value. Thus during development sterols (desmosterol, 7-dehydrocholesterol, etc.) other than cholesterol may be present. Gas-liquid chromatography has successfully been used to separate and analyze the various sterols in myelin (Fumagalli, Grossi, Paoletti, and Paoletti, 1964) and 7-dehydrocholesterol may be conveniently determined from the extinction at 282.5 mμ. Traces of sterols may also be analyzed by a combination of chromatographic procedures and mass spectrometry (Weiss, Galli, Grossi, and Paoletti, 1968). Mature brain contains only very small amounts of sterols other than cholesterol, and the latter is present in the unesterified form (Adams and Davison, 1959). It has been claimed by Young and Hulcher (1966) that 4 percent of myelin total lipid is esterified cholesterol. It appears likely that the long-chain fatty acid cholesterol esters found by Young and Hulcher were formed by esterification during the preparation and separation of the lipid extract.

(2) Galactolipids. Galactolipid determinations relying on the anthrone or orcinol reaction give higher values than can be accounted for by cerebrosides present, and this is particularly true during development. In addition, total galactolipid includes gangliosides and sulphatides as well as the various cerebrosides, so that weight assessments based on multiplying lipid galactose by 4.6 necessarily give imprecise answers.

(3) Gangliosides. The quantitative isolation and analysis of gangliosides depends on several factors. Consequently, great care has to be exercised in order to completely extract these more water-soluble glycolipids. Svennerholm (1964) uses a preliminary extraction with boiling chloroform-methanol (1:2, v/v) for two hours, followed by separation on a silicic acid column and elution with chloroform-methanol (1:4, v/v). Gangliosides may be analyzed by the determination of lipid-bound N-acetyl-neuraminic acid (NANA) and galactosamine. Alternatively, gangliosides can be recovered by aqueous partition of an initial complete chloroform-methanol (2:1, v/v) extract (for details see Suzuki, 1965a, 1965b). In Suzuki's procedure the separated upper phase is dialyzed, and total ganglioside is determined by analysis of its NANA content.

(4) Phospholipids. Although analysis of lipid phosphorus gives exact results, there are many different phospholipid species with different molecular weights present in myelin. It is, therefore, preferable to record analyses in terms of moles of phospholipid.

Analysis of Separated Lipid Fractions. Complete lipid analysis of samples is considerably simplified by preliminary chromatographic separation. This is carried out either on a column (Davison and Wajda, 1959a; Svennerholm, 1964), or by thin layer chromatography (Cuzner and Davison, 1967; Norton and Autilio, 1966). Where large amounts of lipid are available, it is possible to make use of chromatographic separation on alumina (Davison and Wajda, 1959a; Svennerholm, 1964) or silicic acid (Fig. 2-2,

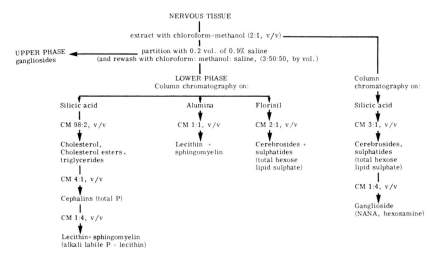

Scheme for the preliminary fractionation of main lipid classes before analysis. (Svennerholm, 1964)

CM = chloroform-methanol mixtures.

FIGURE 2-2.

Rouser, O'Brien, and Heller, 1961; Rouser *et al.* 1964; O'Brien and Sampson, 1965). Galactolipid and sulphatides may be isolated by column chromatography on DEAE in the acetate form (Svennerholm and Thorin, 1962; McKhann and Ho, 1967). These macromethods have been widely applied to the analysis of whole brain and white matter, but insufficient lipid is usually available for this technique to be applied to small myelin samples. Amounts of lipid ranging from 1 to 5 mg (often available in myelin preparations) may be transferred to thin layer chromatographic plates prepared with silicic acid (e.g. Kiesel gel G). The plates are developed with suitable solvent mixtures (e.g. chloroform:methanol:aqueous ammonia 62.5% w/v) and lipid species visualized (e.g. by exposure to iodine vapor or by staining with bromothymol blue 0.04% w/v in 0.01N KOH); for some estimations it may be necessary to run duplicate samples, one of which is covered and the other sprayed as a marker. Each lipid area may be ringed, and the silicic acid zone removed to a small column for elution with suitable solvent mixtures (Cuzner and Davison, 1967). Further subfractionation can be effected by prepacking the chromatography column with a suitable adsorbent before transferring the powdered silicic acid lipid zone to the column and submitting the whole to stepwise gradient elution. Other authors (e.g. Skipski, Peterson, and Barclay, 1964; Jatzkewitz, 1961) have adopted alternative methods for recovery and analysis of lipids. Dawson has used an ingenious method based on differential hydrolysis rates. He has used either paper chromatography (Dawson, 1960) or high voltage ionophoresis (Dawson, Hemington, and Davenport, 1962) for the separation and analysis of phospholipids. Standard analytical methods may be used for the estimation of each lipid (Table 2-I) with, in addition, gas-lipid chromatography of sterols and fatty acids. It should also be possible to apply some of the recent techniques (Renkonen, 1966) for the analysis of lipid subspecies to myelin. Gangliosides may be separated by qualitative thin layer chromatography using chloroform-methanol, 2.5N NH_4OH (60:40:9, by volume), as the solvent, followed by spraying with a suitable resorcinol reagent. Individual major gangliosides may be determined by quantitative thin layer chromatography by using the conditions described by Korey and Gonatas (1963) and Suzuki (1965).

TABLE 2-I

SOME METHODS FOR THE ANALYSIS OF LIPIDS

Lipid to be Analyzed	Solution to be Used	Method	Reference
Gangliosides (total)	Crude lipid extract	NANA estimation	Svennerholm (1957) Miettinen and Takki-Luukkainen (1959)
Gangliosides (individual)	Crude lipid extract followed by TLC	Hexosamine Stearate (GLC)	Elson and Morgan (1933) Kishimoto, Davies, and Radin (1965)
Neutral fats	Fraction from column chromatography	Glycerol estimation	Van Handel and Zilversmit (1957)
Cholesterol	Lipid extracts	Cholesterol	Sperry and Webb (1950) Davison, Dobbing, Morgan, and Payling Wright (1958) Hanel and Dam (1955)
Galactolipids	Total lipid extract followed by chromatography	Hexose estimation Hexose estimation Sphingosine estimation	Svennerholm (1956) Radin (1958) Lauter and Trams (1962)
Sulphatide	Total lipid extract + chromatography	Hexose Sphingosine Sulphate	see galactolipids Davison and Gregson (1962) Kean (1968)
Phospholipids	Total lipid extract + chromatography	Phosphorus	Martland and Robinson (1926) Bartlett (1959) Fiske and Subarrow (1925) as modified by Ernster, Zetterström, and Lindberg (1950)
Choline phospholipids	Total lipid extract + chromatography	Choline	Smits (1957) Böttcher, Pries, and Van Gent (1961)
Ethanolamine and serine containing lipid	Total lipid extract + chromatography	Ethanolamine + serine	Axelrod, Reichenthal, and Brodie (1953)
Plasmalogen	Total lipid extract + chromatography	Amino nitrogen Iodination Aldehydogenic groups	Lea and Rhodes, (1954) Williams, Anderson, and Jasik (1962) Gray and MacFarlane (1958)

Selective hydrolysis methods for the analysis of phospholipids: Dawson (1962), Brockerhoff (1963), and Hübscher, Hawthorne, and Kemp (1960).

Lipid Composition of Vertebrate Myelin Samples

Myelin accounts for about 50 percent of the dry weight of ox white matter and for 65 percent of the total lipid (Norton and Autilio, 1966). Varying proportions of lipid are present in myelin isolated from the brain of different vertebrate species (Cuzner, Davison, and Gregson, 1965b). In the adult rat about 30 percent of the dry weight is protein, the rest being lipid. In species such as the frog and dogfish, relatively more protein is present, and in this respect the myelin has a composition closer to that of other biological membranes. In general, the lipid composition of the total central nervous system is similar to that of the white matter (Table 2-II), and there are relatively small differences between various species. Often larger differences are to be found between

TABLE 2 - II
THE CHEMICAL COMPOSITION OF MYELIN

Constituent	Rat (brain)	Human (brain)	Ox (brain)	Ox (peripheral nerve)
Protein (% dry wt.)	36[1]	21.8[2] 29.7[3] 47[1]	29.5[1]	24.1[4]
Lipid composition µmols/mg lipid				
Cholesterol	0.670[1]	0.850[1]	0.622[1]	0.645[4]
Total galactolipid	0.356[6]	0.295	0.442	—
cerebroside	0.222	0.248	0.283	0.161
sulphatide	0.045	0.051	0.041[3]	0.016
gangliosides	0.003[8]	—	0.003[8]	—
Total phospholipid	0.630	0.560	0.580	—
ethanolamine phospholipid	0.283	0.250	0.205	0.197
serine phospholipid	0.098	0.108	0.109	0.109
choline phospholipid	0.165	0.111	0.112	0.158
inositol monophosphatide	0.028	0.009	0.018	—
sphingomyelin	0.054	0.085	0.089	0.203
phosphatidic acid	0.042[7]	—	—	—
cardiolipin	0.005[7]	0.0025	—	—
Total plasmalongen	0.310	0.236	0.170	—
Guinea pig forebrain myelin, calculated results				
Triphosphoinositides	0.03[5]			
Diphosphoinositides	0.01[5]			

[1]Cuzner *et al.* (1965).
[2]O'Brien and Sampson (1965).
[3]Norton and Autilio (1966).
[4]O'Brien, Sampson, and Stern (1967).
[5]Eichberg and Dawson (1965).
[6]Norton, unpublished results.
[7]Sheltawy and Dawson (1968).
[8]Calculated as monosialogangliosides after Suzuki *et al.* (1967).

analyses reported by various laboratories studying myelin from the same species of animal; this may be ascribed to different techniques used for lipid analysis.

In the entire rat brain about 35 percent of the total cholesterol is localized in myelin, and in ox white matter about 50 percent of the sterol is found in this fraction (Norton and Autilio, 1966; Soto, 1964). Myelin, like other plasma membranes, differs from intracellular membranes in being rich in cholesterol in comparison to phospholipid. It also contains relatively little polysaccharide and only small, although definite, amounts of ganglioside. Table 2-III shows the differences in composition of rat liver plasma membrane and rat brain myelin. There are also marked differences in fatty acid content of the various types of membrane. For example, the cell plasma membrane lipids are esterified with shorter chains than the more saturated fatty acids of myelin. In addition to having a high cholesterol-phospholipid ratio, myelin is characterized by its content of cerebrosides (about 53% of that in whole brain). This galactolipid is present in much smaller

TABLE 2 - III
COMPOSITION OF RAT LIVER PLASMA MEMBRANE
AND RAT BRAIN MYELIN*

	Liver Cell Membrane	Myelin
Lipid % dry wt	40.3	68.8
Protein	57.9	31.2
Lipids as % (by wt) of total lipid		
Total neutral glycerides (mainly triglyceride)	4.7	0
Total sterols	15.7	27.4
Cholesterol, free	13.6	27.3
Cholesterol, ester	3.2	0
Free fatty acid	6.8	0
Total galactolipid	—	31.7
Total phospholipid	39.0	44.9
Ethanolamine phospholipid	6.0	17.7
Phosphatidylserine	3.2	7.6
Phosphatidylinositol	2.8	1.2
Phosphatidylcholine	14.3	11.5
Sphingomyelin	7.2	3.1

*Rat liver cell membranes were prepared by the method of Neville (1960) and were essentially free of mitochondria and endoplasmic reticulum (Skipski, Barclay, Archibald, Terebus-Kekish, Reichman, and Good, 1965). Myelin was prepared and analyzed from 425-day-old rat brain (Norton, 1968). In the table only the most prominent lipids are listed. See also Pfleger, Anderson, and Synder (1968).

amounts in other types of membrane. The most abundant myelin phospholipid is phosphatidal ethanolamine. Less abundant are phosphatidylcholine (lecithin), phosphatidylserine and sphingomyelin. Small amounts of phosphatidic acid, inositol phosphatide, and polyphosphoinositides are present, and only traces of cardiolipin. The small amount of triphosphoinositide that are present in the brain are predominantly localized in myelin (Norton and Autilio, 1966; Eichberg and Dawson, 1965). This agrees with the results of Sheltawy and Dawson (1966), who showed that myelinated peripheral nerve contains relatively high proportions of triphosphoinositide to only a small amount in nonmyelinated nerve. However, the most striking difference in the lipid composition of peripheral compared to central myelin is that the former contains less galactolipid and significantly more sphingomyelin. The glycerophosphatides from peripheral nerve (ox spinal root) myelin contain low proportions of polyunsaturated fatty acids, whereas linoleate comprises 5.6 percent of the total lecithin fatty acid. In central myelin linoleate accounts for only 0.5 percent of the total (O'Brien *et al.,* 1967). There are also differences in the proportions of sphingolipid long-chain fatty acids (C_{25} and C_{26}). In the peripheral nerve myelin sphingolipids, very long chain fatty acids make up less than 2 percent of the whole, while in the central nervous system myelin they account for 5 to 20 percent of total fatty acids.

Protein Composition of Vertebrate Myelin Samples

It has long been known that nervous tissue contains a tryptophan-rich, keratin-like protein which resists digestion at different extremes of pH and withstands proteolytic attack (Adams and Davison, 1965). Since neurokeratin is predominantly found in nerve tracts, it has been considered a fundamental myelin protein. Further advance in our knowledge of the nature of neurokeratin and the myelin proteins had to await the development of less drastic extraction methods. It was, therefore, an important step when Folch and Lees (1951) noted solubilization of protein by extraction of nervous tissue with chloroform-methanol. Since this protein was soluble in organic solvents, and since it contained lipids, it was named proteolipid. This name was given to distinguish the protein from the water-soluble type of lipoprotein. The denatured proteolipid (together with some lipid) can be separated from chloroform-methanol by either evaporating to dryness (Folch *et al.*, 1957) or by treating the extract with an aqueous solution of controlled ionic strength and pH (Webster and Folch, 1961). The released protein is resistant to both endopeptidase and exopeptidase action and has a high sulphur content. Consequently, in many respects it is similar to the classical neurokeratin.

Proteolipids are five times more concentrated in white than in grey matter (Folch and Le Baron, 1957), and histochemical evidence suggests that this protein is localized in myelin (Adams, 1957; Koenig, 1959; Adams and Davison, 1965). However, Amaducci (1962) and his colleagues (Amaducci, Pazzagli, and Pessina, 1962) found no direct correlation between the concentration of myelin lipids (as indicated by cerebroside content) and that of proteolipids in different parts of the central nervous system. A possible explanation of the failure of Amaducci to demonstrate a correlation between proteolipid protein and cerebroside content in different areas of the brain has been provided by the work of Lees (1968). She has shown that extractability of proteolipid protein may be related to the salt concentration of the preparation. Samples of purified myelin have a relatively low electrolyte content in comparison to unwashed whole brain homogenates, and proteolipid protein can be readily extracted. On the other hand, less chloroform-methanol soluble protein can be obtained from comparable amounts of whole nervous tissue. Thus, Lees (1968) found the proportion of protein extracted from subcellular fractions to be between 156 and 175 percent of that present in whole unfractionated white matter. During myelination proteolipid concentration has been found to increase at a rate which is comparable to that of other myelin constituents (Folch, 1955; Uzman and Rumley, 1958; Greaney, 1961; Mokrasch and Manner, 1963) and almost all the protein of isolated central nervous system myelin is soluble in chloroform-methanol mixtures. It is, therefore, generally agreed that the proteolipid is a component of the myelin sheath. This does not mean, however, that it is absent from other cellular components.

It is now known that myelin from the central nervous system also contains other types of protein (Table 2-IV). Thus the basic protein antigen which produces experimental encephalomyelitis

TABLE 2 - IV
MYELIN PROTEINS*

Percentage Distribution of Bovine Myelin Protein		
	Brain	*Sciatic Nerve*
Basic protein	29.0	21.2
Proteolipid	53.5	23.4
Triton-salt insoluble	16.5	54.4

*Myelin has been treated with 0.5 M ammonium acetate and 0.5% triton X-100 (Eng. *et al.*, 1968). The soluble protein is treated with four volumes of ether, the basic protein separates in the aqueous layer and proteolipid protein remains insoluble. The triton-salt insoluble protein is further treated with chloroform-methanol to give an insoluble protein (Wolfgram, 1966).

(Kies, Thompson, and Alvord, 1965) has been found in myelin, and it is quantitatively extracted by chloroform-methanol. Autilio (1966) has separated the various myelin proteins into two main fractions. This was achieved by passing chloroform-methanol extracts of myelin through a polystyrene gel column when two protein peaks are obtained. Extracts in chloroform-methanol-hydrochloric acid partitioned with water separate 35 to 38 percent of the total protein into the upper phase. On Sephadex G-100 separation, this sample gives two fractions. The minor part is proteolipid protein and the major protein (85% of the upper phase protein), which represents about 30 percent of the total myelin protein, has an amino acid composition indistinguishable from that of the basic encephalitogenic protein. This latter protein has been separated from bovine, rabbit, and human central nervous tissue by chromatography on carboxymethylcellulose and Sephadex G-50. Recent work shows it to have a molecular weight of approximately 18,000. This confirms the earlier work of Kies, Einstein, and Lowden, and their colleagues (Laatsch *et al.*, 1962; Lowden, Moscarello, and Moreki, 1966; Roboz-Einstein, Castejtley, Davis, and Rauch, 1965). The higher molecular weight protein that remains in the chloroform-methanol lower phase after partitioning with CHCl₃:CH₃OH:0.04N HCl (Autilio, 1966) has a composition corresponding to that of the classical proteolipid protein (Table 2-V). These results suggest that proteolipid protein accounts for only 55 to 65 percent of the total myelin protein.

TABLE 2 - V

AMINO ACID COMPOSITION OF BOVINE MYELIN PROTEIN (mole %)*

	Basic Protein[1]	Proteolipid[2]	Triton-salt[3] Insoluble
Lysine	8.2	4.3	6.4
Histidine	5.9	1.9	2.1
Arginine	11.2	2.6	5.4
Aspartic	6.8	4.2	9.1
Threonine	4.3	8.5	4.8
Serine	9.6	5.4	5.4
Glutamic	6.4	6.0	12.0
Proline	6.8	2.9	4.3
Glycine	15.6	10.3	7.4
Alanine	8.6	12.5	7.8
Valine	0.8	6.9	5.4
½ Cystine	Tr	4.2	0.9
Methionine	1.2	1.7	2.0
Isoleucine	1.2	4.9	4.0
Leucine	6.0	11.1	8.9
Tyrosine	2.6	4.7	2.7
Phenylalanine	4.9	7.8	3.9

*Tryptophan analyses are not included, and cystine analysis is uncorrected for acid hydrolysis, (after Eng *et al.*, 1968).
[1]Nakao, A.; Davis, W.J., and Einstein, E.R. (1966).
[2]Tenenbaum, D., and Folch Pi, J. (1966).
[3]Wolfgram, F. (1966).
Eng. *et al.* (1968).

Eng (Eng, Chao, Gerstl, Pratt, and Tavastsjerna, 1968) has adopted a different method for the isolation of myelin proteins. In this procedure samples are extracted with Triton-X-100. After centrifugation the soluble fraction has been found to contain mainly basic protein; the triton-insoluble fraction is reextracted to solubilize proteolipid so that an insoluble residue is left which contains a small amount of a third type of protein having a composition similar to that of a protein isolated from peripheral nerve (Wolfgram, 1966; Wolfgram and Kotorii, 1968a, 1968b). Using gel filtration Eng *et al.* (1968) estimate a minimum molecular weight of 150,000 for the proteolipid type protein. Samples have also been characterized by electrophoresis (see Fig. 2-3). Adams and Fox (1968) have examined myelin proteins by electrophoresis on polyacrylamide gels with a phenol-formic acid water solvent system. They fractionated rat brain myelin on a 10 to 30 percent sucrose gradient and found a continuous band of myelin. Successive samples were extracted with chloroform-methanol, and the proportion of soluble and insoluble material was different in various parts of the gradient. The electrophoretic patterns also differed. Cotman and Mahler (1967) have separated adult rat brain myelin by acrylamide gel electrophoresis. Myelin was treat-

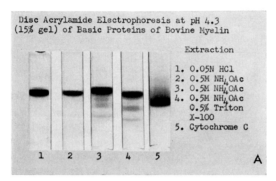

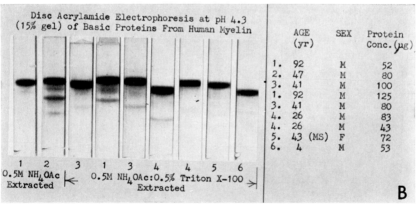

FIGURE 2-3. Disc acrylamide electrophoresis at pH 4.3 (15% gel) of basic proteins from bovine and human myelin. Figure 2-3A shows five samples of bovine myelin extracted with (1) 0.05N HCl, (2). Figure 2-3B shows six samples of human myelin (ages 26-92 years old) extracted with (1) and (2) 0.5M NH₄OAc, the rest have been extracted with 0.5M NH₄OAc: 0.5% Triton X-100. Sample six is from a four-year-old male brain. (Results kindly supplied by Dr. L. F. Eng.)

ed with phenol, acetic acid, and water (2:1:1, w/v/v) to give a
turbid solution. This gave two fast, and two, or possibly three
slower moving bands, but they found it difficult to solubilize myelin, and other workers have found further protein bands (e.g.
Roboz-Einstein, Csejtev, and Marks, (1968).

In contrast to the high proteolipid protein content of brain
and spinal cord at normal pH, much less protein can be removed
from peripheral nerve by extraction with chloroform-methanol.
However, Wolfgram (1966) has obtained a tenfold increase in
soluble protein species by extraction of peripheral nerve with
chloroform-methanol at pH 2 (by addition of 1N HCl). This
same lipoprotein is present in both white and grey matter but in
relatively lower proportions than in central nervous tissue (Wolfgram and Kotorii, 1968a). The amino acid composition of the
Wolfgram lipoprotein is similar in both central and peripheral
nervous tissue. In particular it is rich in dicarboxylic amino acids
(22% total amino acid residues) and basic amino acid (14.6%
total acid residues).

Enzymes in Myelin

The histochemical observations of Tewari and Bourne (1960)
suggest that many enzymes are localized in myelin. However, on
reexamination of this work, Adams (Adams *et al.*, 1963) concluded that such findings could be the result of artefacts, for the
lipophilic character of myelin can serve to trap the diffused reaction product in some histochemical reactions. In other cases (e.g.
Wolfgram and Rose, 1960) prolonged incubation of sections was
used to demonstrate enzyme activity in myelin, but Adams showed
that if short incubation times are used, very little enzyme activity
is present. Nevertheless, there was evidence for the presence of
some alkaline phosphatase in peripheral nerve myelin and of endopeptidase and exopeptidase activity in central nervous system
myelin. These conclusions are confirmed when the enzyme activity
of separated rat brain myelin fractions is determined (Table 2-VI).
Definite amounts of proteolytic and aminopeptidase activity is
localized in myelin. There is little polyphosphoinositide mono-
esterase activity (Salway *et al.*, 1968), but significant quantities of

TABLE 2-VI
ENZYME ACTIVITY IN RAT AND MOUSE BRAIN MYELIN

Enzyme	Enzyme Activity in Myelin (percentage of total recovery) In Whole Brain	Localization
Total ATPase[1]	2.2	microsomes
ATPase (Na[+], K[+] activated) [1]	2.2	nerve endings and membranes
Acid phosphatase[1]	3.2	lysosomes
Alkaline phosphatase[1]	2.9	capillary and vascular endothelium
Glutamic acid decarboxylase[1]	2.0	presynaptic nerve endings
Succinic dehydrogenase[1, 3]	2.3-4	mitochondria
Cytochrome oxidase[2]	2.5	mitochondria
GABA-transaminase[2]	1	mitochondria (at postsynaptic sites?)
Glucose-6-phosphate dehydrogenase[1]	2.7	soluble cytoplasm?
Lactate dehydrogenase[2, 3]	0-2	soluble cytoplasm
Leucine aminopeptidase[1]	17	myelin
Alanyl-β-naphthylamidase[5]	15	myelin (spinal cord)
2′,3′-cyclic nucleotide 3′-phosphohydrolase[4]	60	myelin
phosphatidic acid phosphomonoesterase[3]	11.7	particulate material

[1]Adams, Davison, and Gregson, (1963)
[2]Waksman, Rubinstein, Kuriyama, and Roberts, (1968)
[3]Salway, Kai, and Hawthorne, (1967)
[4]Kurihara and Tsukada, (1967)
[5]Beck, Hasinoff, and Smith (1968)

phosphatidic acid phosphatase are present. More recently, it has been claimed that monoamine oxidase is localized in peripheral nerve myelin (Harkonen, Mustakallio, and Niemi, 1966) and that glycolytic enzyme activity (Miani, Cavallotti, and Caniglia, 1969) and a cyclic nucleotidase (2′,3′-cyclic nucleotide 3′-phosphohydrolase) is present in central myelin (Kurihara and Tsukada, 1967, 1968). It would be wiser to wait for confirmation of some of these observations before considering their possible significance.

DEVELOPING NERVOUS TISSUE

Although the beginning of myelination merges into the final stages of cellular proliferation, in its later stages of its development, much of the increase in wet weight of the brain can be attributed to the deposition of myelin (Davison and Dobbing, 1968). Measurements of brain wet weight increment give no more than a very imperfect assessment of myelination; more exact information may be obtained by following accumulation of specific myelin constituents (e.g. cerebroside, proteolipid, etc.) or by isolation and analysis of myelin. Nevertheless, striking differences

in the timing of the maximum rate of increase of wet weight for
each species suggests big differences in the pattern of myelination

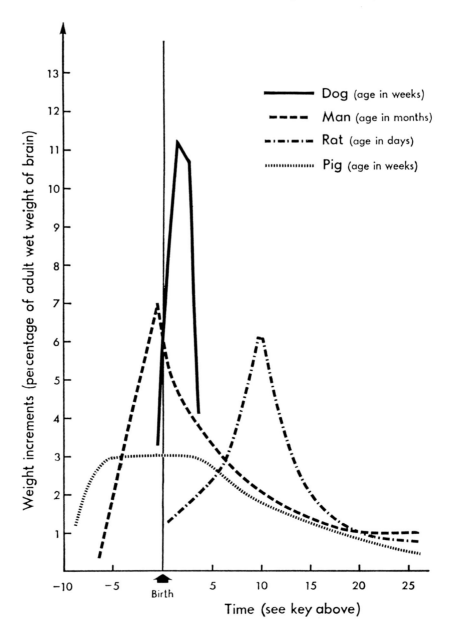

in various vertebrates. Thus the maximum rate of brain wet weight increment occurs at about ten days after birth in the rat but precedes birth in the guinea pig, while in man the peak increase in brain weight is around the time of birth (Fig. 2-4). Histological observations confirm the conclusion that onset of myelination occurs at different times in various species and at different times in each area of the nervous system. In general, myelination first occurs in the phylogenetically older parts of the central nervous system. For example, Uzman and Rumley (1958) found that up to ten days of age, the mouse brain is substantially free of myelin. Early myelin formation then becomes evident in the pons, in the mesencephalic and diencephalic portions of the spinothalamic tracts, and in the interpeduncular commissures. Only at twenty days does myelination start in the corpus callosum. However, the most striking additions to the whole myelin content of the brain are seen histologically in the twenty-three-day-old to adult stages. The same pattern of development is also seen in man, but its timing in relation to birth is quite different. Myelination occurs in various tracts of the spinal cord from the twenty-second to the thirty-sixth week of fetal life (Keene and Hewer, 1931), but only light myelination of the corpus callosum is apparent in the second month of extra-uterine life (Langworthy, 1932). On the other hand, in the guinea pig, domestic pig (Ziolo,

←————————

FIGURE 2-4. The timing of brain growth in different species in relation to birth. Curves of the rate of brain growth in different species are expressed as weight increments (percentage of adult wet weight of brain) per unit period of time. Donaldson (1911) proposed that the growth characteristics of rat brain became comparable with those in man if account were taken of their thirty-fold difference in life span. This concept has been extended to dogs and pigs. Brain weight data are taken from the following sources: man (Spector, 1956), rat (Dobbing, unpublished); dog (Himwich and Petersen, 1959), and pig (Dickerson and Dobbing, unpublished). The assumption that brain development is in any way related to life span is of course quite arbitrary. The diagram shows the species variation in the timing of the brain growth spurt. The earlier part of each growth spurt mainly represents cell division and increase of cell size (Dickerson and Dobbing, unpublished); this period overlaps with one of subsequent lipid accumulation representing myelination. (Reproduced by courtesy of the British Council and Dr. J. Dobbing.)

1965), and lamb (Romanes, 1947), even myelination of the brain
is well advanced before birth. Although it is possible to pinpoint
the onset of myelination, it is not possible to histologically assess
the termination of the process. Some indication of the ending of
myelination comes from biochemical studies. Thus accretion of
the typical myelin lipids continues for a considerable period — at
least for about 180 days postnatal in the case of rat brain sulphatide
(Davison and Gregson, 1962). Norton has measured the dry
weight of myelin from developing rat brain, and his findings suggest that there is a continual logarithmic deposition of myelin,
certainly in rats up to 425 days of age. Myelination is also probably an extended process in other species. For example, the human
brain increases in weight until adolescence, and it seems likely
that deposition of myelin continues until fifteen to twenty years
of age. (The significance of this is discussed in Ch. 3.)

Early Stages of Myelination

Myelination is preceded by multiplication of glial cells (Bensted, Dobbing, Morgan, Reid, and Payling Wright, 1957) and of
Schwann cells (Friede and Samorajski, 1968) in the central and
peripheral nervous systems respectively. Electron microscope evidence shows that the first lipoprotein lamellae formed by the
satellite cells are sometimes loosely wound around the axon.
Discontinuities, folds, trapped vesicles, and irregular repeating
periods may be seen by electron microscopy (De Robertis, Gerschenfeld, and Wald, 1958; Peters, 1960) and only later is the
more uniform, tightly packed pattern of adult myelin attained.

During the early stages of myelination, lipid droplets are
present. These occur mainly in the grey matter, and later these
sudanophilic, Marchi-positive droplets become orientated around
the nerve axon. But this is only a transient phase, for the newly
formed sheaths soon lose their Marchi-positive character. In the
developing human brain, lipid has been found in glial and endothelial cells up to about eight months gestation. As myelination
begins, there is a decrease in the number of lipid-containing cells
as well as in the number of lipid droplets observed in each cell.
Mickel and Gilles (1968) have postulated that some endothelial

and perithelial cells in premature white matter may be adapted for the transfer of myelin lipid precursors. There is also evidence to suggest that myelination is performed by not fully differentiated, multipotential neuroglial cells (the so-called myelination glia, Friede, 1966), which after myelinogenesis may differentiate into oligodendrocytes and astrocytes (Wendell-Smith, Blunt, and Baldwin, 1966; Mitrova, 1967).

Changes in Chemical Composition of Nervous Tissue During Myelination

Lipids in Whole Brain

During myelination the lipid content of both brain and nerve undergoes a substantial increase. Several group of workers have measured changes in the lipid content of the developing brain in order to correlate altering chemistry with changes in central nervous system morphology and functional maturation of the brain. Although there is not complete agreement in the literature about all the results obtained (for cerebroside see Cuzner and Davison, 1968; Galli and Cecconi, 1967; Norton, 1968), one of the most comprehensive of such studies is that of Wells and Dittmer (1967) on the developing rat brain (Table 2-VII).

It will be noted that some lipids (e.g. gangliosides, phosphatidylcholine, phosphatidylethanolamine, and cholesterol) are present in relatively high concentration in the 6-day-old postnatal rat brain. Others such as cholesterol esters and desmosterol (Smith, Fumagalli, and Paoletti, 1967; Banik and Davison, 1967), which are present in the early stages of development, are found in only traces in rat brain twenty-one days old. Before ten to twelve days in the rat brain, the concentration of sphingomyelin, triphosphoinositide, phosphatidic acid, inositol plasmalogen, galactosyldiglyceride, and sulphatide is less than 10 percent of that found in the adult. But as myelination commences, there is a steady increase in the amount of these lipids. Cholesterol, present early in relatively high concentration, undergoes a less dramatic increase in the rat brain during the period of 12 to 330 days after birth. Cerebroside (but not sulphatide)is virtually absent from the brain until mye-

TABLE 2-VII
LIPID COMPOSITION OF DEVELOPING RAT BRAIN*

Lipid	Concentration (μmol/gm wet weight)							
	3 Days	6 Days	12 Days	18 Days	24 Days	42 Days	180 Days	330 Days
Phospholipids								
Phosphatidylcholine	14.72	14.82	20.38	24.38	24.79	24.95	24.65	24.89
Phosphatidylethanolamine	5.25	5.66	7.96	9.37	11.00	10.89	10.72	10.49
Phosphatidylglycerol	0.12	0.20	0.16	0.20	0.29	0.27	0.28	0.29
Phosphatidylinositol	1.21	1.38	1.59	1.86	2.04	2.17	2.20	2.30
Phosphatidylserine	2.91	3.56	4.51	6.10	7.04	8.25	8.50	8.97
Phosphatidylglycerol phosphate	0.10	0.13	0.20	0.16	0.16	0.17	0.06	0.04
Phosphatidic acid	0.14	0.21	0.26	0.39	0.70	1.03	1.31	1.36
Diphosphatidylglycerol	0.19	0.21	0.34	0.52	0.57	0.68	0.60	0.55
Diphosphoinositide	0.01	0.05	0.05	0.16	0.15	0.19	0.21	0.20
Triphosphoinositide	0.03	0.04	0.05	0.14	0.17	0.24	0.41	0.39
Choline plasmalogen	0.04	0.06	0.07	0.09	0.16	0.22	0.35	0.34
Ethanolamine plasmalogen	2.19	2.75	4.73	7.02	11.3	13.5	13.0	13.2
Inositol plasmalogen	less than 0.01		0.05	0.08	0.13	0.13	0.13	0.11
Plasmalogenic acid	0.02	0.05	0.15	0.17	0.18	0.15	0.20	0.12
Ethanolamine phosphoglyceryl ether	0.18	0.23	0.38	0.69	1.02	1.06	1.04	1.13
Sphingomyelin	0.23	0.26	1.04	2.15	3.19	3.62	3.70	4.10
Galactolipids								
Cerebroside	less than 0.05		2.3	5.8	10.3	18.6	21.8	22.5
Sulphatide	0.14	0.32	0.79	1.28	2.04	3.22	4.22	4.48
Galactosyldiglyceride	0.05	0.06	0.31	0.86	1.29	1.46	1.56	1.62
Ganglioside								
Hexosamine	0.31	0.73	0.84	0.96	1.01	1.06	1.15	1.13
Sialic acid	0.51	1.27	1.45	1.74	1.97	2.08	2.18	2.07
Sterols								
Cholesterol	10.7	12.6	22.6	32.2	38.3	39.5	40.2	40.6
Cholesterol ester	2.0	less than 5% of total sterol					—	—
Desmosterol	2.4	2.9	3.6	1.6	0.4	—	—	—
Brain weight (g)	0.40	0.61	1.11	1.34	1.55	1.63	1.85	1.86
Percent recovery of phosphorus in combined fractions	97.0	96.5	98.0	98.5	98.0	97.0	97.0	98.0

*In general, brains of six rats were pooled and analyzed in duplicate (Wells and Dittmer, 1965). Data after Wells and Dittmer (1967) and desmosterol results from Smith et al., 1967; Banik and Davison, 1968; and Norton, 1968.

lination commences, and then the initial rate of cerebroside accumulation is relatively lower than that for the other myelin lipids (see Fig. 2-5). The overall picture, but not the timing of such changes in lipid content of the developing central nervous system, is similar in all species so far examined. The same is true for specific areas of the nervous system. Thus in the kitten optic nerve (Table 2-VIII) Banik, Blunt, and Davison (1968) showed that accretion of cholesterol and phospholipid preceded deposition of cerebroside. In the sixteen-day-old kitten, even when myelination is well established, unexpectedly small amounts of cerebrosides are found. Although the optic nerve myelin was sudanophilic and stained with luxol-fast blue, it did not appear to react with osmium tetroxide (see also Wolman, 1957).

In the most immature human brain (4-month-old fetus) examined by Menkes, Philippart, and Concone (1966), polar glycolipids (possibly of the hematoside and globoside type) were

TABLE 2-VIII
FATTY ACIDS OF KITTEN OPTIC NERVE AND RAT MYELIN*

	Optic Nerve			Myelin			
C-numbers of Fatty Acids	10-day-old Kitten	19-day-old Kitten	Adult Cat	Adult Cat	15-day-old Rat	Adult Rat	Coconut Fed Adult Rat
12:0	2.0	Trace		Trace			
14.0	5.8	6.6	2.83	1.95	1.47		
15:0	1.6	1.5	0.37	0.76			
15:1	0.38	Trace	1.6	1.79	1.4		
16:0	44.9	31.9	27.3	15.83	29.8	13.8	14.9
16:1	Trace	Trace	Trace	3.9	2.8	2.0	2.8
17:0	Trace	0.98	0.5	Trace			
17:1	Trace	1.6	1.63	3.04	2.3	1.4	0.8
Unidentified						1.4	0.9
18:0	7.8	6.5	13.5	19.65	22.3	19.0	21.6
18:1	33.8	33.4	42.6	36.86	24.6	35.1	37.5
18:2	3.7	11.3	3.2	3.12	1.5	0.9	0.4
20.0		5.8	4.4	8.76			
20:1			0.84	Trace	2.0	4.2	4.7
20:4			0.76	3.87	11.5	5.4	5.6
22:4						1.5	1.6
22:5ω^6						5.3	4.2
22:5						0.7	1.0
22:6ω^3						4.0	1.4

*The results show the composition of fatty acids released by mild alkaline hydrolysis of lipid extracts. Methods employed as described by Banik, Blunt, and Davison (1968). Results for 15-day-old rat myelin (Banik and Davison, unpublished) and for adult myelin (Rathbone, 1965) are shown. Female rats (160-190 gm) 8-12 weeks old were fed diets containing 15% total calorie intake as coconut oil for 34 weeks, and the results of this experiment are also included. Composition of fatty acids are shown as a percentage of total fatty acid.

present in small amounts as were cerebrosides and sulphatides. Svennerholm (1964) has also reported the presence of other glyco-lipids, ceramide, and ceramide trihexosides glucocerebrosides, as well as gangliosides, in the fetal human brain (Table 2-IX). Cere-brosides and sulphatides isolated from the immature nervous sys-tem were found to contain a small proportion of hydroxy acids

TABLE 2-IX
GLYCOLIPIDS OF DEVELOPING HUMAN BRAIN*

Glycosphingolipid	23 Weeks Fetus	33 Weeks Premature	Full Term
Lipid as mg 100 gm fresh brain weight			
Glucocerebrosides	0.8	0.8	0.8
Galactocerebrosides	1.6	6.0	7.0
Ceramidedihexosides	4.0	1.0	1.0
Ceramidetrihexosides	1.0	0.5	0.4
Aminoglycolipids	2	2	2
Sulphatides	1.0	3.5	3.0
Gangliosides	90	100	125

*Svennerholm (1964).

and considerable amounts of palmitic (16:0) and stearic (18:0) acids; but as myelination commenced, a second type of cerebroside and sulphatide appeared to be deposited. This so-called myelin cerebroside contained large proportions of hydroxy and long-chain fatty acids (24:0 and 24:1). It was suggested by Menkes and his colleagues that only the primary fatty acids synthetase system lead-ing to synthesis of $C_{16:0}$ chains was present in the immature brain, and that the biochemical machinery for chain elongation appeared later in development. Svennerholm and Ställberg-Sten-hagen (1968) point out the considerable difficulties in preparing pure cerebroside and sulphatide samples. This is particularly true in fetal material where the glycolipids predominate. The existence of a nonmyelin type of cerebroside containing 16:0, 18:0, and 18:1 fatty acids in fetal brain may, therefore, require reappraisal; but it should be pointed out that Menkes *et al.* (1966) examined material at a very early stage of development (4-months fetus). On the other hand, the brains studied by Svennerholm and Ställ-berg-Stenhagen were from newborn infants. In the studies of Svennerholm and Ställberg-Stenhagen, the ratio of hydroxy acids to normal acids was found to increase slightly during myelination and then remained rather constant; in adults the ratio for cerebroside was about 2, and for sulphatides 0.6 to 0.8. In adult nervous tissue the two predominant fatty acids of cerebrosides and sulphatides were the C_{24} *mono*unsaturated and 2-hydroxy saturated acids. The infant brain galactolipids had (compared with child and adult) a lower percentage of C_{22} to C_{26} fatty acids and a much lower percentage of *mono*enoic acids, both of normal and hydroxy acids.

In general, fatty acid changes in relation to age were the same for cerebroside and sulphatides, but the change in sulphatide fatty acid pattern occurred later in development, a finding consistent with the hypothesis that the cerebrosides are precursors of the sulphatides. The adult pattern of fatty acid composition with regard to degree of unsaturation and total percentage of C_{22} to C_{26} acids is reached as early as two years of age in man, but the percentage of odd-numbered (C_{23} and C_{25}) fatty acids continues to increase up to the age of ten to fifteen years.

The fatty acid composition of the galactolipids of peripheral nerves mainly differs in its lower proportion of C_{25} and C_{26} acids and higher proportions of C_{22} and C_{16} acids. The composition of peripheral nerves is in this respect thus intermediate between these of brain and of other organs.

Changes in Fatty Acid Composition of Developing Central Nervous System. The absence of osmophilia in the sixteen to twenty-three day old kitten optic nerve prompted Banik *et al.* (1968) to examine the fatty acids contained in the developing optic nerve. It was found (Table 2-VIII) that there were distinct changes in the proportions of fatty acids released by mild alkaline saponification from the maturing nerve lipid. During development there was an increase in the proportion of longer chain fatty acids and an increase in their degree of unsaturation. Similar results have been reported for fatty acid changes in human brain (Menkes *et al.*, 1966; Lesch, Meier, and Bernhard, 1966; Ställberg-Stenhagen and Svennerholm, 1965). For example, the proportion of stearic acid (18:0) in human brain sphingomyelin decreases with age from 80 percent in the newborn to 40 percent in the adult, whereas the long-chain C_{22} to C_{26} increase from about 10 to 50 percent of the total fatty acid. Lesch *et al.* (1966) found the palmitic acid content of the glycerophospholipids of premature to be higher than that in the newborn infant brain. Marshall, Fumagalli, Niemiro, and Paoletti (1966) have isolated phosphatidylcholine from the developing rat brain and also found that there is an elongation of fatty acid chain length with maturation. These various changes in fatty acid composition may well reflect the increasing deposition of myelin, for it contains predominantly unsaturated long-chain fatty acids (Rathbone, 1965). Rathbone found that there were only small changes in the fatty acid composition of myelin, even after feeding weanling rats for eight months on a diet rich in unsaturated fatty acids (Table 2-VIII).

Lipid Changes in Relation to Myelination

In the brain, accumulation of lipid is largely restricted to the white matter (Robins and Lowe, 1961), and histological examination shows that much of this lipid is accumulated in myelin (Adams and Davison, 1965). It might therefore have been anticipated that during development myelin constituents would accumulate in the brain (Folch, 1955) at similar rates and in proportion to that found in isolated mature myelin. Such an expectation is, however, only partially fulfilled, for the maximum rate of cholesterol and phospholipid deposition precedes that for cerebrosides (Fig. 2-5) and sulphatides (Davison and Gregson, 1962). In the later stages of brain development, increment of brain lipids is in proportion to that expected from the known composition of isolated myelin (Kishimoto, Davies, and Radin, 1965b).

It would appear from the biochemical evidence that a high proportion of the cholesterol and some phospholipid in the brain is synthesized prior to myelination, and that there is a redistribution of some of the brain lipids into myelin (see Figs. 2-6 and 2-7) as myelination proceeds. On the other hand, a much closer relationship exists between the rate of cerebroside synthesis and the formation of myelin (Fig. 2-8), suggesting an important role for the galactolipids (Uzman and Rumley, 1958) in relation to the membrane protein.

Although it has been previously considered that the composition of myelin is identical throughout all stages of development, Horrocks and his colleagues (Horrocks, Meckler, and Collins, 1966; Horrocks, 1968) first reported differences in the lipid con-

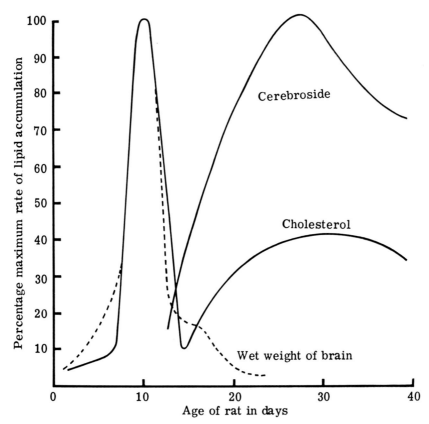

FIGURE 2-5. Changes in the rate of cholesterol and cerebroside accumulation and increase in wet weight in the rat brain during development. Results are the percentages of the maximum daily rate of increment (see Cuzner and Davison, 1968.)

tent of myelin isolated from developing mouse brain. They found increases in galactolipids, cholesterol phosphatidylinositol, and ethanolamine phospholipid, and decreases in lecithin content with increasing age. Cuzner and Davison (1968) have repeated these experiments using the brain of rats from the age of ten days after birth and onwards. Samples of myelin were obtained by layering crude nuclear and mitochondrial suspensions over 0.8M sucrose and subjecting the separated myelin to osmotic shock before final sedimentation. Analysis showed that this so-called early myelin was relatively deficient in cerebroside and richer in phospholipid than that isolated from rats older than twenty-five to thirty days of

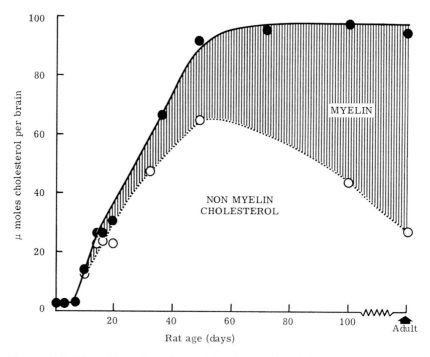

FIGURE 2-6. Disposition of cholesterol in the myelin of developing rat brain. The results show the accumulation of cholesterol as a function of increasing age in the rat (●). Cholesterol localized in myelin is indicated by the hatched area.

age (Table 2-X). In addition, myelin from ten- to twenty-day-old rats contained relatively more short than long-chain saturated acids (obtained by mild alkaline hydrolysis) compared to that from adult rats (Banik and Davison, 1968). Eng and Noble (1968) and Norton (1968) have also reported similar changes in the composition of myelin from developing rat brain. These authors find less marked changes in total galactolipid compared to those reported by Cuzner and Davison (1968) for cerebroside, but there are certainly difficulties in the estimation of glycolipids in the developing brain.

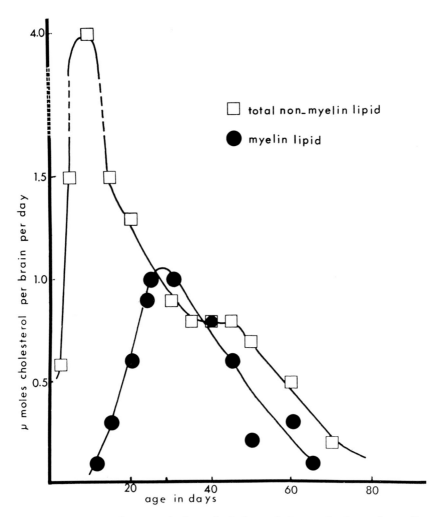

FIGURE 2-7. Rate of accumulation of cholesterol in rat brain and myelin. The distribution of lipid as micromols of cholesterol deposited per day is shown in nonmyelin (□) and myelin (●), (Cuzner, 1968).

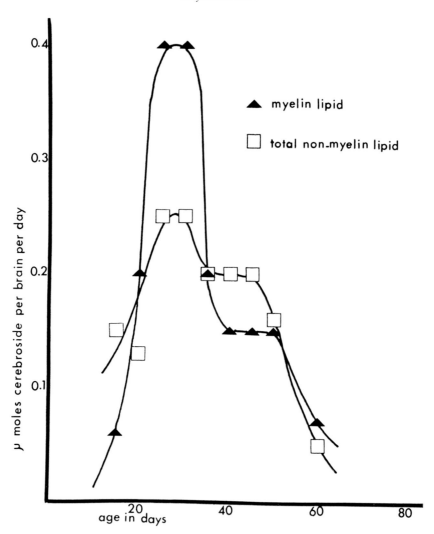

FIGURE 2-8. Rate accumulation of cerebroside in rat brain and myelin. The distribution of lipid as micromols of cerebroside deposited per day is shown in nonmyelin (□) and myelin (▲), (Cuzner, 1968).

Separation of a Second Component from Developing Brain Myelin. Small amounts of ganglioside are present in adult brain (Norton and Autilio, 1966; Soto, Bohner, and Calvino, 1966). In adult rat myelin 89 percent of the glycolipid is monosialoganglio-

TABLE 2-X
COMPOSITION OF MYELIN IN DEVELOPING RAT BRAIN*

Myelin Preparation

	Crude	Crude	Purified	Crude	Purified	Crude	Purified
Age of rat (days)	9 - 10	15 - 16		19 - 22		Adult type	
Protein % dry weight	10[1]	19.0[1]	21.8[1] 25.8	18.0[1]	22.7[1] 29.6[3]	36[4] 23.0[1]	23.7[1] 31.2[3]
Molar Percentage Lipid							
Cholesterol	40.5[2] 29.0	40[2]	35.4 36.6	36[2]	37.8 37.6[1]	42.5	39.9 39.9[1]
Total galactolipid	— 15.1	—	14.1 20.2	—	17.8 20.5	—	23.9 24.3
Cerebroside	2.2 —	4	— —	6.4	— —	14.8	— —
Total phospholipid	57 55.9	55.5	50.5 43.0	57	44.4 41.9	40.0	36.2 36.2
Lecithin (% total phospholipid)	41 50.6[1]	27	41.7 35.1	37	36.8 34.3	10.5	24.2 24.2

[1]Eng and Noble (1968) [3]Norton (1968)
[2]Cuzner and Davison (1968) [4]Cuzner, Davison, and Gregson (1965)
*Crude myelin was prepared as described by Cuzner and Davison 1968 on discontinuous sucrose gradients (Laatsch *et al.*, 1962; Eng and Noble, 1968). Purified myelin was prepared on a continuous sucrose gradient (Autilio *et al.*, 1964).

side (G_4), but in purified myelin from young animals the proportion of G_4 is much less, while six times as much trisialoganglioside (G_1) is present (Table 2-XI). Work by Suzuki, Poduslo, and Norton (1967) and Norton, Poduslo, and Suzuki (1966) suggests that contrary to the belief that gangliosides are exclusive constituents of the neuron and its synaptic membranes (Lapetina, Soto, and De Robertis, 1967), a small amount of ganglioside may be present in the myelin. Further evidence from control experiments in young and adult animals and from distribution studies is consistent with this view (Suzuki, Poduslo, and Poduslo, 1968; Su-

TABLE 2-XI
GANGLIOSIDES IN RAT BRAIN MYELIN*

Age (days)	Total NANA			Distribution of Gangliosides			
	μmg/100 mg	μg/Brain	% Recovery	$G_1(G_{T1})$	$G_2(G_{D1b})$	$G_3(_{D1a})$	$G_4(G_{M1})$
15	48.7	1.95	0.23	11.8	13.7	18.7	55.8
20	44.7	5.36	0.55	11.6	14.0	16.6	57.8
30	39.6	9.50	0.88	8.4	11.0	9.8	70.8
60	39.5	16.2	1.18	4.4	6.3	6.7	82.6
144	35.6	19.9	1.43	1.5	2.7	2.3	93.5
190	51.7	33.0	2.48	0.9	2.6	4.5	92.0
425	68.0	61.8	4.57	1.9	3.8	5.3	89.0

After Suzuki, Poduslo, and Norton, 1968.
*The results are expressed as the mole % of total major gangliosides, calculated with the assumption that G_1 is a trisialo-, G_2 and G_3 disialo-, and G_4 in a monosialo-ganglioside. Gangliosides are termed according to Korey and Gonatas 1963 with the corresponding Svennerholm (1963) nomenclature in parentheses.

zuki, 1967). It remains to be decided whether or not the ganglioside is a contaminant (perhaps a component of the axon) or
whether it is, as seems likely, an integral part of the myelin sheath.
Certainly, this interesting work of Suzuki and his colleagues demonstrates a marked changing pattern in the proportion of the
different gangliosides in developing myelin.

In their studies, Eng and Noble (1968) compared the composition of myelin isolated by layering over 0.8M sucrose with that of
further purified preparations prepared by separation on a continuous sucrose gradient. The purified myelin fraction was found
to have a lipid composition closer to that of adult myelin (Table
2-X) and similar to the chemical composition of purified myelin
found by Norton and Poduslo (in preparation) in rats from
fifteen to thirty days of age.

In the method used by Norton and Poduslo, the crude myelin
fraction was first washed with cold water, and myelin was prepared by sedimentation at 10,000 g for 15 minutes. In this way,
highly purified myelin was isolated (as judged by nucleic acid
and protein analysis and by electron microscope and enzymic
criteria), and an accompanying contaminating membrane fraction
was thereby eliminated in the supernatant. This latter fraction
has been isolated by prolonged centrifugation of the supernatant
wash (Norton, Davison, and Spohn, 1969). Analysis shows it to be
relatively richer in phospholipid and more deficient in cerebroside
than is myelin. The same fraction contains a higher proportion of
short-chain saturated fatty acids than myelin and more protein.
Thus its chemical composition more closely resembles that of the
brain microsomes than that of adult myelin. However, the contaminating membrane fraction does not contain high concentrations of nucleic acids or certain marker enzymes (e.g. ATPase) as
might be expected if it were typically microsomal. Using cesium
chloride or sucrose gradient centrifugation, Norton, Davison, and
Spohn (1969) have been able to separate crude myelin from
fifteen-day-old rat brain into the two fractions. The contaminating
membrane fraction was found to consist predominantly of numerous small, single membrane vesicles like those seen in certain
microsome subfractions or as reported by De Robertis, Iraldi,

Arnaiz, and Salganicoff (1962) in their B fraction from rat brain. The chemical composition of the contaminating membrane fraction was similar to that obtained by centrifugation of the supernatant wash. This work agrees with that of Eng and Noble (1968). They found that "early" myelin contained a small fraction of lower density, which contained less protein, galactolipid, cholesterol, and ethanolamine plasmalogen and more phospholipid than the adult myelin. Electron microscope examination of a sixteen-day-old preparation of the less dense material showed an amorphous field with occasional myelin figures but no intact microsomal or mitochondrial elements. The occurrence of this fraction in the myelin prepared by the procedure of Laatsch *et al.* (1962) accounts for some of the changes in lipid composition observed in crude myelin fractions from developing brain.

Norton (1969) has pointed out that relatively minor contamination of isolated myelin fractions becomes of considerable significance in preparations from immature brain. The latter contain small amounts of myelin while in the adult the proportion of myelin is considerably greater, so that the same degree of contamination becomes relatively trivial. The possibility of contamination by the brain microsomal fraction was examined. No cross-contamination in the crude myelin prepared by centrifugation could be demonstrated when labeled subfractions of brain were added to an unlabeled, fifteen-day-old rat brain homogenate (Norton, Davison, and Spohn, 1969). These various experiments suggest that the contaminating fraction in early myelin is closely connected with the synthesis of the myelin sheath. On the basis of its resemblance in chemical composition to that of both plasma membrane and crude glial preparations from oligodendrogliomas (see Table 2-XII), Davison, Cuzner, Banik, and Oxberry, (1966) have suggested that the contaminant in early myelin may be a transition stage between oligodendroglial membrane and myelin.

Thus, the glial membrane, at first loosely wound around the axon, may be later converted into compact myelin by the insertion of cerebroside and possibly cholesterol into the membrane structure. In membrane biosynthesis of this type it is possible that the protein specifies the final lipid pattern (see Dallner, Siekevitz,

TABLE 2-XII

LIPID COMPOSITION OF GLIA, NEURONS, AND EARLY MYELIN FRACTIONS*

| | Molar Ratios of Lipid Where Cholesterol = 1 | | | | | | | | |
	Neuron[1]	Neuron[2]	Glia[1]	Glia[2]	Glia[3]	Oligoden-droglioma	Early[1] Myelin	Purified Myelin	Myelin[3] Contaminant
Cholesterol	1.0	0.52	1.0	0.65	1.0	1.0	1.0	1.0	1
Total galactolipid	—	—	—	—	0.2	—	0.14	0.3	0.1
Cerebroside	0.0	—	0.12	—	0.14	0.02	0.1	0.13	0.14
Total phospholipid	2.0	2.0	1.47	1.47	0.7	0.87	1.36	1.04	2.2
Phosphatidylcholine	0.77	0.73	0.43	0.58	0.21	—	0.44	—	
Ethanolaminephospholipid	0.73	0.61	0.52	0.52	0.27	—	0.47		
Phosphatidylserine + inositol	0.27	0.24	0.23	0.20	0.14	—	0.32		
Sphingomyelin	0.47	0.11	0.17	0.08	0.08	—	0.13		
Protein % dry wt	—	57	—	44.5	74.1	—	47	23.5	43.2

[1]Davison et al. (1966)
[2]Freysz, Bieth, Judes, Sensenbrenner, Jacob, and Mandel (1968)
[3]Fewster and Mead (1968)
[4]Norton et al. (1969)

*Crude neurons and glia or neuropil preparation were prepared by the methods of Rose (1966), Fewster et al. (1967) and Satake and Abe (1966). In the latter isolation method the sample is treated with acetone-glycerol, and lipids (particularly cholesterol) may be lost. In order, therefore, to facilitate comparison, the results of Freysz et al. (1968) are calculated in relation to the phospholipid content found by Davison et al. (1966). Myelin analyses were on 15- to 16-day-old rats. The data of Fewster and Mead (1968) for preparation 1 of glia cells has been recalculated from dry weights using the average molecular weights they quote.

and Palade, 1966a, 1966b; Cook, 1968) and that changes in protein structure account for alterations in the membrane. The overall process may perhaps be under hormonal control (e.g. thyroxine, Hamburgh, 1966, or estradiol, Curry and Heim, 1966).

Kornguth, Anderson, and Scott (1966) have observed positive immune reactions to basic protein antibody preceding by two days the appearance of Weigert myelin staining. However, it is also possible that rabbit antiserum reacts with nuclear histones rather than myelin protein. Fluorescent antiserum reactions were first seen in the cervical spinal cord of fetal rats twenty-one days old, although at this time only occasional myelin sheaths could be detected by electron microscopy. The appearance of the basic myelin-type protein immediately before active myelination suggests the possibility that the basic protein is itself involved in the initiation of this process. According to Kornguth and his colleagues, this protein, elaborated by the neuron, stimulates the Schwann or glial cell to initiate the wrapping process. Such an interaction between neuron and satellite cell could be involved in the information process by which the cell is influenced to wrap its plasma membrane around the axon. This hypothesis would be consistent with the finding that certain axons of a fiber bundle are myelinated while adjacent fibers are unmyelinated. The subsequent repression of synthesis of this cationic protein by the spinal ganglion cell may either cause or be the effect of the end of the active myelination process. Benson (1966) (see Fig. 2-9) envisages a possible rearrangement of glial or Schwann cell membrane lipoprotein subunits into the more compact organization of mature myelin with an intermediate phase separating the globular from the unit membrane type of structure. The possible transition of one form of membrane into another is clearly of considerable interest (Luzzati and Husson, 1962; Lucy, 1968) but further clarification of these various possibilities must await labeling experiments and chemical analysis of purified glial or Schwann cell plasma membrane. Methods that have so far been employed for the isolation of glial cells often contain heterogeneous cell populations and in some cases the plasma membrane fraction is missing (Fewster, Scheibel, and Mead, 1967; Johnston, and Roots, 1965). Moreover, contamination of cells by even small amounts of myelin

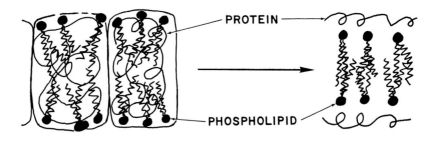

SCHWANN OR GLIAL
CELL MEMBRANE

MYELIN
UNIT MEMBRANE

FIGURE 2-9. Scheme for the formation of myelin from the neuroglial or Schwan cell membrane. (See Benson, 1966.)

(e.g. 5% myelinated axons) could produce confusing results, for compared to the many lamellae present in myelin, the cell membrane is only one unit membrane in thickness. The presence of myelin in glia cells isolated by Fewster *et al.* (1967) could account for some of the galactolipid found in their preparations (Fewster and Mead, 1968).

Changes in Protein and Enzymes during Development of Nervous System Proteins

In the rat the protein content of the brain increases with age from 5 percent at birth to 10 percent of the wet weight in the thiry-day-old animal. Thereafter, there is an increase in absolute content of brain protein. This ends at about fifty days of age, after which the weight only increases slowly (Pitts and Quick, 1967). During development there is some evidence to suggest alterations in the chemical composition of brain proteins (Prensky and Moser, 1967). Certainly, there are changes in enzyme proteins and in the chemical constitution of the proteolipid proteins. Starch gel electrophoresis shows that most of the two hundred proteins of adult rat brain are present at birth. One exception is the characteristic acidic (S-100) protein described by Moore. This first appears at ten days of age and finally comprises 0.5 to 1 percent of the total soluble proteins of rat brains. Moore has found that the amount of the S-100 protein increases sharply between sixteen and twenty-three days after birth and afterwards continues to rise only slowly (Schmitt and Davison, 1965). However, from its distribution in nervous tissue (Moore, Perez, and Gehring, 1968; Hyden and McEwen, 1966; Perez and Moore, 1968), it seems likely that it is not localized in myelin. Hyden and McEwen's studies with immunological methods suggest that the protein is present in glial cytoplasm, Perez and Moore (1968) had proposed that the S-100 protein is concentrated in the axis cylinder of peripheral nerve, for there is a good correlation between degradation of axons and loss of S-100 in nerves undergoing Wallerian degeneration.

Mokrasch and Manner (1963) and Greaney (1961) have demonstrated a steady increase of proteolipid during myelination, and the association of this protein with myelin has been confirmed both by histochemical studies (Koenig, 1959) and by the identification of proteolipid protein in isolated myelin fractions. During development the concentration of basic amino acids in brain protein increases, which suggests that there is an increase in the histone-type proteins in the central nervous system (Kornguth *et al.,* 1966). In the human brain there is evidence to suggest that the basic encephalitogenic protein accumulates with increasing age (Einstein and Csejtev, 1966), and this is borne out by the observations of Eng and his colleagues. In the ten-week, four-year and adult human brain, proteolipid protein accounts for 68, 60 and 52 percent respectively of the total myelin protein (see Fig. 2-5). There is relatively little change in concentration of the triton-salt insoluble protein (17%-20%), but an increase of 16 to 30 percent in basic protein from the ten-week to adult brain (Eng, Chao, Gerstl, Pratt, and Tavastsjerna, 1968).

There are a number of difficulties to be faced in attempting to relate myelination or indeed any phase of morphological development with specific changes in enzyme activity. The problem is that the cellular heterogeneity of the brain and differences in the timing of maturation in different areas of the nervous system have to be considered (see Davison and Dobbing, 1968). While histochemical observations can be of value in relating enzyme activity to individual cell types and in assessing the time that particular enzymes appear, in general, attempts at quantitative measurement have met with little success. In addition, measurements of enzyme activity are only meaningful if related to rate-controlling stages in a metabolic pathway. For these reasons it is intended to comment only briefly on the relationship between enzyme activity and myelination.

Oligodendroglial Enzyme Activity. Although relatively little enzyme activity is associated with myelin immediately before and during the process of myelination, there are notable increases in enzyme activity (see Friede, 1966). Blunt, Wendell-Smith, and Baldwin (1967) have shown that the histochemical profile for oxidative enzyme activity is not established in oligodendrocytes of a kitten optic nerve until the end of the fourth postnatal week. Conversely, it has been shown (Banik, Blunt, and Davison, 1968) that sudanophilic myelin sheaths are present within the kitten optic nerve from the sixth day onwards. By twenty-eight days postnatal, however, the myelin sheaths become osmiophilic for the first time. It is probable, therefore, that earlier reports of an association between processes of myelination and oxidative activity in oligodendrocytes are related in some way to the processes of myelin maturation rather than to myelin deposition.

In the cerebellum of developing rats, Lehrer and Bornstein (1965) have shown that glucose-6-phosphate dehydrogenase activity reaches a peak at eight days. Afterwards it declines. Similar changes are seen in NADP*-dependent isocitric and 6-phosphogluconate dehydrogenase activity. β-Hydroxybutyric dehydrogenase activity in the rat brain is also initially low after birth, but it rises to a peak during the period of most active postnatal cerebral development and then declines again to very low levels after brain maturation is complete (Klee and Sokoloff, 1967). The dehydrogenase is found only in mitochondria, and it is distributed equally in grey and white matter, which suggests that it may be localized in glia rather than neurons. The striking increase in the β-glucuronidase of developing rat cerebellum from zero to nine days (Robins and Lowe, 1961) and the subsequent decrease suggests

---

*Nicotinamide adenine dinucleotide phosphate.

that differentiating glial cells of the presumptive white matter are an especially rich source of the enzyme. Nevertheless, it is unlikely that the enzyme has any role in myelin synthesis. The activity of β-galactosidase may also be related to the presence of growing and differentiating glia, but the enzyme's peak activity declines with the onset of maximal myelination.

Observations on the whole animal that suggest increased enzyme activity is associated with myelinating glia are supported by various studies on fetal white matter and tissue culture of nervous tissue. Thus Meyer and Meyer (1964) have found high concentration of glucose-6-phosphate dehydrogenase in oligodendrocytes of the white matter. Further, during development increasing concentration of oxidative enzymes of the Krebs cycle are found in the oligodendroglia. Blunt, Wendell-Smith, and Paisley (1967) have shown that enzymes of the pentose phosphate oxidative pathway are present in the glioblasts present in kitten optic nerve during early deposition of myelin. They also occur at a later stage in development in mature astrocytes and oligodendrocytes. Yonezawa, Bornstein, Peterson, and Murray (1962) have found that the oxidative enzymatic activity (nucleotide diaphorase and succinic dehydrogenase) of oligodendroglia and Schwann cells parallels the progress of myelination. Since optimum myelin formation occurs in tissue cultures maintained with elevated glucose supplements, there may be a special linkage between myelin formation and glucose utilization. This is possibly related to the demands of the pentose phosphate pathway and the NADPH synthesis.

Histochemical examination also shows that preceding myelination there is a marked increase in oxidative enzyme activity. In the initial stages of morphological maturation, dehydrogenase activity is localized almost exclusively within the perikaryon, but higher dehydrogenase activity accompanies the growth of dendrites. An increase in succinic dehydrogenase activity occurs in the glia near to the nuclei of the myelinating rat cerebellar white matter at about twelve days of age, but by the fourteenth day it then spreads throughout the white matter, and by the sixteenth day it is concentrated in the white matter of the foliae (Friede, 1957).

Blunt and Wendell-Smith (1967) in studies on the developing

cat optic nerve have found that glioblasts which exhibit α-glycero-phosphate dehydrogenase activity also show strong activity of NAD⁺ and NADP⁺ tetrazolium reductase and enzymes of the pentose shunt pathway. This could be taken to indicate that glio-blasts are responsible for the initial deposition of myelin sheaths. The later and differentiated astrocytes and oligodendrocytes show different kinds of histochemical profiles. The astrocytes are char-acterized by strong GPDH* activity, and the oligodendrocytes, by activity of the citric acid cycle enzymes (Blunt, Wendell-Smith, Paisley, and Baldwin, 1967). Both types of differentiated macro-glia show glucose-6-phosphate and 6-phosphogluconate dehydro-genase activity. For these reasons, and because of an exclusive association between astrocytes and myelinated axons in the lamina cribosa of cat optic nerve (Wendell-Smith, Blunt, and Baldwin, 1966), it has been suggested that oligodendrocytes may act as energy donors to axons at nodes of Ranvier, and that the macro-glial cell type implicated in myelin sheath support is the astrocyte. Friede, Fleming, and Knoller (1963) found that in oligodendro-cytes the dehydrogenases involved in the pentose shunt and in glycolysis are more active than the enzymes of the Krebs cycle. This may be related to their synthetic activity. However, as pointed out by Bunge (1968), myelin support may be the func-tion of only some oligodendrocytes. This probability, that the simpler forms of interfascicular oligodendrocytes are not connect-ed to myelin, taken in conjunction with the fact that the inter-nodes vary greatly in size would explain at least part of the cytological heterogeneity of this cell type.

Lipid and Protein Synthesis during Development

Central Nervous System

Myelination is accompanied by increased lipid synthesis and a concomitant increase of enzyme activity and coenzyme concen-tration. Thus in the rat brain, cholesterol biosynthesis, as judged both by *in vivo* and *in vitro* studies (for references see Davison, 1965, 1968), reaches a maximum at about fifteen days after birth.

---

*Glucose phosphate dehydrogenase (reduced).

In adult animals there is only very restricted synthesis of cholesterol in the central nervous system. Experiments *in vivo* suggest that two enzyme systems are rate limiting in cholesterol biosynthesis, the Δ^{24} reductase step, and a stage in the conversion of 8,9-double bond to 5,6-double bond compounds (Holstein, Fish, and Stokes, 1966). Biosynthesis of cerebrosides by rat brain slices reaches a maximum rate in animals of about eleven days old (Maker and Hauser, 1967), but the activity of sulphatide synthesizing enzymes in rat brains studied *in vitro* shows maximum activity at around nineteen days after birth (Balasubramanian and Bachhawat, 1965). *In vivo* the maximum period of biosynthesis of brain cerebrosides and sulphatides is in rats of fifteen days old. Incorporation of ^{35}S-sulphate into brain sulphatide reaches a maximum in rats between fifteen to twenty days old (Chase, Dorsey, and McKhann, 1967) and follows the earlier formation of 3′-phosphoadenosine 5′-sulphatophosphate, which reaches a maximum at about twelve days after birth (Balasubramanian and Bachhawat, 1965). Hence the timing of maximum incorporation immediately precedes the time for the maximum rate of accretion of glycolipid. In the rat brain this is at about twenty-five days after birth (see Fig. 2-7). This data suggests that the rate of deposition is not controlled by the availability of cerebroside synthetase activity, but by some other factor, such as the rate of membrane protein formation.

Similarly increased synthesis of brain phospholipid has been demonstrated in myelinating animals (for reviews see Sperry, 1962; Davison and Dobbing, 1968). This can also be related to increased synthetase activity. For example, McCaman and Cook (1966) find maximum phosphocholine-glyceride transferase activity in the brain of actively myelinating rabbits. Another enzyme whose activity is associated with lipid biosynthesis — glycerol phosphate dehydrogenase — also shows a close relationship to the progress of myelination. In the rat brain its activity in cerebral hemispheres and brain stem is low up until ten days after birth; after that, activity increases to thirty to forty days of age, and in older animals there is only a slow increase in absolute enzyme activity (Laatsch, 1962; De Vellis and Schjeide, 1968). Salway *et al.* (1968) have found that diphosphoinositide kinase and tri-phosphoinositide phosphomonoesterase activities increase most rapidly during myelination. This suggests a close relationship between triphosphoinositide metabolism and myelin. This may be expected from the increase during myelination in triphosphoinositide compared to diphosphoinositide concentration (Rossiter and Gardiner, 1965).

Increase of the amount of proteolipid protein in the brain is accompanied by an increased rate of biosynthesis (Klee and Soko-loff, 1965a, 1965b). Thus on the basis of specific activity measurements, the maximum rate of incorporation of ^{14}C-leucine into proteolipid protein of brain stem slices occurs in five- to ten-day-old rats (De Vellis, Schjeide, and Clemente, 1967). In peripheral nerve protein synthesis as judged *in vitro* studies (Matheson, 1968) using ^{14}C-glycine is most active in the newborn rat. However, in terms of total incorporated radioactivity, maximal synthesis probably occurs somewhat later. The actual localization and mechanism of myelin protein biosynthesis remains a problem of some interest. In studies on the Mauthner neurone of the goldfish, Edström has reported finding an RNA in both the axon and myelin sheath which has a similar base composition to ribosomal RNA. It appears that the myelin sheath RNA itself may be involved in local protein synthesis, for puromycin-sensitive incorporation of ^{14}C-lysine into myelin protein can be shown not only *in vivo* but also in pieces of spinal cord incubated *in vitro*. Edström (1966) points out that the only enzymes found by Adams *et al.* (1963) in the myelin sheath were those concerned with protein metabolism. The cyclic 2',3' AMPase found in myelin may have a similar role. Mokrash and Manner (1963) find the highest serine incorporation to be in the mitochondrial fraction from developing rat brain. Since this fraction may contain "early" myelin, their result would be consistent with that of Edström. On the other hand, Adams and his colleagues have found changes in the characteristics of the polysomes from developing brain that coincide with the period of myelination. This lends weight to the idea that myelin-protein synthesis may be performed by the granular endoplasmic reticulum.

Peripheral Nervous System

Lipogenesis has been examined in developing and adult peripheral nerve by Majno and Karnovsky (1958). In their *in vitro* studies they concluded that although peripheral nerve contains myelin sheaths, supporting cells, and axons, it behaves in a completely dissimilar way to white matter of the central nervous system. White matter has a Q_{0_2} of more than twice that of peripheral nerve but builds considerably less lipid per unit of time than peripheral nerve, and its pattern of substrate utilization is different, particularly with regard to uptake of phosphate (Table 2-XIII). When correlated with the cell population of the nerve, lipid synthesis is lowest in the newborn rat and the greatest activity is reached at about twenty days after birth. Grey matter slices are always most active in lipogenesis, except when acetate is employed as the substrate (presumably found by Majno and Karnovsky to be related to the relative inertness of adult brain cholesterol). Even in the mature sciatic nerve, lipogenesis is not uniform. There is a twenty percent drop in lipid content in a proximodistal direction, and this can be correlated with a similar decrease in lipogenic activity in the distal as compared to the proximal part of the nerve.

During development, oxygen uptake of nerve is nearly as high as that of the cerebral cortex. It reaches a maximum at about ten days and drops progressively to attain a constant level at five months. Lipogenesis from acetate also follows a similar sequence (Fig. 2-10) reaching 162 percent of that in the newborn on the first postnatal day, and eventually in 500-day-old animals, reaching only 4 percent of uptake into newborn nerve.

TABLE 2-XIII
IN VITRO CHARACTERISTICS OF RAT NERVOUS TISSUE*

	Dry wt	Lipid	Q_{0_2}	Relative Incorporation Acetate	Phosphate
Grey matter	19.5%	3.7%	11.2	25	760
White matter	34.5	13.6	2.5	10	49
Peripheral nerve	31.0	9.0	1,1	100	100

Specific activity: cpm/100 mg lipid.

*Data for adult rats (250 - 280 gm) taken from Majno and Karnovsky (1958). $Q_{0_2} = \mu l$ O_2/hr/mg dry tissue for 1st hour incubated.

Correlation with light microscope histological findings shows that the initial rise in lipid-synthesizing activity corresponds to the period during which myelin is first demonstrable. No myelin can be demonstrated at birth in the sciatic nerves (Noback, 1954)

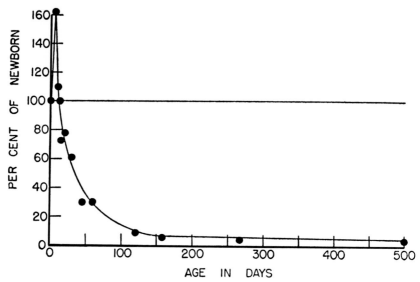

FIGURE 2-10. Incorporation of [1-14C] acetate into the lipids of rat peripheral nerves at various ages. Results are expressed as a percentage of the specific activity (cpm/100 mg) of nerve lipids from newborn animals. There was no overlap in values obtained from six experiments for each of the first three points on the curve. Maximum incorporation at the fifth day coincides with maximal respiratory activity in the nerve (Majno and Karnovsky, 1958). (By courtesy of the authors and the *Journal of Experimental Medicine*).

using methods based on osmic acid preparations. (In the electron microscope loosely packed early myelin can be first seen in significant amounts in 4-day-old rats.) A few myelinated fibers are present, however, in the brachial plexus, which at birth resembles a sciatic nerve at the age of three days. This is in agreement with previous findings of others and may be taken to indicate that maturation and myelination of the nervous system proceeds in a craniocaudal direction. At six days most of the visible nerve fibers are myelinated. Thereafter the myelin sheaths become thicker, and the axons, larger, while the lipid content rises from 1 to 10 percent (Majno and Karnovsky, 1958).

From the curves depicted (Fig. 2-11), one may surmise that the nerves attain relative maturity only towards day 150. Metabolic studies on rat nerves must therefore be accurately standardized with respect to age. This data of Majno and Karnovsky is in close agreement with that derived from histological measurements. Hatai (1903), counting the myelinated fibers in the ventral roots of rat spinal nerves, concluded that maturity was reached between one hundred and two hundred days (see also Friede and Samorajski, 1968).

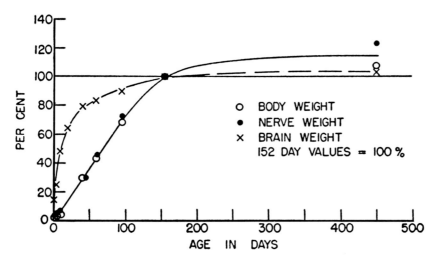

FIGURE 2-11. Growth patterns of the brain, peripheral nerves, and whole body of male albino rats. The curves refer to weights at various ages. The values corresponding to rats 152 days old are set at 100 percent. (By courtesy of G. Majno and M. L. Karnovsky and the *Journal of Experimental Medicine.*)

THE METABOLISM OF MYELIN

Cholesterol Metabolism

The earlier observations of Waelsch, Sperry and Stoyanoff (1940) and also those of Bloch and his colleagues (1943) led to the idea that in the adult brain the myelin lipid cholesterol is

metabolically stable. Waelsch *et al.* (1940) fed deuterated water to
newborn and mother rats. The isotope was actively incorporated
into the unsaponifiable lipids of the young rat brains, but relatively little was taken up into the sterols of the adult. Similarly,
Bloch, Berg, and Rittenberg (1943) fed deuterated cholesterol
to an adult dog, and although sterols in all other organs were
labeled, those in the central nervous system were not labeled. It
has been thought that experiments of this type simply reflect the
establishment during development of a barrier between brain
and blood, a barrier which prevents the exchange of labeled precursors (see Dobbing, 1968a). However, the rate of entry and
uptake of ^{14}C-cholesterol can be directly related to a rate curve for
brain cholesterol accumulation (Dobbing, 1963a; Dobbing and
Sands, 1963), suggesting that blood-brain effect is more a reflection of metabolic needs than a true physical barrier.

It was clearly necessary, therefore, to verify the hypothesis of
the metabolic stability of cholesterol by following the long-term
fate of labeled cholesterol in the brain, and so study its metabolism
more directly. Davison, Dobbing, Morgan, and Payling-Wright
(1958) injected [4-^{14}C] cholesterol into day-old chickens and fifteen-day-old rabbits and traced its incorporation and persistence
in various tissues of the body. While [4-^{14}C] cholesterol was found
to remain in the nervous system for longer than a year with little
change, radioactivity was soon lost from the plasma, liver and
kidneys. Some slow turnover of [4-^{14}C] cholesterol was noted in
the grey matter, but no significant loss of total ^{14}C-sterol occurred
in the white matter (Fig. 2-12). Similar experiments by McMillan, Douglas and Mortensen (1957) and by Pritchard (1963) in
the rat and Kritchevsky and Defendi (1961, 1962) in the chicken
also indicate the general stability of brain cholesterol.

The possibility of the reutilization of radioactive cholesterol
within the brain was also examined. It was found by Davison and
Wajda (1959b) that radioactive cholesterol specifically labeled at
the four-carbon position (Fig. 2-13) could be isolated from the
nervous system a year or more after injection of [4-^{14}C] cholesterol
into developing animals. In addition, radioactivity was not found
in other central nervous system lipid as might have been expected

RADIOACTIVITY IN WHITE AND GREY MATTER OF BRAIN FOLLOWING INJECTION OF [4-¹⁴C] CHOLESTEROL INTO 17 DAY OLD RABBITS.

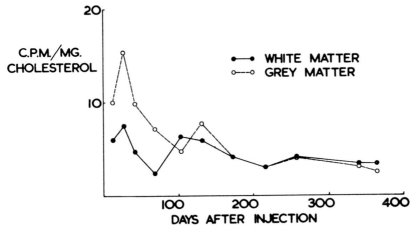

FIGURE 2-12. Radioactivity in white and grey matter of brain (expressed, after correction for growth, as counts per minute per mg cholesterol) at various intervals after the injection of [4-14C] cholesterol into seventeen-day-old rabbits. (After Davison *et al.* 1959 and by courtesy of the *Lancet*.)

if there had been complete catabolism of the labeled sterol. However, these experiments do not disprove the possible reutilization of the intact sterol molecule, or even its resynthesis from a partially degraded fragment of the cylcopentanoperhydrophenanthrene nucleus.

Phospholipid Metabolism

It was now necessary to examine the long-term metabolism of all the myelin components in turn in order to more specifically relate the findings for cholesterol to the metabolism of the whole myelin sheath. Since serine is involved at an early stage in the biosynthesis of sphingolipids (Brady, 1964; see Davison, 1968), and since sphingolipids are prominent myelin constituents, the metabolism of neural lipids with this amino acid as a precursor was studied. Eleven-day-old rabbits were injected with [3-14C] serine

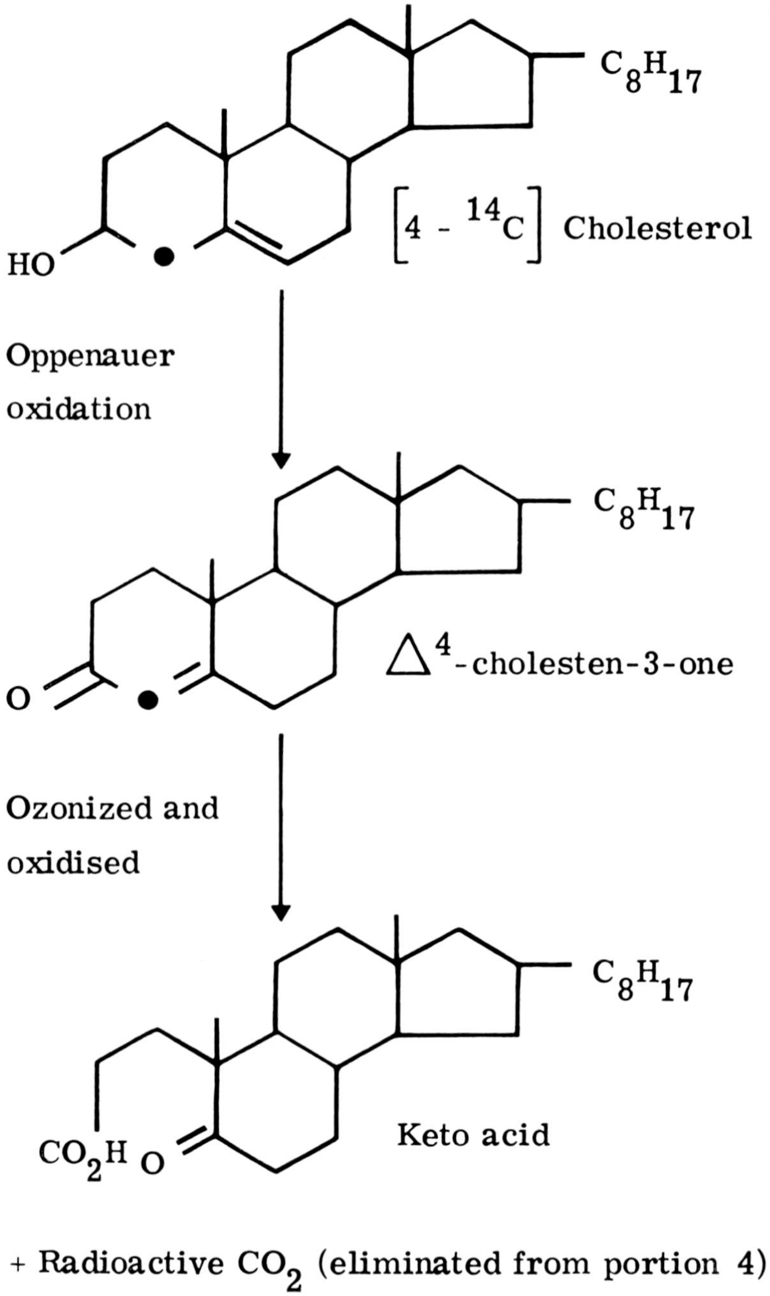

C_8H_{17}
[4 - ^{14}C] Cholesterol
HO
Oppenauer
oxidation
C_8H_{17}
Δ^4-cholesten-3-one
O
Ozonized and
oxidised
C_8H_{17}
Keto acid
CO_2H O
+ Radioactive CO_2 (eliminated from portion 4)

FIGURE 2-13. Elimination of radioactive carbon from [4-^{14}C] cholesterol. (After Davison and Wajda, 1959.)

and the subsequent metabolism of the individual ^{14}C-labeled lipids was followed (Davison, Morgan, Wajda, and Payling-Wright, 1959). There was long-term persistence of radioactive carbon with little turnover in the neutral sphingolipids (cerebrosides and sphingomyelin), in cholesterol, or in the *phospholipids.* Dawson and Richter (1950) and Ansell and Dohmen (1957) had previously shown relatively rapid labeling of brain phospholipids *in vivo,* so that the finding in the experiments using ^{14}C-serine of metabolically stable phospholipid in both central and peripheral nervous system was quite unexpected. These results prompted Davison and Dobbing (1959) to reexamine the metabolism of nervous system phospholipid. ^{32}P-phosphate was injected into developing rats, the animals were killed at intervals, and the radioactivity was determined in phospholipids and acid soluble extracts of the brain. It was found that rapid uptake of ^{32}P-phosphate into brain phospholipid was only sustained for six hours. After this time the rate of incorporation of ^{32}P into phospholipid fell, even if the results were corrected for the acid-soluble ^{32}P precursor content of the brain. It appeared therefore that only a relatively small phospholipid compartment (e.g. polyphosphoinositides) in nervous tissue underwent rapid exchange. It eventually took about ten days after injection for the incorporation of ^{32}P into brain phospholipid to be maximal. After reaching a peak incorporation, the ^{32}P-labeled lipid in brain and sciatic nerve underwent slow turnover. On extending the experiment for 179 days, it was possible to show that a proportion of the phospholipid of rat nervous tissue appeared to be metabolically inert. In further studies on rabbits the metabolically stable phospholipids were found by Davison and Dobbing (1960a, 1960b) to be predominantly located in the white matter. It was of considerable interest when Ansell and Spanner (1961) showed that twenty-four hours after injection of ^{32}P-phosphate into adult rats, the specific activity of the corpus callosum sphingomyelin was lower than that of all other regions in the brain. Since the white matter contains large amounts of myelin, and since sphingomyelin is a typical myelin constituent, this evidence further supported the hypothesis of the relative metabolic stability of myelin. August, Davison, and Williams (1961) attempted to confirm the hypothesis of metabolic stability by isolating myelin from the brain of animals previously injected with radioactive precursors. Radioactive phosphate was injected into both thirteen- to sixteen-day-old and adult rats. Then a crude myelin fraction was isolated by a modification of the methods of Korey (1957) and Whittaker (1959). In confirmation of the hypothesis, extensive labeling was found in the myelin of the young rats up to thirty-six days after injection, and considerable radioactivity was still localized in the myelin of the adult animals (Table 2-XIV and 2-XV). This latter observation was

TABLE 2-XIV

INCORPORATION OF ^{32}P AND ^{14}C ACETATE INTO BRAIN MYELIN*

Age When Injected	Precursor	Time After Injection (days)	Specific Radio- activity of Myelin cpm/mg P
14 days	^{32}P phosphate	36	5.92
Adult	^{32}P phosphate	2	4.4
15-16 days	[1-^{14}C] acetate	1	cpm/mg lipid 4830
Adult	[1-^{14}C] acetate	1	56

*Uptake of precursor (1μci/gm body weight) has been determined in myelin after intraperitoneal injection of phosphate (August *et al.*, 1961) and acetate (Smith and Eng, 1965).

entirely unexpected, for it was difficult to understand how an apparently inert structure could incorporate radioactive precursors to such an extent, particularly as there is much less incorpora-

TABLE 2-XV

RADIOACTIVITY INCORPORATED INTO INDIVIDUAL MYELIN LIPIDS OF YOUNG AND ADULT RAT BRAIN*

	Adult	Radioactivity cpm/mg Lipid Young Animals
Sphingomyelin	22	2500
Cerebroside	13	6048
Ethanolamine phosphatide	32	3220
Cholesterol	33	5000
Serine phosphatide	31	2040
Choline phosphatide	117	4760
Inositol phosphatide	—	2000

*[1-^{14}C] acetate was injected 1μCi/gm body wt into 15- to 16-day-old and adult rats, the animals killed 1 day later, and myelin obtained by centrifugation (Smith and Eng, 1965).

tion into brain lipid with acetate as precursor. Later work provided a possible explanation for the apparent enigma.

It is known that some brain phospholipids undergo quite rapid turnover. While the greater mass of adult brain phospholipid remains stable, this small amount of metabolically active phospholipid undergoing rapid exchange accounts for the earlier observations of Dawson and Richter (1950) and Ansell and Dohmen (1957). Hokin and Hokin, (1955, 1964) showed that phosphatidic acid and inositol phospholipids are readily labeled in mouse brain. Larrabee and Leight (1965) and Pumfrey (1968) have shown similar rapid labeling of nervous tissue phospholipids. This labeling is probably connected with neural transmission processes for stimulation, either electrically or by addition of neurohormones, leads to increased uptake that is particularly evident in the inositol phospholipid fraction. Rapid turnover of brain polyphosphoinositides, however, has been more directly related to myelin metabolism. The specific radioactivities of myelin polyphosphoinositides have been determined three hours after injection of inorganic ^{32}P-phosphate into adult guinea pig, or thirty minutes after incubation of brain subcellular fractions with γ-^{32}P-ATP. Eichberg and Dawson (1965) found that *in vivo* there was rapid labeling of inositol di- and tri-phosphoinositide in purified myelin isolated from the brain. As expected, little exchange of other myelin phospholipids was noted. The exception was phosphatidic acid in which the uptake was about a sixth of that in the polyphosphoinositides. On incubation *in vitro* of radioactive ATP with brain subcellular fractions, there was marked incorporation of ^{32}P-phosphate into the phosphatidic acid of all fractions, particularly into the microsomes. There was also some labeling of triphosphoinositides in the crude myelin-rich nuclear fraction, and extensive labeling of diphosphoinositides in the crude mitochondrial fraction. This led to the suggestion that the rapidly metabolizing polyphosphoinositides are localized in a specific area of the central nervous system (e.g. axolemma or the node of Ranvier), for the great mass of lipid and protein is relatively inert, and it is difficult to envisage only one dynamic component in a tightly packed lamellar structure. Following intraventricular injection of ^{14}C-labeled ethanolamine into young adult rats, the highest activity was found by Ansell and Spanner (1967) to be in the "light" myelin obtained from the crude mitochondrial fraction (Table 2-XVI). In contrast the "heavy" myelin incorporated

TABLE 2-XVI

UPTAKE OF [1,2-^{14}C] ETHANOLAMINE INTO MYELIN OF RAT BRAIN*

Phosphatidyl Ethanolamine	*Counts/sec/mole*		
Time After Injection	*3 hr*	*24 hr*	*63 days*
Whole brain	350	429	22
Small myelin	319	433	41
Large myelin	85	184	34
Microsomes	360	419	—
Prepared by the method of Eichberg *et al.* (1964).			

*Radioactive ethanolamine (0.817 μCi) was given by intraventricular injection into 12- to 14-week-old rats (Ansell and Spanner, 1967, 1968).

much less radioactive ethanolamine. This disproportionate labeling suggested possible contamination of the light myelin fraction, but its specific radioactivity was higher than that of any other fraction, and its radioactivity was not lost on further purification. Electron microscopy of the light myelin failed to show the presence of any mitochondria, and nor was the ATPase activity consistent with possible microsomal contamination. Ansell and Spanner (1967) therefore concluded that in the adult brain there is a small pool of metabolically active myelin which may be related to that described by Davison and Gregson (1966) in their studies on brain sulphatide metabolism.

Cerebroside and Sulphatide Metabolism

Similar long-term experiments with labeled serine, hexoses, and sulphate have shown that the cerebrosides and sulphatides resemble other myelin lipids in their metabolic stability. For example, ^{35}S-sulphate incorporated into the brain, spinal cord, and sciatic nerve sulpholipids of fifteen-day-old rats remains with relatively little loss (Fig. 2-14), and in the central nervous system much of the radioactive sulphatide persisting for more than a year has been localized in myelin isolated by differential centrifugation (Davison and Gregson, 1962). When ^{35}S-sulphate was given by intraventricular injection into adult rats, it was possible to follow the metabolism of isolated myelin and show that a quantitatively small pool (equivalent to about 0.2% of the total brain sulpha-tide) underwent relatively fast exchange. The remainder turned

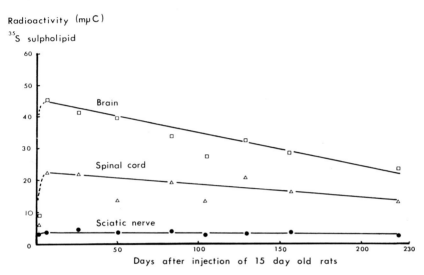

FIGURE 2-14. Incorporation and persistence of ^{35}S-sulphate into the neural lipids of the growing rat brain. Fifteen-day-old rats were given 8 μCi of ^{35}S-sulphate by intraperitoneal injection. Data for brain (□), spinal cord (Δ) and sciatic nerve (●) is after Davison and Gregson (1962).

over very much more slowly. It was suggested that this dynamic sulphatide pool was probably localized at a specific anatomical site, such as the node of Ranvier or the axolemma. However, com-pared to the microsomal and mitochondrial fractions (Cumar, Barra, Maccioni, and Caputto, 1968), in sixteen- to twenty-day-old rat brain preparations, there was relatively little synthesis of sul-pholipid by isolated myelin preparations (PAP[35]S, Tween 20).

Radioactive sulphate was also injected intraperitoneally into four-day-old rats, and the distribution and fate of labeled sulpha-tide was studied in the brain subcellular fractions (Fig. 2-15). During development there was a redistribution of radioactivity in the subcellular fractions, so that ^{35}S-sulphatide was reduced in all fractions, while radioactivity appeared in newly formed myelin.

These experiments were interpreted as indicating the transference of glia cell membrane from the microsome fraction into myelin. Herschkowitz, McKhann, and Shooter (1968) have detected a water-soluble sulphatide-containing lipoprotein in seventeen-day-

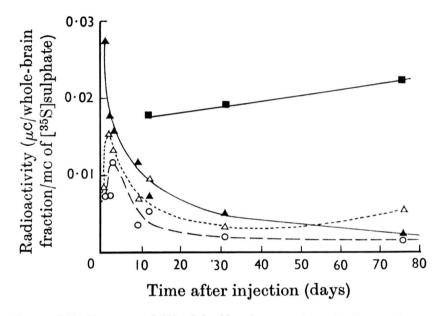

FIGURE 2-15. Turnover of ^{35}S-sulphatide of neonatal rat brain membrane fractions. The four-day-old rats were given 25μCi of carrier-free ^{35}S-sulphate by intraperitoneal injection. Animals were killed at various times up to seventy-six days after injection; in the early experiments brains from two to four animals were pooled to allow separation of about 2 gm of nervous tissue. Fractionation and determination of radioactivity were as described in the text. Results shown are radioactivity (μCi) per whole brain fraction corrected to 1μCi of ^{35}S-sulphate injected. Myelin (■) was only separated in animals older than twelve days. Radioactivity in mitochondria, including synaptic endings (▲), microsomes (△), and supernatant (O), are shown. Results for the nuclear fraction are not included. (By courtesy of the *Biochemical Journal*.)

old rat brain. Using ^{35}S-sulphate, they have found a precursor-product relationship, which suggests that sulphatide synthesized in the microsomes is transported, via the cytoplasm, to the myelin membrane in the form of a lipoprotein (see Fig. 2-16). Other experiments by Pritchard (1963), Torvik, and Sidman (1965) and Banik and Davison unpublished) indicated that myelin becomes labeled when various radioactive precursors are introduced into the brain of newborn animals well before the onset of myelination.

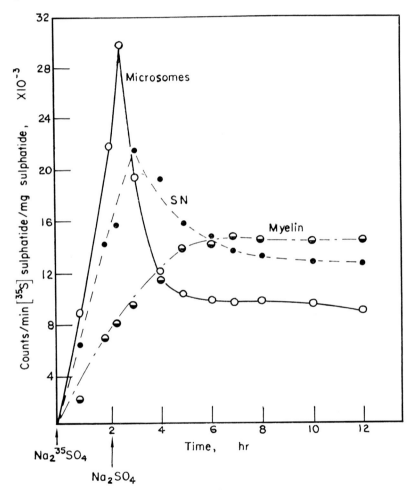

FIGURE 2-16. Turnover of ^{35}S-sulphatide in subcellular fractions of developing rat brain. Seventeen-day-old animals were injected with 2μCi of ^{35}S-sulphate per gram body weight and with 0.5 ml of 7% (w/v) Na$_2$SO$_4$ after 2 hours. (Herschkowitz, McKhann, and Shooter, 1968). SN = soluble sulphatide containing lipoprotein. (By courtesy of the authors and the *Journal of Neurochemistry*.)

Stable and Nonstable Lipids in Rat Myelin

Spinal cord from forty-day old rats has been incubated for two hours at 37°C with [U-^{14}C] glucose, or [I-^{14}C] acetate, and purified myelin isolated (Smith, 1967). The relative specific activity of the myelin depends on the substrate supplied, but in general, about four times as much radioactivity is taken up into inositol phosphatide and lecithin compared to that in cerebrosides and cholesterol. This *in vitro* observation is consistent with the results obtained *in vivo* by Smith and Eng (1965). Smith and Eng (1965) extended work on myelin metabolism and chose [1-^{14}C] acetate as a precursor. Acetate was chosen in order to extensively label fatty acids and was used in preference to substances which may label other parts of the lipid molecule. Following injection of acetate into fifteen- to sixteen-day-old and adult rats, myelin was isolated at intervals up to one year thereafter. The individual lipids were separated on two-dimensional chromatograms, and specific radioactivity was determined. After allowing for an initial exchange period, the turnover rates of lipids were calculated on data corrected for the effects of growth. Unfortunately, it was not possible to do a direct calculation of turnover on the basis of total brain lipid radioactivity. Their results showed that some myelin lipids (e.g. lecithin) undergo faster turnover than others (e.g. sulphatide), and this was true if turnover rates were calculated from a time beginning at two months after labeling or on direct comparison with metabolism of sulphatide. It was suggested that the higher rate of lecithin metabolism could be ascribed to turnover of fatty acid in the lysolecithin and fatty acid cycle of the brain (Webster and Alpern, 1964).

Myelin fractions from adult rats were completely inactive with respect to fatty acid synthesis *in vitro* (Aeberhard and Menkes, 1968), and in short-term *in vitro* and in long-term *in vivo* experiments, no difference was noted in the rates of turnover of the α and β long-chain fatty acids (Smith, 1967). This suggests that lecithin is metabolized as an intact molecule. The results showed two classes of myelin lipid — stable and nonstable (Table 2-XVII). Eng and Smith (1966) proposed that the stable lipids, namely,

TABLE 2-XVII

CALCULATED TURNOVER RATES FOR RAT MYELIN CONSTITUENTS

	*Half-lives**
Cholesterol	7 - 8 months
Sphingomyelin	10 months
Cerebroside	$>$ 1 year
Sulphatide	$>$ 1 year
Ethanolamine phospholipid	7 months
Serine phosphatide	4 months
Choline phosphatide	2 months
Inositol phosphatide	5 weeks

*Half-lives calculated from Smith and Eng's data 2 months to 1 year after injection.

cholesterol, cerebroside, sulphatide, ethanolamine, and sphingo-myelin, form an inert membrane complex into which the more easily metabolized lipids (e.g. lecithin and inositol phospholipid) loosely interdigitate. They point out that there is a remarkably constant molar proportion of the stable and nonstable lipids iso-lated from the myelin of a number of different species (see Table 2-XVIII). Nevertheless, Cuzner, Davison, and Gregson (1965a, 1966) found little evidence of different turnover rates of indi-vidual phospholipids following prior labeling of adult or new-born rat brain with phosphate and after injecting [1-¹⁴C] acetate into fifty-three day old rats previously given tritium when nine and thirteen days old. However, interpretation of experiments using radioactive phosphate is particularly complicated by the

TABLE 2-XVIII

THE ENG-SMITH RATIO IN MYELIN

Species	Central Nervous System		
	Stable	Labile	
Rat	1.06	0.41	Eng and Smith (1966)
Man	0.86	0.28	Norton, Poduslo, and Suzuki (1966)
Squirrel monkey	0.95	0.28	Horrocks (1967)
Ox	0.92	0.31	Norton and Autilio (1966)
	Peripheral Nervous System		
Rat	1.08	0.57	Evans and Finean (1965)
Man	—	—	
Squirrel monkey	1.03	0.29	Horrocks (1967)
Ox	0.92	0.66	O'Brien, Sampson, and Stern (1967)

*The ratio of the sum of moles of galactolipids, ethanolamine phospholipid, and sphingomyelin is compared to the sum of moles of lecithin, inositol, and serine phospholipid when cholesterol = 1.

continuing presence of ^{32}P-phosphate in the blood stream, and the levels of ^{14}C taken up into the individual phospholipids was low, making difficult the reliable assessment of turnover rates. A possible explanation of some of these results is that reutilization of cholesterol, cerebrosides and other lipids can occur whereas lecithin released from myelin is metabolized by catabolic enzymes. This possibility is supported by studies of Banik and Davison (1967, 1969), in which they traced the metabolism of 7-dehydrocholesterol and desmosterol in myelin fraction isolated from developing rat brain. Four-day-old rats were given either triparanol or AY 9944 (Hill and Dvornik, 1966) to block cholesterol biosynthesis, and the disappearance of cholesterol precursors incorporated into myelin was subsequently traced. There was extensive accumulation (up to 50% of total sterol) of both desmosterol and 7-dehydrocholesterol in the myelin isolated in animals of twenty days of age. Yet thirty days later only traces of cholesterol precursors could be detected in myelin. These experiments therefore suggest that the loosely packed developing early myelin may be capable of undergoing metabolic changes. This work implies that turnover of myelin lipids may occur only during the first transition of myelination (e.g. in the rat up to about 30 days after birth), but for further information see Smith (1968).

Myelin Protein Metabolism

Central Nervous System

The original observations of Furst, Lajtha and Waelsch (1958) showed that up to forty-five minutes after injecting ^{14}C-lysine into two young adult monkeys, there was remarkably little uptake of the amino acid into the brain proteolipid proteins, especially those of the white matter (Table 2-XIX). This was consistent with the idea that the myelin proteins were relatively inert. In a long-term study (Davison, 1961) [1-^{14}C] glycine was given by intraperiteonal injection to eleven-day-old rats and labeling of the central nervous system chloroform-methanol soluble and insoluble protein followed. It was found (Fig. 2-17) that there was only very slow loss of ^{14}C from the chloroform-methanol soluble protein fraction, although other proteins underwent relatively rapid

TABLE 2-XIX
INCORPORATION OF ¹⁴C-LYSINE INTO BRAIN PROTEINS
OF ADULT MONKEY*

| | *Specific Activity (count/µg lysine/min)* | |
	Rest of Proteins	*Proteolipid Proteins*
Cortex	1.90	0.21
Cerebellum	1.67	0.22
White matter	1.10	0.06
Hind and midbrain	1.21	0.15
Rest of brain	1.53	0.15

*Results after Furst *et al.* (1958), 13.6µCi/kg body wt into adult monkeys (1-1.5µCi/kg weight).

turnover. Since much of the chloroform-methanol soluble protein is localized in myelin, it was concluded that myelin protein had a

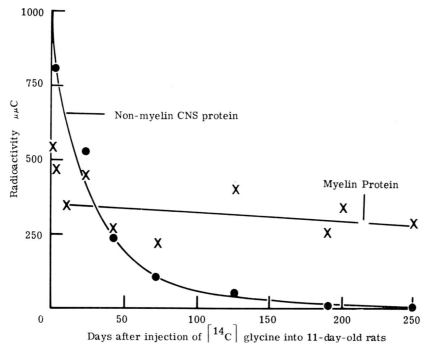

FIGURE 2-17. Metabolism of ¹⁴C-labelled myelin and nonmyelin proteins in the rat central nervous system. ¹⁴C-glycine was injected into eleven-day-old rats and persisting radioactivity determined in proteolipid protein (●) and nonproteolipid, chloroform-methanol insoluble protein (×). Figures for the latter are divided by ten to bring on to the scale. (By courtesy of the *Biochemical Journal.*)

metabolic stability comparable to that of the major lipid components. This conclusion was supported by the finding of a high proportion of the persisting ^{35}S-labeled protein in the myelin fraction isolated from rats injected one year previously with ^{35}S-methionine. Eng and Smith (unpublished) also using ^{14}C-glycine have studied the metabolism of basic, proteolipid and acid extractable protein in rat brain and spinal cord myelin. They find no marked difference in the metabolism of any of the three individual proteins, which behave metabolically in a similar way to the less stable myelin lipids (i.e. half-life of about 30-60 days). Von Hungen, Mahler, and Moore (1968) have examined protein turnover in subcellular fractions of adult rat brain following injection of ^{3}H-leucine. Although in this design of experiment it would be difficult to detect metabolically stable protein (Davison, 1968), however the nuclear protein was found to contain a long-lived component ($t_{0.5}$ about 40 days).

Peripheral Nerve

Radioactivity persisting after injection of [1-^{14}C] glycine into eleven-day-old and adult rats in peripheral nerve chloroform-methanol insoluble protein has also been studied (Davison, 1961). Much less radioactivity was found to be incorporated into the nerve proteins of adult compared to young animals. The specific activity of sciatic nerve protein in the mature series of rats declines during the period studied, and only about 7 percent of the original activity remained 190 to 197 days after injection. In those rats injected with [1-^{14}C] glycine, when eleven days old, 25 percent of the original radioactivity remained 250 days after injection (Table 2-XX). These experiments suggest that the peripheral nerve myelin proteins are also relatively metabolically stable.

LIPID METABOLISM AT THE CELLULAR LEVEL

The cellular location of labeled lipids in autoradiograms of mouse brains has been followed by Torvik and Sidman (1965), who injected either simple precursors (^{14}C- and ^{3}H-acetate or ^{14}C-serine) or 7α-^{3}H-cholesterol into mice of various postnatal

TABLE 2-XX

PERSISTENCE OF RADIOACTIVITY IN PROTEIN RESIDUE FROM SCIATIC NERVE OF YOUNG AND ADULT GROUPS OF RATS AT INTERVALS AFTER INJECTION OF [1-14C] GLYCINE*

Rats Injected with 5 μCi of [1-14C] Glycine When 11 Days Old				Rats Injected with 16.6 μCi of [1-14C] Glycine When Adult			
Time after injection (days)	Wt of sciatic nerve (mg)	Wt of chloroform-methanol insoluble protein residue (mg)	Specific activity corrected for growth and dose	Time after injection (days)	Wt of sciatic nerve (mg)	Wt of chloroform-methanol insoluble residue (mg)	Specific activity corrected for dose
1	16	1.1	265	1	134	18.3	30
42	60	2	87	4	115	11	5.7
72	131	11	254	18	139	15.7	12.0 (1.6)[1]
126	166	18	140	49	123	7.4	1.9
189	92	12	210 (63)[1]	190	115	17.8	2.3 (0.4)[1]
250	90	10	67 (46)[1]	197	140	14.4	1.3 (0.6)[1]

[1]Radioactivity of alkali-insoluble protein residue of sciatic nerve

*Specific activity is given as radioactivity $\mu\mu$Ci/mg of protein residue corrected for a dose of 10μCi of [1-14C] glycine/100 gm body wt. Specific activities for young rats are also corrected for the dilution effect of growth.

ages. Radioactivity in the brain was determined at intervals of up to six months after injection by counting autoradiographic grains over untreated and lipid-extracted light microscope sections. Incorporation and replacement of isotope was most rapid in lipids of nerve cell bodies. It was slower in the neuropil (containing high concentration of surface and intracellular membrane of neuronal and glial processes) and least in white matter. It was argued by Torvik and Sidman that the choroid plexi and nerve cell bodies serve as monitors of circulating, labeled lipid precursors, as these tissue constituents appear to be rapidly and intensely labeled twenty minutes after injection. Since these areas of the nervous system quickly loose their radioactivity, it was deduced that no significant reutilization takes place. This observation is therefore consistent with experiments on specifically labeled cholesterol and on brain protein turnover where all nonmyelin proteins undergo rapid exchange although myelin proteins are stable. Torvik and Sidman also found that the persistent label is diffuse in white matter and not located in the perinuclear cytoplasm of glial cells. This supports the concept that the relatively stable lipids are mainly in the myelin sheath. However, some stable lipid components were found in areas apparently devoid of myelin (e.g. molecular layer of the cerebellum).

Another finding of interest was that labeled lipid was present in the neuropil and white matter (corpus callosum) four months after injection of $[1\text{-}^{14}\text{C}]$ acetate into five-day-old mice (1 week before visible myelination begins in the corpus callosum). This is again consistent with other work in which it was reported that ^{35}S-labeled myelin sulphatide could be isolated months after injection of ^{35}S-sulphate into four-day-old rats. It may be that the radioactive isotope is incorporated into the oligodendroglial plasma membrane before myelination commences.

The radioautographic studies also confirmed that incorporation of isotopes into the white matter lipids of the adult animals was definitely less than in younger animals. Thus three hours after injection of ^{14}C-acetate into the newborn mouse, neuronal perikarya were proportionately much more heavily labeled than any components of the corpus callosum. After two months white matter was found to be weakly labeled, neuropil even more weakly and the nerve cells were practically negative. This agrees with other work showing incorporation and persistence of isotopic precursor into adult myelin.

CONCLUSION

Although it was considered at one time that the biochemistry of myelin was a subject of remote interest, this view has been considerably modified as a result of the increasing attention of research workers to this area of neurochemistry (for reviews see Smith, 1967; Norton, 1968; Davison, 1968a, 1968b, and 1968c; O'Brien, 1969; Mokrasch, 1969). The developing brain provides an ideal system for the study of the biosynthesis of large amounts of membrane structure. Current ideas on the mechanism of the transformation of plasma membrane into the specialized structure of the myelin sheath should be relevant to our understanding of the more general processes controlling membrane formation and its molecular structure. Nor is an appreciation of the biochemistry of myelination without practical significance. The demonstration of the relative metabolic inertness of the greater part of the myelin sheath is an essential prerequisite for the hypothesis of the vulnerable period in brain development (see Dobbing, 1968), and it forms a basis for the explanation of sequences of dysmyelination. On the other hand, the discovery of a small, dynamic part in the otherwise stable myelin sheath presents a challenging observation which may provide a clue to a "weak link" in its structure. Of special interest is the possible role of triphosphoinositide, for not only does this compound seem to be concentrated in myelin, but unlike other myelin phospholipids it undergoes rapid turnover.

No doubt, further work using improved separation methods and appropriate labeling procedures will throw light on some of these intriguing questions.

REFERENCES

ADAMS, C. W. M.: A *p*-dimethylaminobenzal-nitrite method for the histochemical demonstration of tryptophane and related compounds. *J Clin Path, 10*:56, 1957.

ADAMS, C. W. M.; ABDULLA, Y. H.; TURNER, D. R., and BAYLISS, O. B.: Subcellular preparation of peripheral myelin. *Nature (London)*, *220*:171, 1968.

ADAMS, C. W. M., and DAVISON, A. N.: The occurrence of esterified cholesterol in the developing nervous system. *J Neurochem, 4*:282, 1959.

ADAMS, C. W. M., and DAVISON, A. N.: The myelin sheath. In Adams, C. W. M. (Ed.) : *Neurohistochemistry*. Amsterdam, Elsevier, p. 332, 1965.

ADAMS, C. W. M.; DAVISON, A. N., and GREGSON, N. A.: Enzyme inactivity of myelin: Histochemical and biochemical evidence. *J Neurochem, 10*:383, 1963.

ADAMS, D. H., and FOX, M. E.: Studies on rat brain myelin. *Biochem J, 108*:36P, 1968.

AEBERHARD, E., and MENKES, J. H.: Biosynthesis of long chain fatty acids by subcellular particles of mature brain. *J Biol Chem, 243*: 3834, 1968.

ALDRIDGE, W. N.: Liver and brain mitochondria. *Biochem J, 67*:423, 1957.

AMADUCCI, L.: The distribution of proteolipids in the human nervous system. *J Neurochem, 9*:153, 1962.

AMADUCCI, L.; PAZZAGLI, A., and PESSINA, G.: The relation of proteolipids and phosphatide peptides to tissue elements in the bovine nervous system. *J Neurochem, 9*:509, 1962.

ANSELL, G. B., and DOHMEN, H.: Metabolism of individual phospholipids in the rat brain during hypoglycemia, anesthesia and convulsions. *J Neurochem, 2*:1, 1957.

ANSELL, G. B., and SPANNER, S.: Studies on cerebral spingomyelin. *Biochem J, 79*:176, 1961.

ANSELL, G. B., and SPANNER, S.: The metabolism of labelled ethanolamine in the brain of the rat *in vivo. J Neurochem, 14*:873, 1967.

ANSELL, G. B., and SPANNER, S.: The long-term metabolism of the ethanolamine moiety of rat brain myelin phospholipids. *J Neurochem, 15*:1371, 1968.

AUGUST, C.; DAVISON, A. N., and WILLIAMS, F. M.: Phospholipid metablosim in nervous tissue. *Biochem J, 81*:8, 1961.

AUTILIO, L.: Fractionation of myelin proteins. *Fedn Proc, 25*:764, 1966.

AUTILIO, L. A.; NORTON, W. T., and TERRY, R. D.: The preparation and some properties of purified myelin from the central nervous system. *J Neurochem, 11*:17, 1964.

Axelrod, J.; Reichenthal, J., and Brodie, B. B.: Direct determination of phosphatidyl ethanolamine and phosphatidyl serine in plasma and red blood cells. *J Biol Chem, 204*:903, 1953.

Balasubramanian, A. S., and Bachhawat, B. K.: Studies on enzymic synthesis of cerebroside sulphate from 3'-phosphoadenosine-5'-phosphosulphate. *Indian J Biochem, 2*:212, 1965.

Banik, N. L.; Blunt, M. J., and Davison, A. N.: Changes in the osmiophilia of myelin and lipid content in the kitten optic nerve. *J Neurochem, 15*:471, 1968.

Banik, N.L. and Davison, A. N.: Desmosterol in rat brain myelin. *J Neurochem, 14*:594, 1967.

Banik, N. L., and Davison, A. N.: Myelin lipid composition during development of the brain. *Acta Polonika*, in press, 1969.

Bartlett, G. R.: Phosphorus assay in column chromatography. *J Biol Chem, 234*:466, 1959.

Beck, C. S.; Hasinoff, C. W., and Smith, M. E.: 1-alanyl-β-naphthylamidase in rat spinal cord myelin. *J Neurochem, 15*:1297, 1968.

Benson, A. A.: On the orientation of lipid in chloroplast and cell membranes. *J Am Oil Chem Soc, 43*:265, 1966.

Bensted, J. P. M.; Dobbing, J.; Morgan, R. S.; Reid, R. T. W.; and Payling Wright, G.: Neurologlial development and myelination in the spinal cord of the chick embryo. *J Embryol Exp Morph, 5*: 428, 1957.

Biran, L. A., and Bartley, W.: Distribution of fatty acids in lipids of rat brain, brain mitochondria and microsomes. *Biochem J, 79*:159, 1961.

Bloch, K.; Berg, B. N., and Rittenberg, D.: Biological conversion of cholesterol to cholic acid. *J Biol Chem, 149*:511, 1943.

Blunt, M. J., and Wendell-Smith, C. P.: Glial α glycerophosphate dehydrogenase and central myelination. *Nature (London), 216*:605, 1967.

Blunt, M. J.; Wendell-Smith, C. P., and Baldwin, F.: An oxidative enzyme study during central myelination. *J Anat (London), 101*: 191, 1967.

Blunt, M. J.; Wendell-Smith, C. P., and Paisley, P. B.: Phosphogluconate oxidative pathway in glial metabolism. *Nature, 215*:523, 1967.

Blunt, M. J.; Wendell-Smith, C. P.; Paisley, P. B. ,and Baldwin, F.: Oxidative enzyme activity in macroglia and axons of cat optic nerve. *J Anat (London), 101*:12, 1967.

BÖTTCHER, C. J. F.; PRIES, C., and VAN GENT, C. M.: A rapid and sensitive colorimetric microdetermination of free and bound choline. *Recl Trav Chim, 80:*1169, 1961.

BRADY, R. O.: Biosynthesis of glycolipids. In Dawson, R. M. C., and Rhodes, D. N. (Eds.): *Metabolism and Physiological Significance of Lipids.* London, Wiley, p. 95, 1964.

BROCKERHOFF, H.: Breakdown of phospholipids in mild alkaline hydrolysis. *J Lipid Res, 4:*96, 1963.

BRODY, T. M., and BAIN, J. A.: A mitochondrial preparation from mammalian brain. *J Biol Chem, 195:*685, 1952.

BUNGE, R. P.: Glial cells and the central myelin sheath. *Physiol Rev, 48:*197, 1968.

CAVANNA, R., and RAPPORT, M. R.: An improved preparation of bovine brain proteolipid. *J Lipid Res, 8:*65, 1967.

CHASE, H. P.; DORSEY, J., and MCKHANN, G. M.: The effect of malnutrition on the synthesis of a myelin lipid. *Pediatrics, 1:*551, 1967.

COOK, G. M. W.: Chemistry of membranes. *Brit Med Bull, 24:*118, 1968.

COTMAN, C. W., and MAHLER, H. R.: Resolution of insoluble proteins in rat brain subcellular fractions. *Arch Biochem Biophys, 120:*384, 1967.

CUMAR, F. A.; BARRA, H. S.; MACCIONI, H. J., and CAPUTTO, R.: Sulfation of glycosphingolipids and related carbohydrates by brain preparations from young rats. *J Biol Chem, 243:*3807, 1968.

CURRY, J. J., and HEIM, L. M.: Brain myelination after neonatal administration of oestradiol. *Nature (London), 209:*915, 1966.

CUZNER, M. L.: Quantitative thin layer chromatography. Ph.D. thesis. Univ. Lond., 1968.

CUZNER, M. L., and DAVISON, A. N.: Quantitative thin layer chromatography of lipids. *J Chromat, 27:*388, 1967.

CUZNER, M. L., and DAVISON, A. N.: The lipid composition of rat brain myelin and subcellular fractions during development. *Biochem J, 106:*29, 1968.

CUZNER, M. L., DAVISON, A. N., and GREGSON, N. A.: Chemical and metabolic studies of rat myelin of the central nervous system. *Ann NY Acad Sci, 122:*86, 1965a.

CUZNER, M. L.; DAVISON, A. N., and GREGSON, N. A.: The chemical composition of vertebrate myelin and microsomes. *J Neurochem, 12:*469, 1965b.

CUZNER, M. L.; DAVISON, A. N., and GREGSON, N. A.: Turnover of brain mitochondrial membrane lipids. *Biochem J, 101:*618, 1966.

DALLNER, G.; SIEKEVITZ, P., and PALADE, G. E.: Biogenesis of endoplasmic reticulum membranes. I. Structural and chemical differentiation in developing rat hepatocyte. *J Cell Biol, 30:*73, 1966a.

DALLNER, G.; SIEKEVIETZ, P., and PALADE, G. E.: Biogenesis of endoplasmic reticulum membranes. II. Synthesis of constitutive microsomal enzymes in developing rat hepatocyte. *J Cell Biol, 30:*97, 1966b.

DAVISON, A. N.: Metabolically inert proteins of the central and peripheral nervous system, muscle and tendon. *Biochem J, 78:*272, 1961.

DAVISON, A. N.: Brain sterol metabolism. *Adv Lipid Res, 3:*171, 1965.

DAVISON, A. N.: Cholesterol metabolism in nervous tissue. In Lajtha, A. (Ed.) : *Handbook of Neurochemistry.* New York, Plenum, 1969, in press.

DAVISON, A. N.: Lipid metabolism of nervous tissue. In Davison, A. N., and Dobbing, J. (Eds.) : *Applied Neurochemistry.* Oxford, Blackwell, p. 178, 1968a.

DAVISON, A. N.: The influence of nutritional disorder on the lipid composition of the central nervous system. *Proc Nutr Soc, 27:*83, 1968b.

DAVISON, A. N.: Progress in pedology. In Linneweh, F. (Ed.) : *Fortschritte der Pädologie.* Heidelberg, Springer-Verlag, p. 65, 1968c.

DAVISON, A. N.; CUZNER, M. L.; BANIK, N. L., and OXBERRY, J. M.: Myelinogenesis in the rat brain. *Nature (London), 212:*1373, 1966.

DAVISON, A. N., and DOBBING, J.: Phospholipid metabolism in nervous tissue. I. A reconsideration of brain and peripheral nerve phospholipid metabolism *in vivo. Biochem J, 73:*701, 1959.

DAVISON, A. N., and DOBBING, J.: Phospholipid metabolism in nervous tissue. II. Metabolic stability. *Biochem J, 75:*565, 1960a.

DAVISON, A. N., and DOBBING, J.: Phospholipid metabolism in nervous tissue. III. The anatomical distribution of metabolically inert phospholipid in the central nervous system. *Biochem J, 75:*571, 1960b.

DAVISON, A. N., and DOBBING, J.: The developing brain. In Davison, A. N., and Dobbing, J. (Eds.) : *Applied Neurochemistry.* Oxford, Blackwell, p. 253, 1968.

DAVISON, A. N.; DOBBING, J.; MORGAN, R. S., and PAYLING WRIGHT, G.: The deposition and disposal of (4-^{14}C) cholesterol in the brain of growing chickens. *J Neurochem, 3:*89, 1958.

DAVISON, A. N., and GREGSON, N. A.: The physiological role of cerebron sulphuric acid (sulphatide) in the brain. *Biochem J, 85:*558, 1962.

DAVISON, A. N., and GREGSON, N. A.: Changes during maturation in the enzymic activity and composition of subcellular fractions obtained from rat brain. *Acta Neurol Scand, 38:*48, 1962.

DAVISON, A. N., and GREGSON, N. A.: Metabolism of cellular membrane sulpholipids in the rat brain. *Biochem J, 98:*915, 1966.

DAVISON, A. N.; MORGAN, R. S.; WAJDA, M., and PAYLING WRIGHT, G.: Metabolism of myelin lipids; in corporation of (3-^{14}C) serine in brain lipids of the developing rabbit and their persistence in the central nervous system. *J Neurochem, 4:*360, 1959.

DAVISON, A. N., and WAJDA, M.: Metabolism of myelin lipids: estimation and separation of brain lipids in the developing rabbit. *J Neurochem, 4:*353, 1959a.

DAVISON, A. N., and WAJDA, M.: Persistence of cholesterol [4-^{14}C] in the central nervous system. *Nature (London), 183:*1606, 1959b.

DAWSON, R. M. C.: A hydrolytic procedure for the identification and estimation of individual phospholipids in biological samples. *Biochem J, 75:*45, 1960.

DAWSON, R. M. C.; HEMINGTON, N. L., and DAVENPORT, J. B.: Improvements in the method of determining individual phospholipids in a complex mixture by successive chemical hydrolyses. *Biochem J, 84:* 497, 1962.

DAWSON, R. M. C., and RICHTER, D.: Phosphorus metabolism in brain. *Proc Roy Soc Biol, 137:*252, 1950.

DE ROBERTIS, E.; GERSCHENFELD, H. M., and WALD, F.: Cellular mechanism of myelination in the central nervous system. *J Biophys Biochem Cytol, 4:*651, 1958.

DE ROBERTIS, E.; IRALDI, A. P. D.; ARNAIZ, R. D. L., and SALGANICOFF, L.: Isolation and subcellular distribution of acetylcholine and acetylcholinesterase. *J Neurochem, 9:*1, 1962.

DE VELLIS, J. ,and SCHJEIDE, O. A.: Time-dependence of the effect of X-irradiation on the formation of glycerol phosphate dehydrogenase and other dehydrogenases in the developing rat brain. *Biochem J, 107:*259, 1968.

DE VELLIS, J.; SCHJEIDE, O. A., and CLEMENTE, C. D.: Protein synthesis and enzymic patterns in the developing brain following head X-irradiation of newborn rats. *J Neurochem, 14:*499, 1967.

Dobbing, J.: The entry of cholesterol into rat brain development. *J Neurochem, 10:*739, 1963.

Dobbing, J.: Vulnerable periods in developing brain. In Davison, A. N., and Dobbing, J. (Eds.) : *Applied Neurochemistry.* Oxford, Blackwell, p. 287, 1968.

Dobbing, J., and Sands, J. A.: The entry of cholesterol into rat brain during development. *J Physiol (London), 166:*45P, 1963.

Donaldson, H. H.: *J Nerv Ment Dis, 38:*257, 1911.

Edström, A.: The ribonucleic acid in the mauthner neuron of the goldfish. *J Neurochem, 2:*309, 1964.

Edström, A.: Amino acid incorporation in isolated mauthner nerve fibre components. *J Neurochem, 13:*315, 1966.

Eichberg, J., and Dawson, R. M. C.: Polyphosphoinositides in myelin. *Biochem J, 96:*644, 1965.

Eichberg, J.; Whittaker, V. P., and Dawson, R. M. C.: Distribution of lipids in subcellular particles in guinea pig brain. *Biochem J, 92:*91, 1964.

Einstein, E. R., and Csejtev, J.: Proteins in the developing human brain. *Trans Am Neurol Ass,* p. 218, 1966.

Elson, L. A., and Morgan, W. T. J.: Colorimetric method for the determination of glucosamine and chondrosamine. *Biochem J, 27:* 1824, 1933.

Eng, L. F.; Chao, F. C.; Gerstl, B.; Pratt, D., and Tavaststjerna, M. G.: The maturation of human white matter myelin. Fractionation of the myelin membrane proteins. *Biochemistry,* 1968.

Eng, L. F., and Noble, E. P.: The maturation of rat brain myelin. *Lipids, 3:*157, 1968.

Eng, L. F., and Smith, M. E.: The cholesterol complex in the myelin membrane. *Lipids, 1:*296, 1966.

Ernster, L.; Zetterstrom, R., and Lindberg, O.: A method for the determination of tracer phosphate in biological materials. *Acta Chem Scand, 4:*942, 1950.

Evans, M. J., and Finean, J. B.: The lipid composition of myelin from brain and peripheral nerve. *J Neurochem, 12:*720, 1965.

Fewster, M. E., and Mead, J. F.: Lipid composition of glial cells isolated from bovine white matter. *J Neurochem, 15:*1041, 1968.

Fewster, M. E.; Scheibel, A. B., and Mead, J. F.: The preparation of isolated glial cells from rat and bovine white matter. *Brain Res (Amsterdam), 6:*401, 1967.

FISKE, C. H., and SUBBAROW, Y.: The colorimetric determination of phosphorus. *J Biol Chem, 66:*375, 1925.

FOLCH, J. P.: In Waelsch, H. (Ed.) : *Biochemistry of the Developing Nervous System.* N.Y., Academic, p. 121, 1955.

FOLCH, J. PI-, and LE BARON, F. N.: In Richter, D. (Ed.) : *Metabolism of the Nervous System.* London, Pergamon, p. 87, 1957.

FOLCH, J. P., and LEES, M.: Proteolipides, a new type of tissue lipoproteins. Their isolation from brain. *J Biol Chem, 191:*807, 1951.

FOLCH, J. P.; LEES, M., and SLOANE-STANLEY, G. H.: A simple method for the isolation and purification of total lipids from animal tissues. *J Biol Chem, 226:*497, 1957.

FREYSZ, L.; BIETH, R.; JUDES, C.; SENSENBRENNER, M.; JACOB, M., and MANDEL, P.: Distribution quantitative des divers phospholipides dans les neurones et les cellules gliales isoles du cortex cerebral de rat adulte. *J Neurochem, 15:*307, 1968.

FRIEDE, R. L.: Die histochemische Reifung des Kleinhirnes der Ratte, dargestellt durch das Verhalten der Succinodehydrogenase. *Arch Psychiat Z Neurol, 196:*196, 1957.

FRIEDE, R. L.: *Topographic Brain Chemistry.* N.Y., Academic, 1966.

FRIEDE, R. L.; FLEMING, L. M., and KNOLLER, M.: A comparative mapping of enzymes involved in hexosemonophosphate shunt and citric acid cycle in the brain. *J Neurochem, 10:*263, 1963.

FRIEDE, R. L., and SAMORAJSKI, T.: Myelin formation in the sciatic nerve of the rat. A quantitative electron microscopic, histochemical and radioautographic study. *J Neuropath Exp Neurol, 27:*546, 1968.

FUMAGALLI, R.; GROSSI, E.; PAOLETTI, P., and PAOLETTI, R.: Studies on lipids in brain tumours I. *J Neurochem, 11:*561, 1964.

FURST, S.; LAJTHA, A., and WAELSCH, H.: Amino acid and protein metabolism of the brain. III. Incorporation of lysine into the proteins of various brain areas and their cellular fractions. *J Neurochem, 2:*216, 1958.

GALLI, C., and CECCONI, R. D.: Lipid changes in rat brain during maturation. *Lipids, 2:*76, 1967.

GRAY, G. M., and MACFARLANE, M. G.: Separation and composition of phospholipids of ox heart. *Biochem J, 70:*409, 1958.

GREANEY, J. F.: The chemical maturation of rat brain. *Fed Proc, 20:*343, 1961.

HAMBURGH, M.: Evidence for a direct effect of temperature and thyroid hormone on myelinogenesis in vitro. *Devl Biol, 13:*15, 1966.

HANEL, H. K., and DAM, H.: Determination of small amounts of total cholesterol. Tschugaeff reaction with a note on the determination of lanosterol. *Acta Chem Scand, 9:*677, 1955.

HARKONEN, M.; MUSTAKALLIO, A., and NIEMI, M.: Monoamine oxidase activity in the peripheral nerve myelin. *J Neurochem, 13:*4, 1966.

HATAI, S.: On the increase in the number of medullated nerve fibers in the ventral roots of the spinal nerves of the growing white rat. *J Comp Neurol, 13:*177, 1903.

HERSCHKOWITZ, N.; McKHANN, G. M., and SHOOTER, E. M.: Studies of water soluble lipoproteins in rat brain. *J Neurochem, 15:*161, 1968.

HILL, P., and DVORNIK, D.: Effect of AY-9944, an inhibitor of cholesterol biosynthesis, on the incorporation of lipid precursors in rat tissue. *Arch Biochem Biophys, 114:*88, 1966.

HIMWICH, W. A., and PETERSEN, J. C.: In Masserman, J. H. (Ed.) : *Biological Psychiatry.* New York, Grune, p. 2, 1959.

HOKIN, L. E., and HOKIN, M. R.: Effects of acetylcholine on turnover of phosphoryl units in individual phospholipids of pancreas slices and brain cortex slices. *Biochim Biophys Acta, 18:*379, 1955.

HOKIN, L. E., and HOKIN, M. R.: Interconversions of phosphatidylinositol and phosphatidic acid involved in the response to acetylcholine in the salt gland. In *Metabolism and Physiological Significance of Lipids.* London, Wiley, p. 423, 1964.

HOLSTEIN, T. J.; FISH, W. A., and STOKES, W. M.: Pathway of cholesterol biosynthesis in the brain of the neonatal rat. *J Lipid Res, 7:* 634, 1966.

HORROCKS, L. A.: Composition of myelin from peripheral and central nervous systems of the squirrel monkey. *J Lipid Res, 8:*569, 1967.

HORROCKS, L. A.: Composition of mouse brain myelin during development. *J Neurochem, 15:*483, 1968.

HORROCKS, L. A.; MECKLER, R. J., and COLLINS, R. L.: Variation in the lipid composition of mouse brain myelin as a function of age. In Ansell, G. B. (Ed.) : *Variations in Chemical Composition of the Nervous System.* Oxford, Pergamon, p. 46, 1966.

HOWELL, J. McC.; DAVISON, A. N., and OXBERRY, J. M.: Observations on the lesions in the white matter of the spinal cord of Swayback sheep. *Acta Neuropath (Berlin), 12:*33, 1969.

HUBSCHER, G.; HAWTHORNE, J. H., and KEMP, P.: The analysis of tissue phospholipids: hydrolysis procedure results with pig liver. *J Lipid Res, 1:*433, 1960.

HYDEN, H., and MCEWEN, B. S.: A glial protein specific for the nervous system. *Proc Nat Acad Sci USA, 55:*354, 1966.

JATZKEWITZ, H.: A new method for the quantitative ultramicrodetermination of sphingolipids from the brain. *Z Phys Chem, 326:*61, 1961.

JOHNSTON, P. V., and ROOTS, B. I.: The neurone surface. *Nature (London), 205:*778, 1965.

KEAN, E. L.: Rapid sensitive spectrophotometric method for quantitative determination of sulphates. *J Lipid Res, 9:*319, 1968.

KEENE, M. F. L., and HEWER, E. E.: Some observations of myelination in the human central nervous system. *J Anat, 66:*1, 1931.

KIBLER, R. F., and SHAPIRA, R.: Isolation and properties of an encephalitogenic protein from bovine, rabbit and human central nervous system tissue. *J Biol Chem, 243:*281, 1968.

KIES, M. W.; THOMPSON, E. B., and ALVORD, E. C.: The relationship of myelin proteins to experimental allergic encephalomyelitis. *Ann NY Acad Sci, 122:*148, 1965.

KISHIMOTO, Y.; DAVIES, W. E., and RADIN, N. S.: Turnover of the fatty acids of rat brain gangliosides, glycerophosphatides, cerebrosides and sulfatides as a function of age. *J Lipid Res, 6:*525, 1965a.

KISHIMOTO, Y.; DAVIES, W. E., and RADIN, N. S.: Developing rat brain: changes in cholesterol, galactolipids, and the individual fatty acids of gangliosides and glycerophosphatides. *J Lipid Res, 6:*532, 1965b.

KLEE, C. B., and SOKOLOFF, L.: Amino acid incorporation into proteolipid of myelin *in vitro*. *Proc Nat Acad Sci USA, 53:*1014, 1965a.

KLEE, C. B., and SOKOLOF, L.: Protein biosynthesis in the developing brain. Abstr., International Conference, Oxford, p. 58, 1965b.

KLEE, C. B., and SOKOLOFF, L.: Changes in D (-) -β-hydroxybutyric dehydrogenase activity during brain maturation in the rat. *J Biol Chem, 242:*3880, 1967.

KOENIG, H.: The proteolipid nature of the neurokeratin network of myelin. *J Neurochem, 4:*93, 1959.

KOREY, S. R.: Some characteristics of a neuroglial fraction. In Richter, D. (Ed.) : *Metabolism of the Nervous System*. London, Pergamon, p. 87, 1957.

KOREY, S. R., and GONATAS, J.: Separation of human brain gangliosides. *Life Sci, 2:*296, 1963.

KOREY, S. R.; ORCHEN M., and BROTZ, M.: Studies of white matter. I. Chemical constitution and respiration of neuroglial and myelin enriched fractions of white matter. *J Neuropath Exp Neurol, 17:* 430, 1958.

KORNGUTH, S. E.; ANDERSON, J. W., and SCOTT, G.: Temporal relationship between myelinogenesis and the appearance of a basic protein in the spinal cord of the white rat. *J Comp Neurol, 127:*1, 1966.

KRITCHEVSKY, D., and DEFENDI, V.: Persistence of sterols other than cholesterol in chicken tissue. *Nature, (London), 192:*71, 1961.

KRITCHEVSKY, D., and DEFENDI, V.: Deposition of tritium labelled sterols (cholesterol, sitosterol, lanosterol) in brain and other organs of the growing chicken. *J Neurochem, 9:*421, 1962.

KURIHARA, T., and TSUKADA, Y.: The regional and subcellular distribution of 2′, 3′-cyclic nucleotide 3′-phosphohydrolase in the central nervous system. *J Neurochem, 14:*1167, 1967.

KURIHARA, T., and TSUKADA, Y.: 2′, 3′-cyclic nucleotide 3′-phosphohydrolase in the developing chick brain and spinal cord. *J Neurochem, 15:*827, 1968.

LAATSCH, R. H.: Glycerol phosphate dehydrogenase activity of developing rat central nervous system. *J Neurochem, 9:*487, 1962.

LAATSCH, R. H.; KIES, M. W.; GORDON, S., and ALVORD, E. C.: The encephalomyelitic activity of myelin isolated by ultracentrifugation. *J Exp Med, 115:*777, 1962.

LANGWORTHY, O. R.: Development of behaviour patterns and myelinization of tracts in nervous system. *Arch Neurol Psychiat (Chicago), 28:*1365, 1932.

LAPETINA, E. G.; SOTO, E. F., and DE ROBERTIS, E.: Gangliosides and acetylcholinesterase in isolated membranes of the rat brain cortex. *Biochim Biophys Acta, 135:*33, 1967.

LARRABEE, M. G., and LEICHT, W. S.: Metabolism of phosphatidyl inositol and other lipids in active neurones of sympathetic ganglia and other peripheral nervous tissues. The site of the inositide effect. *J Neurochem, 12:*1, 1965.

LAUTER, C. J., and TRAMS, E. G.: A spectrophotometric determination of sphingosine. *J Lipid Res, 3:*136, 1962.

LEA, C. H., and RHODES, D. N.: Phospholipids. 2. Estimation of amino nitrogen in intact phospholipids. *Biochem J, 56:*613, 1954.

LEES, M. B.: Effect of ion removal on the solubility of rat brain proteins in chloroform-methanol mixtures. *J Neurochem, 15:*153, 1968.

LEHRER, G. M., and BORNSTEIN, M. B.: Carbohydrate metabolism of the developing brain *in vivo* and *in vitro*. In Ansell, G. B. (Ed.) :

Variation in Chemical Composition of the Nervous System as Determined by Developmental and Genetic Factors, Int. Neurochem. Conf., Oxford, p. 67, 1965.

LESCH, P.; MEIER, S., and BERNHARD, K.: Brain lipid analysis. The neutral lipids in the brain of prematures and newborns. *Helv Chim Acta, 49:*1215, 1966.

LOWDEN, J. A.; MOSCARELLO, M. A., and MORECKI, R.: The isolation and characterization of an acid-soluble protein from myelin. *Canad J Biochem, 44:*567, 1966.

LOWRY, O. H.; ROBERTS, N. R.; LEINER, K. Y.; WU, MEI-LING.; FARR, A. L., and ALBERS, R. W.: The quantitative histochemistry of brain. III. Ammon's Horn. *J Biol Chem, 207:*39, 1954.

LUCY, J. A. :Ultrastructure of membranes: Micellar organization. *Brit Med Bull, 24:*127, 1968.

LUZZATI, V., and HUSSON, F.: The structure of the liquid-crystalline phases of lipid—water systems. *J Cell Biol, 12:*207, 1962.

McCAMON, R. E., and COOK, K.: Intermediary metabolism of phospholipids in brain tissue. III. Phosphocholine-glyceride transferase. *J Biol Chem, 241:*3390, 1966.

McKHANN, G. M., and HO., W.: The *in vivo* and *in vitro* synthesis of sulfatides during development. *J Neurochem, 14:*717, 1967.

McMILLAN, P. J.; DOUGLAS, G. W., and MORTENSEN, R. A.: Incorporation of C^{14} of acetate [1-C^{14}] and pyruvate [2-C^{14}] into brain cholesterol in the intact rat. *Proc Soc Exp Biol, NY, 96:*738, 1957.

MAJNO, G., and KARNOVSKY, M. L.: A biochemical and morphological study of myelination and demyelination. 1. Lipide biosynthesis in vitro by normal nervous tissue. *J Exp Med, 107:*475, 1958.

MAKER, H. S., and HAUSER, G.: Incorporation of glucose carbon in gangliosides and cerebrosides by slices of developing rat brain. *J Neurochem, 14:*457, 1967.

MARSHALL, E. R.; FUMAGALLI, R.; NIEMIRO, R., and PAOLETTI, R.: The change in fatty acid composition of rat brain phospholipids during development. *J Neurochem, 13:*857, 1966.

MARTLAND, M., and ROBISON, R.: Possible significance of hexose phosphoric esters in ossification. 6. Phosphoric esters in blood plasma. *Biochem J, 20:*847, 1926.

MATHESON, D. F.: Incorporation of ^{14}C glycine into protein of the adult rat peripheral nerve: Effects of inhibitors. *J Neurochem, 15:*179, 1968.

MENKES, J. H.; PHILIPPART, M., and CONCONE, M. C.: Concentration and fatty acid composition of cerebrosides and sulphatides in mature and immature human brain. *J Lipid Res, 7:*479, 1966.

MEYER, I., and MEYER, P.: Enzyme histochemistry of the growing and adult oligodendrocyte. *Acta Neurol Scand, 40:*89, 1964.

MICKEL, H. S., and GILLES, F. H.: Changes in glial cells during myelinogenesis. *J Neuropath Exp Neurol, 1:*146, 1968.

MIETTINEN, T., and TAKKI-LUUKKAINEN, I. T.: Use of butylacetate in determination of sialic acid. *Acta Chem Scand, 13:*856, 1959.

MITROVA, E.: Karyometric investigation of glia in the cerebellum in the course of myelination. *Z Mikr Anat Forsch, 77:*304, 1967.

MOKRASCH, L. C.: In Lajth, A. (Ed.) : *Handbook of Neurochemistry,* Plenum Press, p. 171, 1969.

MOKRASCH, L. C., and MANNER, P.: Incorporation of ^{14}C amino acids and [^{14}C] palmitate into proteolipids of rat brain *in vivo. J Neurochem, 10:*541, 1963.

MOORE, B. W.; PEREZ, V. J., and GEHRING, M.: Assay and regional distribution of a soluble protein characteristic of the nervous system. *J Neurochem, 15:*265, 1968.

MIANI, N.; CAVALLOTTI, C., and CANIGLIA, A.: Synthesis of adenosine triphosphate by myelin of spinal nerves of rabbit. *J Neurochem, 16:*249, 1969.

NAKAO, A.; DAVIS, W. J., and EINSTEIN, E. R.: Basic proteins from the acidic extract of bovine spinal cord. I. Isolation and characterization. *Biochim Biophys Acta, 130:*163, 1966.

NEVILLE, D. M.: The isolation of a cell membrane fraction from rat liver. *J Biophys Biochem Cytol, 8:*413, 1960.

NOBACK, C. R.: Metachromasia in the nervous system. *J Neuropath Exp Neurol, 13:*161, 1954.

NORTON, W. T.: The variation in chemical composition in myelin in disease and during development. *Charing Cross Hospital Gazette,* no. 8, 1967-68.

NORTON, W. T.: In press, 1969.

NORTON, W. T., and AUTILIO, L. A.: The lipid composition of purified bovine brain myelin. *J Neurochem, 13:*213, 1966.

NORTON, W. T.; DAVISON, A. N., and SPOHN, M.: In preparation, 1969.

NORTON, W. T.; PODUSLO, S. E., and SUZUKI, K.: Subacute sclerosing leukoencephalitis. II. Chemical studies including abnormal myelin and an abnormal ganglioside pattern. *J Neuropath Exp Neurol, 25:*582, 1966.

NORTON, W. T.; PODUSLO, S. E., and SUZUKI, K.: Rat brain myelin:

Compositional changes during development. Abstr. First Meeting Intern. Soc. Neurochemistry, Strasbourg, France, p. 161, 1967.

O'BRIEN, J. S.: Lipids and myelination. In Himwich, W. A. (Ed.): *Developmental Neurobiology.* Springfield, Thomas, 1970.

O'BRIEN, J. S., and SAMPSON, E. L.: Lipid composition of the normal human brain; grey matter, white matter myelin. *J Lipid Res, 6:* 537, 1965a.

O'BRIEN, J. S.; SAMPSON, E. L., and STERN, M. B.: Lipid composition of myelin from the peripheral nervous system. Intradural spinal roots. *J Neurochem, 14:*357, 1967.

PEREZ, V. J., and MOORE, B. W.: Wallerian degeneration in rabbit tibial nerve: changes in amounts of the S-100 protein. *J Neurochem, 15:*971, 1968.

PETERS, A.: The formation and structure of myelin sheaths in the central nervous system. *J Biophys Biochem Cytol, 8:*431, 1960.

PETERSON, V. P., and SCHOU, M.: Intracellular distribution of brain phospholipides. *Acta Physiol Scand, 33:*309, 1955.

PETRUSHKA, E., and GUIDITTA, A.: Electron microscopy of two subcellular fractions isolated from cerebral cortex homogenate. *J Biophys Biochem Cytol, 6:*129, 1959.

PFLEGER, R. C.; ANDERSON, N. G., and SYNDER, G.: Lipid class and fatty acid composition of rat liver plasma membranes isolated by zonal centrifugation. *Biochemistry, 7:*2826, 1968   .

PITTS, F. N., and QUICK, C.: Brain succinate semialdehyde dehydrogenase. II. Changes in the developing rat brain. *J Neurochem, 14:* 561, 1967.

PRENSKY, A. L., and MOSER, H. W.: Changes in the amino acid composition of proteolipids of white matter during maturation of the human nervous system. *J Neurochem, 14:*117, 1967.

PRITCHARD, E. T.: The formation of phospholipids from ^{14}C labelled precursors in developing rat brain *in vivo. J Neurochem, 10:*495, 1963.

PRITCHARD, E. T., and FOLCH-PI, J.: Tightly bound proteolipid phospholipid in bovine brain white matter. *Biochim Biophys Acta (Amsterdam), 70:*481, 1963.

PUMPHREY, A. M.: [32]P Orthophosphate incorporation into brain-slice phospholipids and their precursors: effects of electrical stimulation. *Biochem J, 108:*38P, 1968.

RADIN, N. S.: Glycolipide determination. *Meth Biochem Analysis, 6:* 163, 1958.

RATHBONE, L.: The effect of diet on the fatty acid composition of serum, brain, brain mitochondria and myelin in the rat. *Biochem J, 97*:620, 1965.

RENKONEN, O.: Individual molecular species of phospholipids. III. Molecular species of ox-brain lecithins. *Biochim Biophys Acta, 125*:288, 1966.

ROBINS, E.; EYDT, K. M., and SMITH, D. E.: Distribution of lipides in the cerebellar cortex and its subjacent white matter. *J Biol Chem, 220*:677, 1956.

ROBINS, E., and LOWE, I. P.: Quantitative histochemical studies of the morphogenesis of the cerebellum. I. Total lipid and four enzymes. *J Neurochem, 8*:81, 1961.

ROBOZ-EINSTEIN, E.; CASTEJTLEY, J.; DAVIS, W., and RAUCH, H.: *Proc Intern Congr Neurol (Vienna), 4*:137, 1965.

ROMANES, G. J.: Prenatal medullation of sheep's nervous system. *J Anat (London), 81*:64, 1947.

ROSE, S. P. R.: Preparation of enriched fractions from cerebral cortex containing isolated, metabolically active neuronal cells. *Nature (London), 206*:621, 1966.

ROSSITER, R. J., and GARDINER, R. J.: Phosphoinositides of developing rat brain. *Int Neurochem Conf (Oxford)*, p. 100, 1965.

ROUSER, G.; GALLI, C.; LIEBER, E.; BLANK, M. L., and PRIVETT, O. S.: Analytical fractionation of complex lipid mixtures: DEAE cellulose chromatography combined with quantitative thin layer chromatography. *J Am Oil Chem Soc, 41*:836, 1964.

ROUSER, G.; O'BRIEN, J., and HELLER, D.: The separation of phosphatidyl ethanolamine and phosphatidyl serine by column chromatography. *J Am Oil Chem Soc, 38*:14, 1961.

SALWAY, J. G.; HARWOOD, J. L.; KAI, M.; WHITE, G. L., and HAWTHORNE, J. N.: Enzymes of phosphoinositide metabolism during rat brain development. *J Neurochem, 15*:221, 1968.

SALWAY, J. G.; KAI, M., and HAWTHORNE, J. N.: Triphosphoinositide phosphomonoesterase activity in nerve cell bodies, neuroglia and subcellular fractions from whole rat brain. *J Neurochem, 14*:1013, 1967.

SATAKE, M., and ABE, S.: Preparation and characterization of nerve cell perikaryon from rat cerebral cortex. *J Biochem (Tokyo), 59*: 72, 1966.

SCHMITT, F. O., and DAVISON, P. F.: Brain and nerve proteins: Functional correlates. *Neurosciences Res Prog Bull, 3*:9, 1965.

SCHWARTZ, A.; BACHELARD, H. S., and McILWAIN, H.: The sodium-stimulated adenosine-triphosphatase activity and other properties of cerebral microsomal fractions and subfractions. *Biochem J, 84:* 626, 1962.

SHELTAWY, A., and DAWSON, R. M. C.: The polyphosphoinositides and other lipids of peripheral nerves. *Biochem J, 100:*12, 1966.

SHELTAWY, A., and DAWSON, R. M. C.: On the phosphatidic acid of myelin. *J Neurochem, 15:*144, 1968.

SKIPSKI, V. P.; BARCLAY, M.; ARCHIBALD, F. M.; TEREBUS-KEKISH, O.; REICHMAN, E. S., and GOOD, J. J.: Lipid composition of rat liver cell membranes. *Life Sci, 4:*1673, 1965.

SKIPSKI, V. P.; PETERSON, R. F., and BARCLAY, M.: Quantitative analysis of phospholipids by thin-layer chromatography. *Biochem J, 90:*374, 1964.

SMITH, M. E.: The metabolism of myelin lipids. *Adv Lipid Res, 5:* 241, 1967.

SMITH, M. E.: The turnover of myelin in the adult rat. *Biochim Biophys Acta, 164:*285, 1968.

SMITH, M. E., and ENG, L. F.: The turnover of the lipid components of myelin. *J Am Oil Chem Soc, 42:*1013, 1965.

SMITH, M. E.; FUMAGALLI, R., and PAOLETTI, R.: The occurrence of desmosterol in myelin of developing rats. *Life Sci, 6:*1085, 1967.

SMITS, G.: Modification of the periodide method for the determination of choline. *Biochim Biophys Acta, 26:*424, 1957.

SOTO, E. F.: Induction of experimental allergic encephalomyelitis with a myelin fraction obtained form bovine white matter. *Neurology (Minneapolis), 14:*938, 1964.

SOTO, E. F.; BOHNER, L. S., and CALVINO, M. C.: Chemical composition of myelin and other subcellular fractions isolated from bovine white matter. *J Neurochem, 13:*989, 1966.

SPECTOR, W. S.: *Handbook of Biological Data.* Philadelphia, Saunders, 1956.

SPERRY, W. M.: The biochemistry of the brain during early development. In Elliott, A. C.; Page, I. H., and Quastel, J. H.: *Neurochemistry.* Springfield, Thomas, p. 55, 1962.

SPERRY, W. M., and WEBB, M.: A revision of the Schoenheimer-Sperry method for cholesterol determination. *J Biol Chem, 187:*97, 1950.

STALLBERG-STENHAGEN, S., and SVENNERHOLM, L.: Fatty acid composition of human brain sphingomyelin: normal variation with age and changes during myelin disorder. *J Lipid Res, 6:*146, 1965.

SUZUKI, K.: The pattern of mammalian brain gangliosides. II. Evaluation of the extraction procedures, post-mortem changes and the effect of formalin preservation. *J Neurochem, 12:*629, 1965a.

Suzuki, K.: The pattern of mammalian brain gangliosides. III. Regional and developmental differences. *J Neurochem, 12*:969, 1965b.

Suzuki, K.: Formation and turnover of the major brain gangliosides during development. *J Neurochem, 14*:917, 1967.

Suzuki, K.; Poduslo, S. E., and Norton, W. T.: Gangliosides in the myelin fraction of developing rats. *Biochim Biophys Acta, 1:44* 375, 1967.

Suzuki, K.; Poduslo, J. F., and Poduslo, S. E.: Further evidence for a specific ganglioside fraction closely associated with myelin. *Biochim Biophys Acta, 152*:576, 1968.

Svennerholm, L.: The quantitative estimation of cerebrosides in nervous tissue. *J Neurochem, 1*:42, 1956.

Svennerholm, L.: Quantitative estimation of sialic acids. II. A colorimetric resorcinol-hydrochloric acid method. *Biochim Biophys Acta, 24*:604, 1957.

Svennerholm, L.: The distribution of lipids in the human nervous system. I. Analytical procedure. Lipids of foetal and newborn brain. *J Neurochem, 11*:839, 1964.

Svennerholm, L., and Stallberg-Stenhagen, S.: Changes in fatty acid composition of cerebrosides and sulfatides of human nervous tissue with age. *J Lipid Res, 9*:215, 1968.

Svennerholm, L., and Thorin, H.: Quantitative isolation of brain sulphatides. *J Lipid Res, 3*:483, 1962.

Tenebaum, D., and Folch-Pi, J.: The preparation and characterization of water-soluble proteolipid protein from bovine brain white matter. *Biochim Biophys Acta, 115*:141, 1966.

Tewari, H. B., and Bourne, G. H.: Neurokeratin network of the peripheral nerve fibre myelin sheath as a centre of metabolic activity. *Nature (London), 186*:645, 1960.

Thompson, E. J.; Goodwin, H., and Cumings, J. N.: Caesium chloride in the preparation of membrane fractions from human cerebral tissue. *Nature (London), 215*:168, 1967.

Torvik, A., and Sidman, R. L.: Autoradiographic studies on lipid synthesis in the mouse brain during postnatal development. *J Neurochem, 12*:555, 1965.

Uzman, L. L., and Rumley, M. K.: Changes in the composition of the developing mouse brain during early myelination. *J Neurochem, 3*:170, 1958.

Van Handel, E., and Zilversmit, D. B.: Micromethod for the direct determination of serum triglycerides. *J Lab Clin Med, 50:*152, 1957.

VON HUNGEN, K.; MAHLER, H. R., and MOORE, W. J.: Turnover of protein and ribonucleic acid in synaptic subcellular fractions from rat brain. *J Biol Chem, 243:*1415, 1968.

WAELSCH, H.; SPERRY, W. M., and STOYANOFF, V. A.: Lipid metabolism in brain during myelination. *J Biol Chem, 135:*297, 1940.

WAKSMAN, A.; RUBINSTEIN, M. K.; KURIYAMA, E., and ROBERTS, E.: Localization of γ-aminobutyric-α-oxoglutaric acid transaminase in mouse brain. *J Neurochem, 15:*351, 1968.

WEBSTER, G. R., and ALPERN, R. J.: Studies on the acylation of lysolecithin by rat brain. *Biochem J, 90:*35, 1964.

WEBSTER, G. R., and FOLCH, J. P.: Some studies on the properties of proteolipids. *Biochim Biophys Acta, 49:*399, 1961.

WEISS, J. F.; GALLI, G., and GROSSI PAOLETTI, E.: Sterols with 29, 28 and 27 carbon atoms metabolically related to cholesterol, occurring in developing and mature brain. *J Neurochem, 15:*563, 1968.

WELLS, M. A., and DITTMAR, J. C.: A comprehensive study of the postnatal changes in the concentration of the lipids of developing rat brain. *Biochemistry, 6:*3169, 1967.

WENDELL-SMITH, C. P.; BLUNT, M. J., and BALDWIN, F.: The ultrastructure characterization of macroglial cell types. *J Comp Neurol, 127:*219, 1966.

WHITTAKER, V. P.: The isolation and characterization of acetylcholine containing particles from brain. *Biochem J, 72:*694, 1959.

WILLIAMS J. N.; ANDERSON, C. E., and JASIK, A. D.: A sensitive and specific method for plasmalogens and other enol ethers. *J Lipid Res, 3:*378, 1962.

WOLFGRAM, F.: A new proteolipid fraction of the nervous system. I. Isolation and amino acid analyses. *J Neurochem, 13:*461, 1966.

WOLFGRAM, F., and KOTORII, K.: The composition of the myelin proteins of the central nervous system. *J Neurochem, 15:*1281, 1968a.

WOLFGRAM, F., and KOTORII, K.: The composition of the myelin proteins of the peripheral nervous system. *J Neurochem, 15:*1291, 1968b.

WOLFGRAM, F., and ROSE, A. S.: Histochemistry of neurokeratin in normal and degenerating sciatic nerve. *Neurology, 10:*365, 1960.

WOLMAN, M.: Histochemical study of myelinization in the rat. *Bull Res Coun Israel Sect E, 6:*3, 1957.

WORTHINGTON, C. R., and BLAUROCK, A. E.: Electron density model for nerve myelin. *Nature, 281:*87, 1968.

YONEZAWA, T.; BORNSTEIN, M. B.; PETERSON, E. R., and MURRAY, M. R.: A histochemical study of oxydative enzymes in myelinating cultures of central and peripheral nervous tissue. *J Neuropath Exp Neurol, 21*:479, 1962.

YOUNG, F., and HULCHER, F. H.: Cholesterol esters in myelin and the component fatty acids. *Proc Soc Exp Biol Med, 123*:385, 1966.

ZIOLO, I.: Myelinization of nerve fibres of pig spinal cord. *Acta Anat (Basel), 61*:297, 1965.

Chapter 3

MYELINATION AND DISEASES OF THE NERVOUS SYSTEM: ABNORMALITIES OF MYELIN COMPOSITION

A. N. DAVISON

A LTHOUGH THE COMMON demyelinating diseases largely affect the mature nervous system, there are a few lipidoses which interfere with myelination of the developing human nervous system. Besides these rare diseases affecting myelination, there is the potentially more serious possibility that mild stress applied during the period of myelination may result in permanent structural deficits in the brain. Whether or not myelination results in intellectual or other deficiencies is not yet established. It is certainly true, however, that as in the demyelinating diseases serious and often fatal neurological damage follows the loss of myelin. The formation of the myelin may also be faulty as in the lipidoses. Besides briefly discussing these topics from a biochemical standpoint, reference will be made in this section to the possibility that the end of myelination in the brain is of special significance in explaining the age onset of the demyelinating diseases.

In the last few years, advances in the field of neurochemistry have made it possible to determine the chemical composition of nervous tissue in much greater detail than was previously possible. The use of gel electrophoresis for the characterization of neural proteins has met with great success, and the development of thin layer and gas-liquid chromatography has simplified the problems of lipid analysis. Much is now known about the enzyme composition of the brain, and work has begun on the evaluation of substrate fluxes and rate-controlling processes within the central nervous system (Lowry, 1968). In addition, the advent of improved centrifugal methods have made possible the isolation of purified myelin. Rather than studying formalin-fixed neural tissue, neurochemists may now employ fresh material for separation into subcellular fractions by either differential or

162

density gradient centrifugation. The application of these various methods has had a very considerable effect on current knowledge related to the biochemistry of myelin both in health and disease.

DYSMYELINATION

It has been suggested that certain of the demyelinating diseases can be attributed to instability of the myelin sheath (O'Brien, 1964, 1967), the instability being produced by incorporation of "faults" into myelin during its development. Essentially this process of so-called dysmyelination must be regarded as a disease of development, for molecular errors may only be actively introduced during the period of myelin formation, since there is relatively little synthesis of myelin in the adult brain. It may be that repair of faulty myelin is still possible in the very early stages of myelination, but that after this initial phase, molecular errors incorporated into the structure would not be easily reversible.

Fatty Acids and Myelin Stability

Vandenheuvel (1963) and O'Brien (1964, 1965, 1967) have stressed the likely effects which could be produced by changes in the fatty acid complement of myelin. Of special significance is the interdigitation of long-chain fatty acids and the packing of the curled chains of the polyunsaturated fatty acids. Compared to other membranes, myelin contains higher proportions of sphingolipids with long-chain fatty acids (19-26 carbon atoms), and these long-chain molecules could well account for the exceptional stability of the structure, as they provide large areas for attraction between $-CH_2$ pairs of adjacent hydrocarbon chains. It follows that any decrease in the proportion of long-chain fatty acids would tend to destabilize the whole structure. Close packing of lipid and hence stability of myelin would also be reduced by any increase or even a decrease (Bernsohn and Stephanides, 1967) in the proportion of polyunsaturated fatty acids, for these curled molecules can only be accommodated in a fixed pattern in the molecular structure of myelin.

There is some evidence that this kind of physical instability of the myelin sheath may be an important factor in some demyelinating diseases. O'Brien (1964) has examined the white matter lipids from two cases of inborn error of metabolism in which myelination is faulty (metachromatic leukodystrophy and Niemann-Pick disease). He demonstrated a seven- to ten-fold deficiency of sphingolipids containing long-chain fatty acids. The defect was specific, since sphingolipids containing shorter chain fatty acids were present in normal or increased proportions and the remaining lipids were diminished. Others have recently found similar deficiencies of sphingolopids containing long-chain faty acids in a variety of diseases affecting myelin: multiple sclerosis (Gerstl, Tavaststjerna, Hayman, Smith, and Eng, 1963), Pelizaeus-Merzbacher disease (Gerstl, Malamud, Hayman, and Bond, 1965), globoid cell leukodystrophy, and infantile Gaucher's disease (Svennerholm, 1963; Ställberg-Stenhagen and Svennerholm, 1965).

Svennerholm (1963) has found normal concentrations of very long chain fatty acids in cerebrosides and sulphatides obtained from the brain of patients with metachromatic leukodystrophy. This finding is not consistent with the view that the biochemical defect in the disease is due to a failure to elongate the fatty acids of sphingolipids beyond eighteen carbon atoms via the "chain elongation system." In the view of Ställberg-Stenhagen and Svennerholm, there is no evidence for a primary failure in elongation of the fatty acids in the cases of leukodystrophy. The changed quotient between fatty acids with fourteen to twenty carbon atoms and those with twenty-two to twenty-six carbon atoms can in their view be completely explained by the changed ratios between axoplasmic tissue and myelin.

Refsum's Syndrome

Another disease in which there appears to be an inborn error in the metabolism of fatty acids is Refsum's syndrome (heredopathia atactica polyneuritiformis). This is a neurological condition in which phytanic acid (3,7,11,15-tetramethyl hexadecanoic acid) has been found to accumulate in the serum (Nevin, Cumings, and McKeown, 1967) and body tissues. The failure in the

α-oxidation mechanism for branched-chain fatty acids is only partial, however, since patients with the disease can metabolize small quantities of 3,6-dimethyloctanoic acid and of 3,14,14-trimethylpentadecanoic acid (Try, 1967).

In Refsum's syndrome there is a marked demyelination within the central nervous system, and electron microscopy shows the presence of abnormal myelin lamellae. MacBrinn and O'Brien (1968) have isolated myelin from a case of the disease and found that some of the normal glycerophospholipid (predominantly lecithin) fatty acids is esterified with phytanic acid. Phytanate was found to be primarily localized in the one position of the lecithin molecule, and more was present in pure myelin than in either grey or white matter. It has been suggested that accumulation of the abnormal, branched fatty acid interfered with the close packing of myelin and so led to its instability (O'Brien, 1967).

Metachromatic Leukodystrophy

This lipidosis is an inborn error of metabolism in which there is a well-defined abnormality of myelin (dysmyelination). Although the myelin has an apparently normal ultrastructure, much less is present than would be expected from controls of the same age. Analysis (Table 3-I) shows that myelin isolated from the

TABLE 3-I
METACHROMATIC LEUKODYSTROPHY*

Age (9 yrs.)	Grey Matter (O'Brien, 1964)		White Matter (O'Brien, 1964)		Myelin (Norton, 1968)	
	M.L.D.†	Control	M.L.D.	Control	M.L.D. (11 yrs)	Control
Water (% dry wt)	83.3	85.8	79.9	77.3	—	—
Total lipid	34.8	47.8	53.5	74.1	63.2	70
Total protein (% of total lipid)	65.2	52.2	46.5	25.9	36.8	30
Cerebrosides	3.5	1.9	6.4	10.6	9.0	22.7
Sulphatides	1.6	0.4	12.6	3.9	28.4	3.8

White matter fatty acids (M.L.D.) as % of normal concentration (O'Brien, 1964)

Sphingolipid chain length:		
14 - 20	Sphingomyelin	82%
21 - 26	Sphingomyelin	30
21 - 26	Cerebroside	13
21 - 26	Sulphatide	206

*Analyses were performed on frozen brains (O'Brien, 1964) and myelin isolated from fresh material in 5% of normal yield (Norton, 1968).
†Metachromatic leukodystrophy.

diseased brain has an abnormally high sulphatide content (up to seven times normal) and that there is a concomitant deficiency in cerebrosides (O'Brien, 1964; Norton and Poduslo, 1966; Cumings, Thompson, and Goodwin, 1968). It has been shown (Mehl and Jatzketwitz, 1965; Austin, Armstrong, and Shearer, 1965) that this accumulation of sulphatide is due to the lack of sulphatase A — an enzyme probably responsible for the removal of sulphate from cerebroside sulphate (sulphatide). Another dysmyelinating disease in which there is an imbalance in galactolipid content is globoid leukodystrophy. In this condition there is a decrease in brain sulphatide content, and this has been correlated with a reduction in cerebroside sulphotransferase activity (Bachhawat, Austin, and Armstrong, 1967).

DAMAGE TO MYELIN DURING DEVELOPMENT
The Vulnerable Period of Development

A variety of conditions are known to reduce the rate and extent of myelination. During this vulnerable period of development, dietary deficiencies and certain metabolic disturbances have been shown to interfere with myelination. In many such cases there is an accompanying intellectual deficit (e.g. in phenylketonuria, in hypothyroidism, and possibly in protein deficiency).

It is now well established that within the central nervous system of the adult animal, the rate of synthesis of certain lipids is much less than in developing animals. It has even been suggested that there is no biosynthesis of cholesterol in the brain of adult animals, although active synthesis occurs in nervous tissue during development. Cerebroside synthesis is maximal in twenty-day-old rat brain and much reduced in the adult. This restricted biosynthesis of typical myelin lipid is consistant with the lack of turnover of the adult sheath that has been demonstrated by long-term studies with isotopes and with the general inability of the mature central nervous system to remyelinate after lesions. The period of myelination may therefore be regarded as of critical importance, and interference with the process may have lasting effects.

The apparent metabolic stability of myelin constituents, once laid down, makes possible the use of analytical procedures to measure brain growth. Factors such as undernutrition, which may operate temporarily to retard growth of the whole organism, reduce the quantities of more labile body constituents, and this invalidates the use of the more labile constituents as an index of maturity. But if myelin lamellae are stable once they have been formed, it follows that the number of lamellae, measured as the total quantity of their constituents is always an index of the amount of myelination which has taken place. It is possible that adverse factors may slow down the rate of deposition of myelin, but it is unlikely that they can have much effect on reducing the amount of metabolically stable material already formed (Davison and Dobbing, 1966; Dobbing, 1968).

In the adult brain much of the wet weight is accounted for by myelin which is not in a dynamic state and cannot easily be drawn upon to meet metabolic demand. This could explain the sparing of adult brain in conditions of undernutrition and other types of stress (see Table 3-II). Consequently, generalized vulnerability of myelin to adverse external factors (as opposed to localized small demyelinating lesions) is likely to be confined to the period of myelination. This is not because the lamellae of immature sheaths are metabolically more labile than in the adult animal. More probably, it is because the supply of precursors of myelin constituents are restricted even before they become available to the brain. Furthermore, the myelin constituents in brain before incorporation may be vulnerable to undernutrition and other types of stress. The enzyme systems and co-factors con-

TABLE 3-II
UNDERNUTRITION AND BRAIN CHOLESTEROL

Age of Rat	Period of Undernutrition	Body Weight Compared to Controls (%)	Deficiency in Brain Cholesterol Compared to Controls Concentration (%)	Deficiency in Brain Cholesterol After Rehabilitation Concentration (%)
New born	3 wk of mild undernutrition	41	14	7.6
3 weeks	8 wk restricted diet	80	None	None
Adult	5 wk very severe undernutrition	46	None	None

(After Dobbing, 1968)

cerned with myelination, many of which are transient and restricted to the period of myelination, may also be affected at this time.

It therefore seems reasonable to propose that effects of both undernutrition and other forms of stress will vary and depend upon when the event occurs in relation to the process of myelination. It is possible that the extent of the recovery, on the return of favorable circumstances, will also depend on the timing of the stress. Consequently, even if metabolic derangement be corrected, it may not be possible to compensate for the developmental abnormality. The hypothesis may also be extended to other metabolically stable brain constituents such as nuclear DNA. This seems to be yet another example of critical, sensitive, or vulnerable periods which have already been described and which may affect not only the physical growth of the organism, but also its intellectual, emotional, and social development (Dobbing, 1968).

It is not suggested of course that defects in myelination form the basis of intellectual or emotional development. Myelin is not even necessarily linked to sensory or motor functions, since in many species the neuronal connections for these processes can be formed before myelination has begun. However, myelination is a major event in growth of the brain once the architecture of the brain has been determined in the earlier stages of development, particularly if the preparatory oligodendroglial proliferation be included as a process leading to myelination. Whether interference with myelination will result in an impairment of future brain function, or whether there are other systems in the brain (developing coincidentally and hence similarly vulnerable) which are more important remains to be discovered.

In reviewing the experimental evidence for these proposals, the species differences in the timing of the period of maximum myelination relative to birth are of vital importance. This is particularly true for the extrapolation of findings from one species to another. Tentative extrapolation to man would place the human infant's vulnerable period about the seventh intrauterine month to the first few months of postnatal life. The full-term neonate, and particularly the prematurely born, would thus be at special risk.

While critical periods have been suggested in earlier stages of brain development when the formation of neurons, for example, is taking place, there has been no systematic search for evidence of a vulnerable period during myelination. Experimental evidence is therefore incomplete and must be inferred from a variety of sources. Even less is known about the eventual effects of deprivation during myelination and any dissussion of the topic must be regarded as speculative.

Dobbing (1964) has been able to demonstrate substantial deficits in brain cholesterol in the first three weeks of life by varying the size of rat litters during the suckling period. These changes may be regarded as an example of quite small restrictions being effective during the vulnerable period on the formation of a typical myelin lipid. Much more severe undernutrition for quite long periods does not reduce the concentration of myelin lipids if the stress is applied twenty-one days after birth. In these circumstances it is possible to restore brain size and myelin content. Severe undernutrition of the adult has negligible effects on the brain.

In experiments with newborn pigs Dickerson, Dobbing, and McCance (1967) have been able to show similar effects to these of undernutrition in rats. Comparison with the prenatal and postnatal growth pattern of well-nourished pigs again demonstrates that severe undernutrition retards development of the central nervous system and that rehabilitation results in incomplete recovery. These changes in myelination following undernutrition can be correlated with certain neurological conditions. Swayback or enzootic ataxia of sheep is associated with a copper deficiency of lambs. Both histological and neurochemical assessment of affected animals show that myelination is retarded. In this disease it has been suggested that lipid biosynthesis is impeded by the reduced levels of cytochrome oxidase present in the central nervous system of swayback lambs. Amyelination is also found in Border disease, another neurological condition of lambs, but this is not accompanied by copper deficiency.

It has been suggested that the vulnerable period of myelination of the human brain extends from a few months before birth until well afterwards. As suggested above, premature infants may therefore be particularly at risk. The effects of undernutrition in man have been studied much less than in animals. Nevertheless, changes in brain weight have been seen in badly undernourished children, and Kwashakior, (Davison, 1968) produced changes in the lipid concentration of the brain. Fishman, Prensky, and Dodge (1969) have reported marked reduction in brain proteolipid protein, cerebrosides, and plasmalogens of infants suffering from malnutrition (see also Benton, Moser, Dodge, and Carr, 1966). Early malnutrition may also produce permanent intellectual damage (Stoch and Smythe, 1967).

There is also good evidence that alterations in myelin content, possibly caused by amyelination, occur in phenyketonuria (Malamud, 1966), although the manner in which high levels of phenylalanine can interfere with myelination are not understood. Menkes (1967) has speculated that in phenylketonuria protein synthesis may be blocked. Barbato, Barbato and Hamanaka (1968) have shown that high levels of phenylalanine in young rabbits inhibit synthesis from ^{14}C-acetate of cerebroside in brain myelin. Experiments of Agrawal, Bone, and Davison (1969) suggest that phenylalanine selectively inhibits the biosynthesis of myelin protein and that the effects on lipid metabolism are secondary to this block. In man changes in the content of cerebroside and sulphatide, as well as a reduction of their $C_{24:1}$ long-chain fatty acids, have been noted (Crome, Tymms, and Woolf, 1962; Gerstl, Malamud, Eng, and Hayman, 1967; Cumings, Grundt, and Yanagihara, 1968). Defects or abnormalities of myelin formation are also evident in the leukodystrophies which are accompanied by pronounced mental retardation. The biochemistry of phenylketonuria is discussed in the following chapter.

The Quaking Mouse

The quaking mouse has a characteristic neurological disease attributable to a recessive autosomal mutant and is characterized by deficient myelination of the developing central nervous system (Sidman, Green, and Appel, 1965). It is first recognized at about

the twelfth day after birth (i.e. shortly after the onset of myelination) and reaches its full expression by about three weeks.
Such an animal has an unsteady gait and a marked tremor of the
hind quarters, and in the adult, epileptic fits can be readily induced by sensory stimulation (Sidman, Dickie, and Appel,
1964).

The entire central nervous system is deficient in myelin, although some fragments of myelin are present in almost all tracts.
No evidence of destruction, globoid cells, metachromatic lipids,
or inflammation have been found, and neurons, axons, and glial
cell appear to be normal. Peripheral nerve myelin is unaffected.

The brain lipid composition of diseased mice and controls
have been examined at a time when the period of the maximum
rate of myelination was completed (7-10 weeks after birth). In
their studies Baumann, Jacque, Pollet, and Harpin (1968) found
that the diseased mouse brain had only a slightly lower wet
weight than that of controls, but lipid and proteolipid content
was reduced to 68 percent of the normal value. The drop was
most marked in the myelin lipids — galactolipid, cholesterol, and
plasmalogens. There was also an increase in the relative proportion of phospholipids. Baumann and her colleagues also observed
a diminution in the content of sphingolipid long-chain fatty
acids (especially C_{24}), but no change was found in the proportion
of polyunsaturated long-chain fatty acids. The proportion of $C_{16:0}$
and $C_{18:0}$ fatty acids in total brain lipids of quaking mice was
found to be greater than in normal animals. Changes of this type
(i.e. increased proportions of short-chain fatty acids, increased
phospholopid, and decreased galactolipid) are reminiscent of the
compositional changes found at an early stage in the development of the myelinating central nervous system. It would therefore be of considerable interest to prepare and analyze myelin
from the brain of diseased mice, since it might be possible to
isolate fractions similar to those found in the developing brain.

The Effect of X-irradiation

Radiosensitivity of the brains of animals decreases with age.
The rat brain is most susceptible to the effects of radiation one
day after birth, at which time both cellular growth and myelina-

tion can be retarded. Irradiation of the two-day-old rat brain, however, produces little cellular destruction (for references see Schjeide, Lin, and De Vellis, 1968; De Vellis, Schjeide, and Clemente, 1967), although after such treatment the oligodendroglia are smaller in size than normal. In addition, myelin sheaths in rats exposed at two days and examined twenty-eight days later are thinner than in controls, and the onset of myelination appears to be delayed. The radiation effect therefore seems to be an example in which tissue response is altered by inhibition of differentiation at the subcellular level rather than by destruction of cells or by their misorientations. Although the formation of neurons is largely completed in the rat brain before birth, glial proliferation is still rapid during the early postnatal and sensitive period, and it is presumably during mitosis that cells are most susceptible to ionizing radiations. Since one of the major roles of glial in the developing brain is the synthesis of myelin, it would be expected that irradiation at the time of glial proliferation would affect myelination. De Vellis and his colleagues (1967) showed that in exposed animals there is a reduction in the total activity of a number of enzymes concerned with lipid biosynthesis. Most marked decreases occurred in glycerolphosphate dehydrogenase and to a lesser extent in isocitric dehydrogenase activity ($NADP^+$ dependent). There was relatively little effect on malate and lactate dehydrogenases, but notable decreases in the lipid and proteolipid protein content of the irradiated rat brain stem. These results are consistent with the histological observations suggesting that irradiation of the neonatal brain interferes with the development of myelin. Schjeide and his colleagues (1968) next isolated myelin from irradiated rats at different times up to 178 days after exposure. The results were compared with analyses from controls, and it was found that considerably less myelin could be recovered from the brain stems of treated rats (Table 3-III.) However, its composition differed only in the fatty acid composition. The proportion of total long-chain fatty acids and $C_{24:1}$ and $C_{26:1}$ was lower than in controls. It was also observed that myelin from more mature animals contained higher proportions of unsaturated fatty acids and relatively more long-chain fatty acids than younger animals. This suggests that x-irradiation at an early age delays the process of myelination, for not only is less myelin isolated from the treated animals, but also the fatty acid composition is similar to that seen in the early stages of myelination.

TABLE 3-III

EFFECTS OF IRRADIATION ON MYELIN FROM RAT BRAIN STEM*

| | | 20 Days Old | | 40 Days Old |
	Control	Irradiated	Control	Irradiated
Myelin dry wt (mg/gm wet wt brain stem)	8.1	4.1	10.8	6.0
Long-chain fatty acids 20:0 to 24:1 of myelin (% total fatty acid)	22.6	20.5	25.2	21.7

*Rats were irradiated with 700 rads of x-rays over the head when 2 days old. Light myelin was isolated by the method of Autilio, Norton, and Terry (1964). Results after Schjeide *et al.* (1968). No differences were noted in the chemical composition of the myelin, except in the fatty acids.

DEMYELINATION

The Age Onset of Multiple Sclerosis

A common feature to multiple sclerosis and experimental allergic encephalitis is that both are conditions largely affecting the mature brain. There is a low incidence of multiple sclerosis in children (McAlpine, Compston, and Lumsden, 1955), and it is known that young animals are resistant to experimental allergic encephalitis (Stone and Lerner, 1965). It has been suggested that multiple sclerosis resembles experimental allergic encephalitis in being an autoimmune disease (Table 3-IV Paterson, 1965; Adams and Leibowitz, 1969). It is therefore worth considering the age-onset effect in terms of a possible immunological response. At present, it is not clear how antigens could be released from myelin to induce an immune response, for Kornguth and Anderson (1965) have evidence from studies with ferritin-labeled antibodies that many of the antigenic determinants of myelin are blocked in intact tissue. Injury or inflammation in the central nervous system might release acid proteinases from lysosomes (Lajtha and Marks, 1966) which, acting as they do *in vitro,* could cause proteolysis of myelin protein with the liberation of polypeptides. These polypeptides (Table 3-V) which have been

TABLE 3-IV

MULTIPLE SCLEROSIS AND SUBACUTE SCLEROSING LEUKOENCEPHALITIS*

Myelin Lipid (% dry wt)	*Average Myelin Composition*			
	Control (Adult) 76.5	Multiple Sclerosis (Adult) 77.0	Control (21 yr) 70	Subacute Sclerosing Leukoencephalitis 73.7
	μmole/gm dry wt			
Cholesterol	0.41	0.37	0.50	0.83
Total phospholipid	0.37	0.40	0.39	0.35
Total galactolipids	0.21	0.22	0.22	0.19
Cholesterol	0.334	0.280	Cumings and Goodwin (1968).	
Cerebroside	0.176	0.166		
Sulphatides	0.039	0.052		

(M.S. white matter contains 70.8% and normal white matter 74.2% myelin)

*Analysis for myelin after Gerstl, Eng, Hayman, Tavaststjerna, and Bond (1967) and Norton (1968).

shown to be encephalitogenic in animals (Carnegie and Lumsden, 1966; Lumsden, Robertson, and Blight, 1966) might be important in the initiation of multiple sclerosis. Such suggestions do not easily explain the low incidence of the disease in children, for the basic protein is present in the developing brain (Eng, Chao, Gerstl, Pratt, and Tavaststjerna, 1968). It is therefore unlikely that the resistance of young animals is due to the absence of an encephalitogenic factor.

TABLE 3-V

EXPERIMENTAL ALLERGIC ENCEPHALOMYELITIS

(The effect of injection of protein or polypeptide + Freund's complete adjuvant into guinea pig.)

	Dose	Clinical Effect	Histological Demyelination	Day of Onset of Neurological Symptoms
Polypeptide (mol wt 3500)	1μg	4/6	6/6	14 - 16
Basic protein (mol wt 16,500)	50μg	3/6	5/6	17 - 19

(After Carnegie, Bencina, and Lamoureux, 1967)

The Neurotoxic Action of Organophosphorus Compounds

Studies on the neurotoxic action of the organophosphorus compounds provide a clue for a possible explanation of the susceptibility of the adult to demyelination. Certain organophosphates (e.g. tri*ortho*cresyl phosphate, mono*ortho*cresyl phosphate, mipafox and di*iso*propylfluorophosphate) have been found to produce secondary-type demyelination in some species (Barnes and Denz, 1953; Aldridge and Barnes, 1966). The process of demyelination has been shown to begin at the muscle spindle and to proceed in a retrograde manner to involve the peripheral nerve fibers and the corresponding tracts of the spinal cord (Cavanagh, 1954). At one time it was considered that neurotoxity could be related to inhibition of the enzyme pseudocholinesterase (Earl and Thompson, 1952), but there is no convincing evidence for such a relationship (Davison, 1953; Thompson, 1954). It does appear that inhibition of an esterase is involved in the selective mechanism of action of these neurotoxic agents (Poulsen and Aldridge, 1964; Johnson, 1968, 1969), but it is not clear how the inhibition produces the pathological changes. Some clue to the mode of action of the organophosphates is given by the fact that whereas fowls are particularly susceptible to paralysis, young birds are unusually resistant (Barnes, personal communication). For example, no neurotoxic effect is seen after oral administration of mono*ortho*cresyl phosphate to fifty-day-old chickens, although the same dose in adult birds produces paralysis in twelve to fourteen days. In seventy-day-old birds a transient ataxia is produced, and a slowly reversible paralysis, in ninety-day-old birds (Turnbull and Davison, 1969).

These observations suggest that neurotoxicity can be correlated with a developmental process which terminates in chickens of about ninety days old. Establishment of the neuronal populations and most metabolic pathways in the nervous system are established early in development, but myelination is a more extended process which ends at about the time when birds become susceptible to demyelination. This suggests that any damage effected by neurotoxic agents can be repaired only at the time when active myelin synthesis is occurring. Consequently, there may be a balance between the rate of demyelination and remyelination. According to this hypothesis, in adult animals the rate of destruction exceeds the very slow rate of myelin synthesis so that nervous system lesions result (Fig. 3-1).

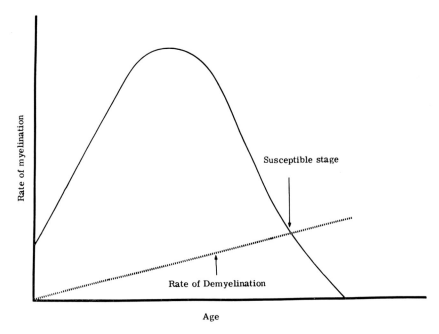

FIGURE 3-1. Myelination and susceptibility to demyelination. It is proposed that demyelination will become apparent only when the rate of demyelination exceeds the rate of myelination. (Courtesy of the Athlone Press, University of London.)

The Mechanism of Demyelination

In some respects the process of demyelination may be regarded as the reverse of myelinogenesis. Cholesterol esters are present in developing nervous tissue, and esterification of cholesterol is a characteristic feature of Wallerian-type degeneration. During myelination there is a deposition of myelin lipid, and during demyelination there is progressive loss of total myelin lipid (Johnson, McNabb, and Rossiter, 1949; McCaman and Robins, 1959). Simon (1966) has convincing evidence from experiments with ^{14}C-cholesterol that in the peripheral nervous system demyelination occurs in an orderly, sequential manner, so that the more recently formed myelin lamellae are first removed (table 3-VI). This view of the mechanism of myelination is supported by the histological studies of Lampert and his colleagues (Lampert and

TABLE 3-VI

CHOLESTEROL TURNOVER IN DEGENERATING PERIPHERAL NERVE*

	Normal Nerve Cholesterol	Cholesterol Ester	Sectioned Nerve Cholesterol	Cholesterol Ester	Cholesterol Total
Amount (μmol)	8.25	0	3.15	1.15	4.3
Specific radioactivity (cpm/μmol)	610	0	1260	1070	1210
Total radioactivity (cpm)	5032	0	3969	1230	5199

Simon (1966)

*[4-^{14}C] cholesterol was injected into rats during the 10th to the 18th day of life. Five months after the final injection, the right sciatic nerve was sectioned and the animals killed 16 days afterwards. No radioactivity was found in the lipids of muscle, heart, liver, or blood, but 150,000 cpm were present in whole brain. The results show that although there was substantial loss of cholesterol (μmols), there was no change in the total amount of radioactive cholesterol, thus indicating a possible loss of the more recently deposited unlabeled sterol.

Carpenter, 1965; Lampert, 1965, 1967). Electron micrographs of the central nervous system in guinea pigs with experimental allergic neuritis show that outer myelin lamellae are often split off first. However, the final clarification of these problems must await combined studies in which isotope precursors are incorporated into myelin, and localization of radioactivity is determined by electron microscopy (see Hendelman and Bunge, 1969).

REFERENCES

ADAMS, C. W. M., and LEIBOWITZ, S.: The general pathology of demyelinating diseases. In Bourne, G. H. (Ed.): *Structure and Function of Nervous Tissue.* New York, Academic, 1969, in press.

AGRAWAL, H. C.,; BONE, A. H., and DAVISON, A. N.: Inhibition of brain protein synthesis by phenylalanine. *Biochem J, 112:*27, 1969.

ALDRIDGE, W. N., and BARNES, J. M.: Further observations on the neurotoxicity of organophosphorus compounds. *Biochem Pharmac, 15:*541, 1966.

AUSTIN, J. H.; ARMSTRONG, D., and SHEARER, L.: Metachromatic form of diffuse cerebral sclerosis. V. The nature and significance of low sulfatase activity: a controlled study of brain, liver and kidney in four patients with metachromatic leucodystrophy (MLD). *Arch Neurol (Chicago), 13:*593, 1965.

AUTILIO, L. A.; NORTON, W. T., and TERRY, R. D.: The preparation and some properties of purified myelin from the central nervous system. *J Neurochem, 11:*17, 1964.

BACHAWAT, B. K.; AUSTIN, J., and ARMSTRONG, D.: A cerebroside sulphotransferase deficiency in a human disorder of myelin. *Biochem J, 104*:15C, 1967.

BARBATO, L.; BARBATO, I. W. M., and HAMANAKA, A.: The *in vivo* effect of high levels of phenylalanine on lipids and RNA of the developing rabbit brain. *Brain Res, 7*:399, 1968.

BARNES, J. M., and DENZ, F. A.: Experimental demyelination with organophosphorus compounds. *J Path Bact, 65*:597, 1953.

BAUMANN, N. A.; JACQUE, C. M.; POLLET, S. A., and HARPIN, M. L.: Fatty acid and lipid composition of the brain of a myelin deficient mutant ,the 'quaking mouse'. *Europ J Biochem, 4*:340, 1968.

BENTON, J. W.; MOSER, H. W.; DODGE, P. R., and CARR, S.: Modifications of the schedule of myelination in the rat by early nutritional deprivation. *Pediatrics, 38*:801, 1966.

BERNSOHN, J., and STEPHANIDES, L. M.: Aetiology of multiple sclerosis. *Nature (London), 215*:821, 1967.

CARNEGIE, P. R.; BENCINA, B., and LAMOUREUX, G.: Experimental allergic encephalomyelitis. Isolation of basic proteins and polypeptides from central nervous tissue. *Biochem J, 105*:559, 1967.

CARNEGIE, P. R., and LUMSDEN, C. E.: Encephalitogenic peptides from spinal cord. *Nature (London), 209*:1354, 1966.

CAVANAGH, J. B.: The toxic effects of tri-ortho-cresyl phosphate on the nervous system—an experimental study in hens. *J Neurol Neurosurg Psychiat, 17*:163, 1954.

CROME, L.; TYMMS, V., and WOOLF, L. I.: A chemical investigation of the defects of myelination in phenylketonuria. *J Neurol Neurosurg Psychiat, 25*:143, 1962.

CUMINGS, J. N., and GOODWIN, H.: Sphingolipids and phospholipids of myelin in multiple sclerosis. *Lancet, 2*:664, 1968.

CUMINGS, J. N.; GRUNDT, I. K., and YANAGIHARA, T.: Lipid changes in the brain in phenylketonuria. *J Neurol Neurosurg Psychiat, 31*:334, 1968.

CUMINGS, J. N.; THOMPSON, E. J., and GOODWIN, H.: Sphingolipids and phospholipids in microsomes and myelin from normal and pathological brains. *J Neurochem, 15*:243, 1968.

DAVISON, A. N.: Some observations on the cholinesterases of the central nervous system after the administration of organophosphorus compounds. *Brit J Pharmacol, 8*:212, 1953.

DAVISON, A. N.: Progress in pedology. In Linneweh, F. (Ed.): *Fortschritte der Pädologie.* Heidelberg, Springer-Verlag, p. 65, 1968.

DAVISON, A. N., and DOBBING, J.: Myelination as a vulnerable period in brain development. *Brit Med Bull, 22*:40, 1966.

DE VELLIS, J.; SCHJEIDE, O. A., and CLEMENTE, C. D.: Protein synthesis and enzymic patterns in the developing brain following head x-irradiation of newborn rats. *J Neurochem, 14*:499, 1967.

DICKERSON, J. T. W.; DOBBING, J., and McCANCE, R. A.: The effect of undernutrition in the postnatal development of the brain and cord in pigs. *Proc Roy Soc B, 166*:396, 1967.

DOBBING, J.: The influence of early nutrition on the development and myelination of the brain. *Proc Roy Soc B, 159*:503, 1964.

DOBBING, J.: Vulnerable periods in developing brain. In Davison, A. N., and Dobbing, J. (Eds.): *Applied Neurochemistry.* Oxford, Blackwell, p. 287, 1968.

EARL, C. J., and THOMPSON, R. H. S.: The inhibitory action of tri-ortho-cresyl phosphate on cholinesterases. *Brit J Pharmacol, 7*:261, 1952.

ENG, L. F.; CHAO, F. C.; GERSTL, B.; PRATT, D., and TAVASTSTJERNA, M. G.: The maturation of human white matter myelin. Fractionation of the myelin membrane proteins. *Biochemistry,* 1968.

FISHMAN, M. A.; PRENSKY, A. L., and DODGE, P. R.: Low content of cerebral lipids in infants suffering from malnutrition. *Nature, 221*:552, 1969.

GERSTL, B.; ENG, L. F.; HAYMAN, R. B.; TAVASTSTJERNA, M. G. and BOND, P. R.: On the composition of human myelin. *J Neurochem, 14*:661, 1967.

GERSTL, B.; MALAMUD, N.; HAYMAN, R. B., and BOND, P. R.: Morphological and neurochemical study of Pelizaeus-Merzbacher disease. *J Neurol Neurosurg Psychiat, 28*:540, 1965.

GERSTL, B.; MALAMUD, N.; ENG, L. F., and HAYMAN, R. B.: Lipid alterations in human brains in phenylketonuria. *Neurology, 17*:51, 1967.

GERSTL, B.; TAVSATSTJERNA, M. G.; HAYMAN, R. B.; SMITH, J. K., and ENG, L. F.: Lipid studies of white matter and thalamus of human brains. *J Neurochem, 10*:889, 1963.

HENDELMAN, W. J., and BUNGE, R. P.: Radioautographic studies of choline incorporation into peripheral nerve myelin. *J Cell Biol, 40*:190, 1969.

JOHNSON, M. K.: An enzyme in hen brain hydrolysing phenyl phenylacetate: a possible connection with the delayed neurotoxic effect of some organophosphorus compounds. *Biochem J, 110*:13P, 1968.

JOHNSON, M. K.: A phosphorlylation site in brain and the delayed neurotoxic effect of some organophosphorus compounds. *Biochem J, 111:*487, 1969.

JOHNSON, A. C.; McNABB, A. R., and ROSSITER, R. J.: Chemical studies of peripheral nerve during Wallerian degeneration. *Biochem J, 45:*500, 1949.

KORNGUTH, S. E., and ANDERSON, J. W.: Localization of a basic protein in the myelin of various species with the aid of fluorescence and electron microscopy. *J Cell Biol, 26:*157, 1965.

LAMPERT, P. W.: Demyelination and remyelination in experimental allergic encephalomyelitis. *J Neuropath Exp Neurol, 24:*371, 1965.

LAMPERT, P.: Electron microscopic studies on ordinary and hyperacute experimental allergic encephalomyelitis. *Acta Neuropath, 9:*99, 1967.

LAMPERT, P., and CARPENTER, S.: Electron microscopic studies on the vascular permeability and the mechanism of demyelination in experimental allergic encephalomyelitis. *J Neuropath, 24:*11, 1965.

LAJTHA, A., and MARKS, N.: In Peeters, H. (Ed.): *Protides of the Biological Fluids.* Amsterdam, Elsevier, *13:*103, 1966.

LOWRY, O. H.: Energy metabolism of the nerve cell. In Rodahl, K., and Issekutz, B. (Eds.): *Nerve as a Tissue.* p. 163, 1968.

LUMSDEN, C. E.; ROBERTSON, D. M., and BLIGHT, R.: Chemical studies on experimental allergic encephalomyelitis. Peptide as the common denominator in all encephalitogenic 'antigens.' *J Neurochem, 13:*127, 1966.

McALPINE, D.; COMPSTON, N. D., and LUMSDEN, C. E.: McAlpine, D.; Compston, N. D., and Lumsden, C. E. (Eds.): *Multiple Sclerosis.* Edinburgh, E. & S. Livingstone, 1955.

MACBRINN, M. C., and O'BRIEN, J. S.: Lipid composition of the nervous system in Refsum's disease. *J Lipid Res, 9:*552, 1968.

McCAMAN, R. E., and ROBINS, E.: Quantitative biochemical studies of Wallerian degeneration in the peripheral and central nervous system. II. 12 Enzymes. *J Neurochem, 5:*32, 1959.

MALAMUD, N.: Neuropathology of phenylketonuria. *J Neuropath Exp Neurol, 25:*254, 1966.

MEHL, E., and JATZKEWITZ, H.: Evidence for the genetic block in metachromatic leucodystrophy. *Biochem Biophys Res Commun, 19:*407, 1965.

MENKES, J. H.: The pathogenesis of mental retardation in phenylketonuria and other inborn errors of amino acid metabolism. *Pediatrics, 39:*297, 1967.

NEVIN, N. C.; CUMINGS, J. N., and McKEOWN, F.: Refum's syndrome. Heredopathia atactica polyneuritiformis. *Brain, 90:*419, 1967.

NORTON, W. T.: The variation in chemical composition in myelin in disease and during development. *Charing Cross Hospital Gazette,* no. 8, 1967/68.

NORTON, W. T., and PODUSLO, S.: Metachromatic leucodystrophy: Chemical abnormal myelin and cerebral biopsy studies of three siblings. In Ansell, G. B. (Ed.) : *Chemical Composition of the Nervouse System.* Oxford, Pergamon, p. 82, 1966.

O'BRIEN, J. S.: A molecular defect of myelination. *Biochem Biophys Res Commun, 15:*484, 1964.

O'BRIEN, J. S.: The stability of the myelin membrane. *Science, 147:* 1099, 1965.

O'BRIEN, J. S.: Cell membranes—composition: structure: function. *J Theor Biol, 15:*307, 1967.

PATERSON, P. Y.: Experimental allergic encephalomyelitis and autoimmune disease. *Adv Immun, 5:*131, 1966.

POULSEN, E., and ALDRIDGE, W. N.: Studies on esterases in the chicken central nervous system. *Biochem J, 90:*182, 1964.

SCHJEIDE, O. A.; LIN, R. I. S., and DE VELLIS, J.: Molecular composition of myelin synthesized subsequent to irradiation. *Radiat Res, 33:*107, 1968.

SIDMAN, R. L.; DICKIE, M. M., and APPEL, S. H.: Mutant mice (quaking and jimpy) with deficient myelination in the central nervous system. *Science, 144:*309, 1964.

SIDMAN, R. L.; GREEN, M. C., and APPEL, S. H.: Catalog of the neurological mutants of the mouse. Harvard University Press, 1965.

SIMON, G.: Cholesterol ester in degenerating nerve: origin of cholesterol moiety. *Lipids, 1:*369, 1966.

STÄLLBERG-STENHAGEN, S., and SVENNERHOLM, L.: Decrease of short chain fatty acid. *J Lipid Res, 6:*146, 1965.

STOCH, M. B., and SMYTHE, P. M.: The effect of undernutrition during infancy on subsequent brain growth and intellectual development. *S Afr Med J, 41:*1027, 1967.

STONE, H., and LERNER, E. M.: Chronic disseminated allergic encephalomyelitis in guinea pigs. *Ann NY Acad Sci, 122:*227, 1965.

SVENNERHOLM, L.: In Folch-Pi, J., and Bauer, H. J. (Eds.) : *Brain Lipids and Lipoproteins and the Leucodystrophies.* New York, Elsevier, p. 104, 1963.

THOMPSON, R. H. S.: Anticholinesterase. Esterase levels in the nervous system of animals during demyelination by tri-ortho-cresyl phosphate. *Chem and Ind,* p. 749, 1954.

TRY, K.: Indications of only a partial defect in the α-oxidation mechanism in Refsum's disease. *Scand J Clin Lab Invest, 20:*255, 1967.

TURNBULL, J. M., and DAVISON, A. N.: In preparation, 1969.

VANDENHEUVEL, F. A.: Study of biological structure at the molecular level with stereo model projections. I. The lipids in myelin sheath of nerve. *J Am Oil Chem Soc, 40:*455, 1963.

Chapter 4

MYELIN DEFICIENCIES RELATED TO INBORN ERRORS OF HUMAN METABOLISM

L. I. WOOLF

M ANY INBORN ERRORS of metabolism are associated with mental retardation. In some of these where the defective enzyme is directly concerned with some constituent of the brain, the chemistry and morphology of both grey and white matter have been intensively investigated. Examples are Tay-Sachs disease, other gangliosidoses, and metachromatic leukodystrophy. In other cases where the primary defect is in the metabolism of an amino acid or a sugar, there has been little or no investigation of the brains. This is, perhaps, understandable; investigation of the chemistry and morphology of the brain in gangliosidosis is intellectually more exciting than in phenylketonuria, for example, where any observed effects are presumably secondary and more or less nonspecific. Moreover, in contrast to the numerous studies of the lipidoses, very little work is being done on the chemistry and morphology of the brain in mental retardation. Study of the brain in these other inborn errors of metabolism is, however, important if we are to discover how a defect in phenylalanine metabolism, to cite a specific example, brings about mental retradation. Nor are these questions purely academic; in some areas one infant in every 4,500 suffers from phenylketonuria (Cahalane, 1968).

Only in two inborn errors of metabolism outside the lipidoses has there been adequate examination of the chemistry and morphology of the brain. These two conditions are phenylketonuria and leucinosis (maple syrup urine disease).

PHENYLKETONURIA
Clinical Features

The presenting symptom is usually profound mental retardation, the median intelligence quotient being below 30. The pa-

183

tients are normal at birth but deteriorate during infancy, so that at six months of age the developmental quotient may be below 50. By two years after birth the majority of those affected, if untreated, have an IQ of 30 or less. There is a slow, continuing, further deterioration during childhood and in some cases adult life.

The frequency distribution of IQ in phenylketonuria yields a bimodal curve. Probably about two thirds of all phenylketonurics fall in the lower IQ group, with a peak below IQ 20, and probably about one third in the higher group, with a peak about IQ 90 to 100. The antimode falls about IQ 65. These two groups differ biochemically and genetically as well as in IQ; the terms *atypical phenylketonuria* and *hyperphenylalaninemia* have been applied to certain individuals in the higher IQ group.

Apart from the intellectual defect, many affected individuals show disorders of behavior. In the lower IQ range the patients are more withdrawn than similarly retarded nonphenylketonuric patients. The phenylketonurics often show autistic behavior with meaningless repetitive movements of fingers, head, or limbs. In the higher IQ ranges, hyperkinesis is sometimes a problem; some of these children exhibit behavioral problems rather than intellectual retardation (Sutherland, Berry, and Shirkey, 1960). In addition, between 20 and 25 percent of phenylketonurics suffer epileptic seizures. This is more common in the lower IQ range but also occurs in a proportion of those with IQ in the normal range (Woolf *et al.*, 1961). Both minor and major seizures occur, sometimes in the same patient. The electroencephalogram is abnormal in 90 to 95 percent of the patients (Fois, Rosenberg, and Gibbs, 1955).

When phenylketonurics are compared with their unaffected siblings at the same age, a relative lack of melanin in skin, hair, and eyes is seen. This has been traced to the competitive inhibition of tyrosinase by the high concentration of phenylalanine (Miyamoto and Fitzpatrick, 1957).

Morphology and Chemistry of the Brain

Early reports indicated that, while brains of phenylketonurics tended to be rather small, there was no gross structural abnormality. In a few cases there was a marked defect of myelination in the white matter, but in most cases this amounted to no more than pale staining of the myelin, i.e. somewhat poor uptake of dyes specific for some component of myelin, and in many patients no abnormality was seen, (Alvord, Stevenson, Vogel, and Engle, 1950; Poser and van Bogaert, 1959; Crome and Pare, 1960; Jervis, 1963). Some workers doubted whether lack of myelin was a feature of phenylketonuria; they suggested that the defective myelination, where observed, might be secondary to epilepsy.

Myelin is of course a spirally arranged plasma membrane. Normal myelin has a characteristic qualitative and quantitative chemical composition which varies with age but within an age group varies little from individual to individual. The white matter of the brain consists of axons, their myelin sheaths, and glial cells with the myelinated axons constituting the great bulk of the white matter after infancy. Quantitative chemical analysis of the white matter from patients and suitable control subjects should therefore indicate any abnormality of myelin. A shortcoming of this method is that it may be difficult to distinguish between a qualitative abnormality of the myelin and a reduced amount of myelin per fiber. However, either of these could be regarded as defective myelination.

In order to throw more light on myelination in phenylketonuria, the brains of four patients who had died were examined for myelin lipids, (Crome, Tymms, and Woolf, 1962). The youngest patients available were selected for this study because it was considered possible that myelination was merely delayed in phenylketonuria. Since the brains had been preserved in neutral formalin in saline, the more labile phosphatides were partly destroyed. However, cerebroside, sulphatide, sphingomyelin, and cholesterol are characteristic myelin components that are stable in formalin. Consequently, it was decided to estimate lipid galactose (i.e. cerebroside and sulphatide combined), free cholesterol, and esterfied cholesterol. Cholesterol esters are not a normal component of myelin, but it was hoped their estimation would throw some light on whether myelin was actively destroyed in phenylketonuria.

White matter from the four brains and from five age-matched

control subjects who had had no neurological disease was dissected free from grey matter, meningeal membranes, and blood vessels. The white matter was washed free of formalin, and the lipids were extracted with chloroform-methanol, 2:1. The washed lipid extract was passed through a column of Florisil® to remove phosphatides, and portions of the eluate were evaporated to dryness, after which galactose was determined by a nonhydrolytic orcinol method (Crome *et al.*, 1962) . The results are shown in Figure 4-1. Other portions of the eluate were analyzed for total and free cholesterol. The results are shown in Table 4-I.

White matter from the phenylketonuric brains had a higher water content and lower solids content than that from age-matched

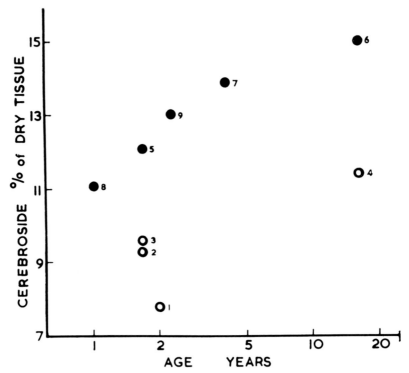

FIGURE 4-1. Cerebroside content of white matter plotted against age (log scale). ●, normal controls, O, phenylketonurics. (Crome, Tymms, and Woolf, 1962. By permission of the editors, *Journal of Neurology, Neurosurgery and Psychiatry*.)

TABLE 4-I
CHOLESTEROL CONTENT OF WHITE MATTER OF
THE FRONTAL LOBE IN PHENYLKETONURIA*

| Case | | Age | | Dry | Cholesterol | | | |
| | | Yr. | Mo | matter % | % Wet Weight | | % Dry Weight | |
					Free	Ester	Free	Ester
1		2	—	19.0	2.00	0.00	10.5	0.0
2		1	8	18.8	2.39	0.01	12.7	0.1
3		1	8	21.9	3.32	0.15	15.2	0.7
	(a)†			15.8	1.92	0.33	12.1	2.2
4		16	—					
	(b)			20.4	2.70	0.02	13.2	0.1
Control 5		1	8	23.3	4.16	0.00	16.5	0.0
Control 6		16	—	24.1	3.66	0.03	15.2	0.12
Control 7		4	—	24.1	3.61	0.03	15.0	0.1
Control 8		1	—	22.5	3.21	0.01	13.7	0.04
Control 9		2	3	25.9	3.58	0.02	13.8	0.1

*From Crome, Tymms, and Woolf (1962) and Crome (1962).
†Area *a* was undergoing active demyelination, as shown histologically; area *b* gave no histological evidence of active demyelination.

normal brains. The content of cholesterol and cerebroside plus sulphatide was also lower in the phenylketonuric brains, both absolutely and as a proportion of total solids. Therefore, as measured by these criteria, white matter from these four patients with phenylketonuria had a lower myelin content than the normal. Histological examination had revealed borderline or doubtful lack of myelin in cases three and four and no abnormality in cases one and two. The variation of chemical composition from case to case is noteworthy.

Although the limited objectives of this investigation were achieved, more questions than answers arose. The lower proportion of total solids could have resulted from a decrease in the number of myelinated fibers and an increase in the number of glial cells. The alternative, simple swelling of the fibers is unlikely to be the whole explanation in view of the small size of the brains. The question remains whether the remaining myelinated fibers were structurally normal at the molecular, ultrastructural, and light microscope levels.

Esterified cholesterol is a crude but useful measure of demyelination. Normal myelin appears to contain no cholesterol esters, and normal brain tissue only traces which are possibly related to the presence of blood. In the destruction of myelin some of the cholesterol is esterified, possibly within the phagocytes, and transported via the blood stream to other organs. The presence at autopsy of appreciable amounts of cholesterol esters therefore signifies relatively recent demyelination, within two or three years before death. The finding of cholesterol esters in considerable amount in the brain of a sixteen-year-old phenylketonuric boy is therefore highly significant evidence of demyelination, (Crome, 1962). On the other hand, the virtual absence of cholesterol esters from three other brains does not conclusively exclude some demyelination, even though their ages were only twenty months, twenty months and two years respectively, (Crome *et al.*, 1962).

Other workers have confirmed some of these findings, have failed to confirm others, and have considerably extended the range of measurements and the conclusions drawn from them. Foote, Allen, and Agranoff (1965), examining the brains of two adult patients with phenylketonuria, could not find any decrease in cerebroside, cholesterol, or phospholipid content. However, these workers noted a decrease in the ratio of unsaturated to saturated fatty acids in all lipid fractions. Menkes (1966) found an even more marked reduction in this ratio in one case, though not in two others. Berry, Cevallos, and Wade (1965) found a reduction in the ratio of monoenoic to saturated fatty acids in the cerebroside of peripheral nerve during the early stages of Wallerian degeneration, and Menkes (1966) suggests that his findings and those of Foote *et al.* (1965) may represent early demyelination. In one of his three cases Menkes found an abnormal branched-chain fatty acid in the cerebroside fraction. Each of the brains examined by Menkes (1966) showed a reduction in the lipid hexose, though the purified cerebroside plus sulphatide fraction was at the lower limit of normal. Free cholesterol was slightly reduced in two of the three brains, and cholesterol esters were absent from all three. Menkes considers that a deficiency of nonhydroxylated fatty acids in the sulphatide fraction may represent one of the more consistent changes in phenylketonuria.

In a very careful study of different areas of the brains of three patients with phenylketonuria, Gerstl, Malamud, Eng, and Kayman (1967) found histological and chemical evidence of a reduction of myelin. These workers confirmed the finding of Crome *et al.* (1962) that the deficiency of myelin increased with increasing age, suggesting progressive demyelination proceeding so slowly that cholesterol esters did not accumulate in appreciable amounts. Gerstl *et al.* (1967) also noted a relative deficiency in long-chain fatty acids and unsaturated fatty acids in the white matter (c.f. Forrsman, Kristensson, Sourander, and Svennerholm, 1967). It is interesting that long-chain fatty acids are deficient in many diseases involving demyelination, perhaps because lipids containing long-chain acids are preferentially attacked.

There is direct evidence of active demyelination in some older patients with phenylketonuria, since sudanophilic areas have been found in the white matter of eight patients (Benda, 1952; Jervis, 1954; Crome, 1962; Malamud, 1966). These areas contain cholesteryl esters resulting from myelin breakdown. The condition has been termed Schilder's disease, but this is a synonym better avoided, since it suggests an etiologic entity which, in fact, does not exist.

It seems very probable that myelin does not need constancy of chemical composition to continue to function. For example, some variation in the relative proportions of the different fatty acids can probably be tolerated. It is possible that the myelin laid down in phenylketonuria is abnormal in composition and/or structure. It is clear that when myelin is destroyed, different molecular species are attacked at different rates, altering the composition of the remaining myelin. We know so little of the process of demyelination that it is useless to speculate on whether some parts of the myelin sheath are attacked before others, whether the myelin undergoes some early chemical changes while retaining its ultrastructural integrity, whether neuron death precedes demyelination, whether the primary attack is on the glial cell, or whether the axon retains its function to some extent during demyelination. Answers to these questions must be sought if we are to understand how the brain is affected in phenylketonuria.

One thing is clear — the lack of myelin, however it is brought about, is the result of the high concentration of phenylalanine in the blood. When phenylketonuric infants are treated with a low-phenylalanine diet so that the concentration in the blood is essentially normal from early infancy onwards, they escape mental retardation and epilepsy, the EEG remains normal, and they show no neurological abnormalities. This is good evidence that myelin is very probably being laid down normally and is not being destroyed in children treated in this way. As yet, the brain of a phenylketonuric child successfully treated by clinical criteria has not been available for study.

MAPLE SYRUP URINE DISEASE (LEUCINOSIS)

Clinical Features

Signs of neurological disease usually show themselves during the first week or two of life. The infant feeds normally at first but fails to suck after the first few days. The infant goes rapidly downhill; rigidity and opisthotonos develop, the Moro reflex is absent, and occasionally there are grand mal seizures. The EEG shows a gross, generalized abnormality. Attacks of apnea develop, and the infant, if untreated, invariably dies during the first two years of life, usually during the first few weeks.

The disease results from the absence of an enzyme essential for the oxidative decarboxylation of the three α-keto-acids derived by transamination from leucine, isoleucine, and valine (Menkes, 1959; MacKenzie and Woolf, 1959; Dancis *et al.*, 1959). In a variant form of the disease, the body appears to retain about 20 percent of the normal ability to decarboxylate the three α-keto-acids; this form is associated with much milder clinical signs (Kiil and Rokkones, 1964; Morris, Lewis, Doolan, and Harper, 1961).

As soon as it appeared that this was an inborn error of metabolism leading to the accumulation of three amino acids, the analogy with phenylketonuria became obvious, and it was suggested that treatment with a diet low in leucine, isoleucine, and valine might be efficacious (MacKenzie and Woolf, 1959). This treatment has now been used in a few cases with very good results, the children surviving without neurologic signs or in some cases any mental retardation, (Snyderman, Norton, Roitman, and Holt, 1964; Ireland, 1965; Westall, 1967).

Morphology and Chemistry of the Brain

With one possible exception (Martin and Norman, 1967) these brains show no structural abnormalities compatible with prenatal damage. The predominant abnormal findings are in the white matter and are edema, status spongiosus, astrocytosis, and deficient myelination. The lack of myelin is far more marked than in phenylketonuria and has been found in all untreated cases coming to necropsy, (Menkes, Hurst, and Craig, 1954; Crome, Dutton, and Ross, 1961; Silberman, Dancis, and Feigin, 1961; Menkes, Phillippart, and Fiol, 1965; Martin and Norman, 1967). The degree of lack of myelin varies from one part of the brain to another. The myelin sheaths are reported by Crome *et al.* (1961) to be greatly reduced in number. Those present are often tortuous with uneven, irregular contours and show localized ballooning into vacuoles from 20μ to greater than 100μ in diameter. These vacuoles account for the spongy, edematous condition of the white matter. There is some sudanophilic and Schiff-positive material in phagocytes around some blood vessels, but this is not greatly in excess of normal, and no sudanophilic material is found elsewhere. The numbers of axons in the white matter and of neurons in the cerebral cortex appear to be approximately normal, though these estimates are subject to error. Apart from relatively minor details, other autopsy reports agree with the above observations.

Chemical investigations of the brain have been carried out on five untreated patients who came to autopsy at the ages of seventeen days, twelve days, four months, twenty months, and twenty-five days, respectively, (Woolf, 1962; Menkes *et al.*, 1965; Menkes and Solcher, 1967; Prensky and Moser, 1966). Woolf (1962) and Prensky and Moser (1966) worked with unfixed material that had been deep frozen while Menkes *et al.* (1965) studied material that had been stored in formalin for less than a year. In spite of this difference, the results obtained for the three patients dying before the age of four weeks agree well (Table 4-II).

Menkes *et al.* (1965) found no abnormalities in lipid composition that could not be related to formalinization, though the

TABLE 4-II

LIPID CONTENT OF BRAIN IN UNTREATED
MAPLE SYRUP URINE DISEASE*

Case†	Age	Total Solids %	Cerebroside	Cholesterol % Dry Weight		Proteolipid Protein % Dry Weight	Author
				Total	Ester		
1 F	17 days	11	0.37	6.9	∼ 0	—	Woolf (1962)
2 P	12 days	8.6, 12.0	0.26, 0.44	6.5	0.3	—	Menkes,
Control P	Stillborn	8.5	0.23	7.7	0.4	—	Phillippart and Fiol (1965)
3 F	25 days	7.84	0.01	7.98	0.63	0.402	
Control F	14 days	10.99	1.084	8.12	0.31	1.188	Prensky
4 F	20 mo	22.40	11.3	13.7	—	4.59	and Moser
Control F	23 mo.	20.61	16.0	16.0	—	7.64	(1966)
Control F	24 mo	23.41	13.3	13.9	—	7.89	
5 P	4 mo	9.1	0.11	6.04	0.54	—	Menkes
Control F	3 mo	12.9	1.3	5.4	—	—	and Solcher
Control F	6½ mo	17.4	1.02	—	—	—	(1967)

*Case 1: mixed grey and white matter, others: white matter from various parts of the brain.
†F: fresh frozen, P: preserved in formalin.

amount of ceramide may have been elevated. The cerebroside fraction of white matter contained galactose, dihydro-, threo-, and erythro-sphingosine, fatty acids, and hydroxyacids in the same relative amounts as in a control brain from a normal one-day-old infant. The distributions of normal and hydroxy fatty acids according to chain length and degree of unsaturation were also normal. The cerebroside contained 18.3% and 20.3% hexose of which 91.5 percent was galactose and 8.5 percent appeared to be glucose (detected and determined by glucose oxidase). Menkes *et al.* (1965) reported that they found a small proportion of glucose in almost every purified brain cerebroside specimen irrespective of age. The sulphatides appeared to be normal in structure for the infant's age, though the amount isolated was small.

Menkes *et al.* (1965) reported that the brain they examined weighed almost twice normal, was edematous with loose-meshed, cystic white matter, and that myelination was less extensive than would be expected for the patient's age. It is difficult to relate these findings to the results of their chemical investigations which suggested a normal proportion of water and myelin lipids in the white matter, as compared with a normal, one-day-old infant. During the first weeks after birth, the composition of the normal brain is changing more rapidly than at any other time, and we would expect greater variation from subject to subject than would occur at a later time. Therefore, it is possible that had Menkes *et al.* used more control brains from infants closely bracketing in age their twelve-day-old patient, they might have found significant chemical differences in the amount and composition of myelin. The infant's brain examined by Prensky and Moser (1966) contained far more water and far less cerebroside than the age-matched controls.

In the two older, untreated patients the deficiency of myelin lipids was more marked. Menkes and Solcher (1967) found virtually no cerebrosides or sulphatides in subcortical white matter from their four-month-old patient, and very little C_{24} sphingomyelin, a component of normal white matter, was present in the brain. In their twenty-month-old patient, Prensky and Moser (1966) found a reduction of brain glycolipids to 77 percent of normal and of proteolipids to 58 percent of normal. This variability in myelin content from case to case can perhaps be correlated with the differences in clinical severity of the disease. In their patient Menkes and Solcher (1967) found great variation in the degree of myelinization from one part of the brain to another and normal myelinization of the spinal cord. In all the cases so far reported in both neonates and older children, the content of cholesterol ester was within normal limits.

Two patients treated from an early age with a diet low in leucine, isoleucine, and valine have died of intercurrent infections. In one patient, who died at the age of five months, and who had been treated since the tenth day of life (Linneweh and Solcher, 1965; Menkes and Solcher, 1967), myelination was apparently normal. There were some slight gliosis and sudanophilic deposits, but no chemical or morphological abnormality of myelin sheaths was noted. The other died at the age of eighteen months, having been treated since twelve weeks after birth (Voyce, Montgomery, Crome, Bowman, and Ireland, 1967). The brain appeared generally normal, but some parts of the white matter, particularly in the temporal lobes, pons, cerebellum, inferior olives, and arcuate nuclei, showed some fibrous gliosis; there was loss of myelin without gliosis at the angle of the lateral ventricles, and the pyramids showed only a pale staining of the myelin. There was little or no evidence of active demyelination. Neurochemical investigation of the frontal lobe (which was histologically normal) by Cumings revealed no abnormality (Voyce *et al.*, 1967). The relatively normal myelinization in these two treated patients is clear evidence that the lack of myelin in untreated maple syrup urine disease is the result of a toxic action of the branched-chain amino acids or their metabolites. The minor abnormalities found in the second case are presumably the result of the considerable delay in instituting treatment. They suggest the irreversibility of some of the changes in the brain brought about by the high blood concentrations of leucine, isoleucine, and valine.

Taking all the reported cases together, it seems that demyelination may play only a minor part in the disease process and that the primary defect is in the initial formation of myelin sheaths. There is little evidence on the nature of the myelin that is laid down, but it seems possible that the chemical composition may be within normal limits.

CONCLUSIONS

The myelin sheath plays a vital role in transmission of an impulse along the axon. In both phenylketonuria and maple syrup urine disease, gross mental and neurological disease are associated with a lack of myelin in the white matter of the brain. It would be tempting to conclude that the lack of myelin explains the disease process in both conditions, but this is not wholly adequate as an explanation. In spite of the clinical and biochemical resemblances between phenylketonuria and maple syrup urine disease, it is possible that the lack of myelin arises in different ways. It seems probable that the metabolism of the glial cells that form myelin sheaths is altered in maple syrup urine disease and that slow, active demyelination occurs in phenylketonuria with reduction in the number of myelin sheaths. Additionally, it is possible that the laying down of myelin is inhibited in phenylketonuria and that some active demyelination occurs in maple syrup urine disease.

Lack of myelin cannot alone explain all the clinical findings in phenylketonuria. The very severely retarded adult reported by Forssman *et al.* (1967) had only occasional foci of myelin pallor, and the content of the various lipids was at the lower limit of the normal range. When some older affected children are given a low phenylalanine diet, within a few days there is an improvement in behavior, a marked decrease in seizure frequency, and a change in the EEG towards the normal. This rapid effect must have some explanation other than the degree of myelination. There is good evidence that a high concentration of phenylalanine in the blood, as in phenylketonuria, reduces the formation of neurotransmitter substances at the synapses, though the mechanism by which this reduction is brought about is open to question (Fellman, 1956; Davison and Sandler, 1958; Sandler, Davies, and Rimington, 1959; Hanson, 1959; Boylen and Quastel, 1961; Tashian, 1961; McKean, Schanberg, and Giarman, 1962; Jervis, 1963). There is evidence that the α-keto-acids which accumulate in maple syrup urine disease also inhibit the enzymes synthesizing neurotransmitter substances, (Tashian, 1961). It remains to be determined whether in maple syrup urine disease there is a significant effect on the synaptic transmission of impulses as well as on the function of the glial cell.

The following sequence of changes in phenylketonuria has been suggested (Crome *et al.,* 1962); high concentrations of phenylalanine or its metabolites may depress neuronal function in such a way as to bring about the rapidly reversible behavioral and neurological abnormalities. If continued long enough, this toxic effect may cause neuronal death, the axons of neurons that succumb early never becoming properly myelinated; where neuronal death occurs after infancy, the axon, becomes demyelinated. Over the years this may happen on so localized a scale that sudanophilic staining is not observed except in a few cases. This hypothesis does not exclude the possibility that glial function is also affected.

About thirty inborn errors of amino acid metabolism, in addition to phenylketonuria and maple syrup urine disease, are known to be associated with mental retardation. In none of these has the structure, ultrastructure, and chemistry of the brain been adequately studied. A study of myelination in these conditions may well throw light on the mechanism by which the metabolic error brings about the mental retardation.

REFERENCES

ALVORD, E. C. JR.; STEVENSON, L. D.; VOGEL, F. S., and ENGLE, R. L.: Neuropathological findings in phenylpyruvic oligophrenia (Phenylketonuria). *J Neuropath Exp Neurol, 9:*298, 1950.

BENDA, C. E.: *Developmental Disorders of Mentation and Cerebral Palsies.* New York, Grune, 1952, p. 451.

BERRY, J. F.; CEVALLOS, W. H., and WADE, R. R.: Lipid class and fatty acid composition of intact peripheral nerve during Wallerian degeneration. *J Amer Oil Chem Soc, 42:*492, 1965.

BOYLEN, J. B., and QUASTEL, J. H.: Effects of L-phenylalanine and sodium phenylpyruvate on the formation of adrenaline from L-tyrosine in adrenal medulla in vitro. *Biochem J, 80:*644, 1961.

CAHALANE, S. F.: Phenylketonuria: mass screening of newborns in Ireland. *Arch Dis Child, 43:*141, 1968.

CROME, L.: The association of phenylketonuria with leucodystrophy. *J Neurol Neurosurg Psychiat, 25:*149, 1962.

CROME, L.; DUTTON, G., and Ross, C. F.: Maple syrup urine disease. *J Path Bact, 81:*379, 1961.

CROME, L., and PARE, C. M. B.: Phenylketonuria—A review and a report of the pathological findings in four cases. *J Ment Sci, 106:* 862, 1960.

CROME, L.; TYMMS, V., and WOOLF, L. I.: A chemical investigation of the defects of myelination in phenylketonuria. *J Neurol Neurosurg Psychiat, 25:*143, 1962.

DANCIS, J.; LEVITZ, M.; MILLER, S., and WESTALL, R. G.: Maple syrup urine disease. *Brit Med J, 1:*91, 1959.

DAVISON, A. N., and SANDLER, M.: Inhibition of 5-hydroxytryptophan decarboxylase by phenylalanine metabolites. *Nature (London), 181:*186, 1958.

FELLMAN, J. H.: Inhibition of DOPA decarboxylase by aromatic acids associated with phenylpyruvic oligophrenia. *Proc Soc Exp Biol Med, 93:*413, 1956.

FOIS, A.; ROSENBERG, C., and GIBBS, F. A.: The electroencephalogram in phenylpyruvic oligophrenia. *Electroenceph Clin Neurophysiol, 7:*569, 1955.

FOOTE, J. L.; ALLEN, R. J., and AGRANOFF, B. W.: Fatty acids in esters and cerebrosides of human brain in phenylketonuria. *J Lipid Res, 6:*518, 1965.

FORSSMAN, H.; KRISTENSSON, K.; SOURANDER, P., and SVENNERHOLM, L.: Histological and chemical studies of a case of phenylketonuria with long survival. *J Ment Defic Res, 11:*194, 1967.

GERSTL, B.; MALAMUD, N.; ENG, L. F., and KAYMAN, R. B.: Lipid alterations in human brains in phenylketonuria. *Neurology (Minneapolis), 17:*51, 1967.

HANSON, A.: Action of phenylketonuria metabolites on glutamic acid decarboxylase and γ-aminobutyric acid-α-ketoglutaric acid transaminase in brain. *Acta Chem Scand, 13:*1366, 1959.

IRELAND, J. T.: In Allan, J. D., and Holt, K. S. (Eds.) : *Biochemical Approaches to Mental Handicap in Childhood.* Edinburg & London, E. & S. Livingstone, 1965, p. 71.

JERVIS, G. A.: Phenylpyruvic oligophrenia (phenylketonuria) . *Res Publ Ass Res Nerv Ment Dis, 33:*259, 1954.

JERVIS, G. A.: In Lyman, F. L. (Ed.) : *Phenylketonuria.* Springfield, Thomas, 1963, pp. 96, 101.

KIIL, R., and ROKKONES, T.: Late manifesting variant of branched-chain ketoaciduria (maple syrup urine disease) . *Acta Paediat, 53:* 356, 1964.

LINNEWEH, F., and SOLCHER, H.: Über den Einfluss diätetischer Prophylaxe auf die Myelogenese bei der Leucinose (maple syrup urine disease) . *Klin Wschr, 43:*926, 1965.

McKEAN, C. M.; SCHANBERG, S. M., and GIARMAN, N. J.: A mechanism of the indole defect in experimental phenylketonuria (rats) . *Science, 137:*604, 1962.

MACKENZIE, D. Y., and WOOLF, L. I.: Maple syrup urine disease: An inborn error of the metabolism of valine, leucine and isoleucine associated with gross mental deficiency. *Brit Med J, 1:*90, 1959.

MALAMUD, N.: Neuropathology of phenylketonuria. *J Neuropath Exp Neurol, 25:*254, 1966.

MARTIN, J. K., and NORMAN, R. M.: Maple syrup urine disease in an infant with microgyria. *Develop Med Child Neurol, 9:*152, 1967.

MENKES, J. H.: Maple syrup disease. *Pediatrics, 23:*348, 1959.

MENKES, J. H.: Cerebral lipids in phenylketonuria. *Pediatrics, 37:*967, 1966.

MENKES, J. H.; HURST, P. L., and CRAIG, J. M.: A new syndrome: Progressive familial infantile cerebral dysfunction associated with an unusual urinary substance. *Pediatrics, 14:*462, 1954.

MENKES, J. H.; PHILLIPPART, M., and FIOL, R. E.: Cerebral lipids in maple syrup disease. *J Pediat, 66:*584, 1965.

MENKES, J. H., and SOLCHER, H.: Maple syrup disease. Effects of dietary therapy on cerebral lipids. *Arch Neurol, 16:*486, 1967.

MIYAMOTO, M., and FITZPATRICK, T. B.: Competitive inhibition of mammalian tyrosinase by phenylalanine and its relationship to hair pigmentation in phenylketonuria. *Nature (London), 179:*199, 1957.

MORRIS, M. D.; LEWIS, B. D., and DOOLAN, P. D.: Biochemical observations in ketoaciduria, a variant of maple syrup urine disease. *Fed Proc, 20:*4, 1961.

POSER, C. M., and VAN BOGAERT, L.: Neuropathologic observations in phenylketonuria. *Brain, 82:*1, 1959.

PRENSKY, A. L., and MOSER, H. W.: Brain lipids, proteolipids and free amino acids in maple syrup urine disease. *J Neurochem, 13:* 863, 1966.

SANDLER, M.; DAVIES, A., and RIMINGTON, C.: Effect of phenylacetic acid on the carcinoid syndrome. *Lancet, 2:*318, 1959.

SILBERMAN, J.; DANCIS, J., and FEIGIN, I.: Neuropathological observations in maple syrup urine disease. *Arch Neurol, 5:*351, 1961.

SNYDERMAN, S. E.; NORTON, P. M.; ROITMAN, E., and HOLT, L. E. JR.: Maple syrup urine disease, with particular reference to dietotherapy. *Pediatrics, 34:*454, 1964.

SUTHERLAND, B. S.; BERRY, H. K., and SHIRKEY, H. C.: A syndrome of phenylketonuria with normal intelligence and behavior disturbances. *J Pediat, 57:*521, 1960.

TASHIAN, R. E.: Inhibition of brain glutamic acid decarboxylase by phenylalanine, valine and leucine derivatives—a suggestion concerning the etiology of the neurological defect in phenylketonuria and branched-chain ketonuria. *Metabolism, 10:*393, 1961.

VOYCE, M. A.; MONTGOMERY, J. N.; CROME, L.; BOWMAN, J., and IRELAND, J. T.: Maple syrup urine disease. *J Ment Defic Res, 11:*231, 1967.

WESTALL, R. G.: Dietary treatment of maple syrup urine disease. *Amer J Dis Child, 113:*58, 1967.

WOOLF, L. I.: Recent work on phenylketonuria and maple syrup urine disease. *Proc Roy Soc Med, 55:*824, 1962.

WOOLF, L. I.; OUNSTED, C.; LEE, D.; HUMPHREY, M.; CHESHIRE, N. M., and STEED, G. R.: Atypical phenylketonuria in sisters with normal offspring. *Lancet, 2:*464, 1961.

Chapter 5

DISEASES AFFECTING MYELINATION IN DOMESTIC ANIMALS

J. McC. HOWELL

INTRODUCTION

EARLIER CHAPTERS HAVE REVIEWED current knowledge of the critical steps in myelination. Although much is known about how this process may be affected under experimental conditions (Ch. 3), considerably less information is available in human disease, and it is not always easy to evaluate the dynamic processes of naturally occurring disease using human material alone. However, such information can be obtained from a study of certain diseases which occur in the domestic animals, many of which may be reproduced under controlled conditions. Such diseases can provide details of the pathogenesis of a lesion; may give an indication of the etiology of a disease process, and provide useful models for the evaluation of therapy. Much more could be learned about the critical steps in myelination by the application of experimental techniques to these naturally occurring diseases.

There are many syndromes in the domestic animals in which myelin is affected, and for an account of these the reader is referred to the book by Innes and Saunders (1962). This chapter describes some of the diseases of myelination which can be used as experimental models for diseases of man. As many will be unfamiliar with these diseases, and as the material has not previously been collected together in this form, the lesions will be described in some detail.

HYPOMYELINOGENESIS CONGENITA

Hypomyelinogenesis congenita is one of the most interesting lesions to have recently been described in the domestic animals. In this syndrome myelination is deficient, and the lesion is probably similar to that described in some cases of phenylketonuria in man (Crome and Pare, 1960; Jervis, 1963).

Pigs

This disease of new born piglets is characterized by tremors of skeletal muscles and was first reported from the United States of America by Kinsley in 1922, but it now appears to have a world-wide distribution (Christensen and Christensen, 1956; Stromberg and Kitchell, 1958; Innes and Saunders, 1962). It has been called congenital tremors, trembling, trembles, dancing pig disease, chorea, and myoclonia congenita. The most severely affected pigs have difficulty in feeding and die, but in less severely affected piglets the symptoms may disappear with time. The condition is usually regarded as a single clinical entity, but there are variations in the pathology and etiology.

Pathology

There are no constant pathological findings, and Done (1968) has proposed the following classification:

Type A. Morphological lesions of the CNS.

1. Cerebellar hypoplasia and defective myelination, particularly in the spinal cord.
2. Defective myelination of the spinal cord, but no cerebellar defects.
3. Subtotal failure of myelination in the CNS with deficiency of oligodendrocytes; no cerebellar hypoplasia.

Type B. No morphological lesions of the CNS.

Retarded myelination may occur throughout the CNS of the piglets but appears to be particularly well marked in the spinal cord (Christensen and Christensen, 1956; Gitter and Bowen, 1962; Emerson and Delez, 1965; Harding, Done, and Darbyshire, 1966). The axons appear to be normal (Fig. 5-1), and there is no reactive gliosis; but in sections stained for myelin, less myelin is present than in controls of the same age. It is of considerable interest that the spinal nerve roots appear to be fully myelinated (Fig. 5-2).

Etiology

Several etiological agents may be capable of producing trembling in new born pigs. Genetic factors (Hupka and Horn, 1956;

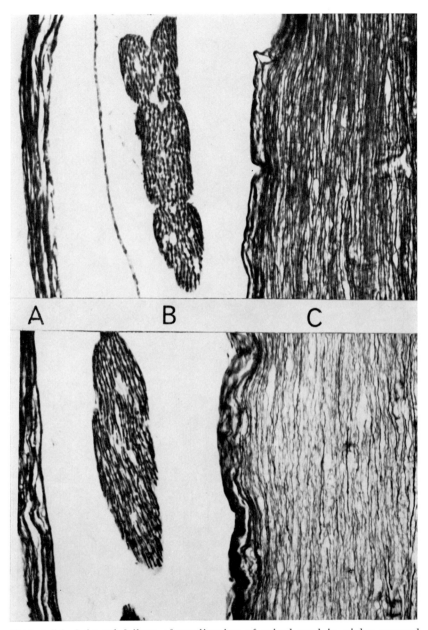

FIGURE 5-1. Subtotal failure of myelination of spinal cord in piglet exposed *in utero* to a strain of swine fever virus. *L.S.,* lateral funiculi of spinal cords at T₉, stained Holmes' silver and luxol blue. The section at the top of the figure is normal; that at the bottom is from an affected piglet, showing numerous axons in a spinal cord virtually devoid of myelin; spinal nerves are unaffected. *A*: dura mater, *B*: dorsal root, and *C*: spinal cord. X155. (By courtesy of Mr. J. T. Done, Weybridge.)

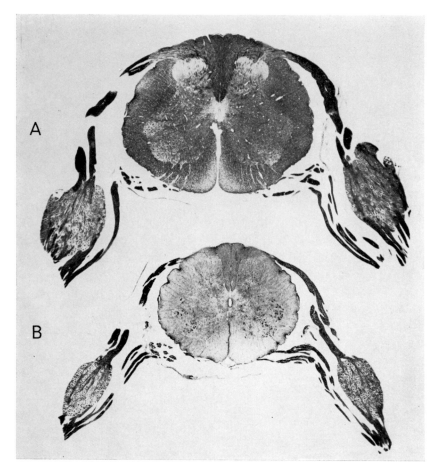

FIGURE 5-2. Spinal hypomyelinogenesis in the newborn pig, resulting from infection of the dam on day ten of pregnancy with a strain of swine fever (hog cholera) virus. Both spinal cords sectioned at T_1, stained Luxol blue and Scarba red and photographed at same magnification. *A*: normal, *B*: affected piglet, showing hypoplasia of spinal cord with almost complete absence of myelin, though spinal nerves are fully myelinated. X14. (By courttesy of Mr. J. T. Done, Weybridge.)

Pobisch, 1961) , hypothyroidism (Florio, Flachat, Cottereau, Flochon, Fedida, and Saint-Cyr, 1956) , and faulty feeding (Christensen and Christensen, 1956) are among the factors that have been suggested. Recent work indicates that type A1 is the result of transplacental infection with swine fever virus, type A2 may also be produced following the infection of pregnant sows by a virus other than that of swine fever, and type A3 is caused by a sex-linked recessive gene (Done and Harding, 1967; Done, 1968).

Sheep

In 1959 Hughes, Kershaw, and Shaw described a disease of lambs occurring in the Welsh border counties and called it *B* or Border disease. The lambs had abnormally pigmented hairy birth-coats, were usually smaller, and grew less quickly than normal lambs. A proportion showed muscular tremors which were some-times violent enough to prevent locomotion, and in some ataxic lambs there was deficiency of myelin. Markson, Terlecki, Shand, Sellers, and Woods (1959) also described the defective formation of myelin in trembling, ataxic lambs, and they called the condition hypomyelinogenesis congenita. Other outbreaks have been described in Great Britain (Barr, 1964; Barlow and Dickinson, 1965), in Canada (Darcel, Avery, and Bainborough, 1961), and in New Zealand (Hartley and Kater, 1962).

Pathology

Histological changes were found in all areas of CNS white matter but tended to vary in extent and degree. Some fibers were not myelinated, and in others the degree of myelination appeared to be reduced (Figs. 5-3 and 5-4). The axons had a normal distribution and morphology, and there were no signs of inflammation or gitter cell* formation (Hughes *et al.,* 1959; Markson *et al.,* 1959; Barr, 1964). Barlow and Dickinson (1965) while recording a decreased affinity for myelin stains, also saw dilatation of myelin sheaths; and in lambs up to one month old, sudanophilic and osmiophilic lipids were found in myelin sheaths, free in the inter-stitial tissue, and in perivascular spaces. However, a significant gitter cell reaction was not seen. Abnormal glial cells were seen which were sometimes seen to be dividing. In a later paper on the electron microscopy of Border disease (Cancilla and Barlow,

---

*Gitter cells are phagocytes containing lipid material.

1968a) , these cells were identified as astrocytes, and the deficiency of myelin was seen to be due to the presence of morphologically normal myelin sheaths with less than the usual complement of

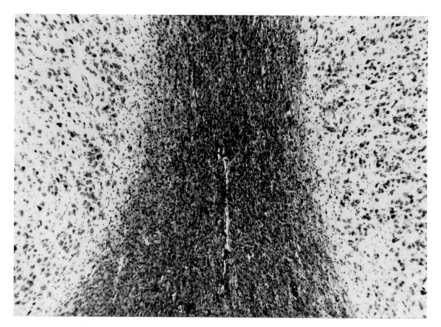

FIGURE 5-3. Cerebral tissue from a one-week-old normal lamb. Cortical tissue on both sides of well-myelinated white matter. Luxol-fast blue, cresyl violet. X78.

lamellae. Evidence of myelin destruction, invasion of the nerve sheaths by macrophages at the nodes of Ranvier, and naked axons surrounded by cells with sequestered myelin debris have also been described. Davison and Oxberry (1966) determined the lipid composition of the white matter of Border disease lambs and compared their results with those previously obtained from young swayback lambs (Howell, Davison, and Oxberry, 1964) . They found reduced amounts of the characteristic myelin lipids (Fig. 5-5) , whereas the content of the nonmyelin lipid lecithin remained little altered and cholesterol esters were absent.

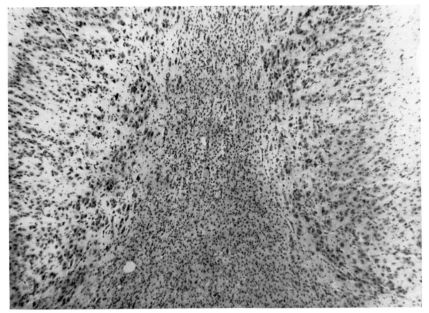

FIGURE 5-4. Similar field to Figure 5-3, but from a one-week-old shaker lamb. The white matter is almost completely unmyelinated. Luxol-fast blue, cresyl violet. X78. (By courtesy of Mr. M. Barr, Penrith.)

Etiology

In 1967 Nott and Shaw postulated that maternal infection during pregnancy might produce Border disease in the lambs. Subsequent experiments (Dickinson and Barlow, 1967; Shaw, Winkler, and Terlecki, 1967) suggested that this is so, for pregnant ewes injected with an inoculum prepared from the tissues of lambs with hypomyelinogenesis gave birth to lambs with hypomyelinogenesis (Table 5-I). The nature of the transmissible agent has yet to be established.

Calves

Hypomyelinogenesis, particularly involving the cerebellum, has been described in Jersey calves (Saunders, Sweet, Martin, Fox, and Fincher, 1952); in Shorthorns and Herefords (Hulland, 1957), and in Angus-Shorthorn crosses (Young, 1962). The symp-

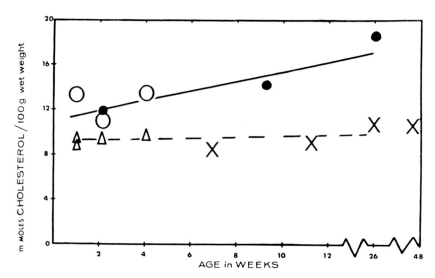

FIGURE 5-5. The cholesterol content of the spinal cord white matter from normal, swayback, and hypomyelinogenesis lambs aged between one and twenty-six weeks of age. (Normal (O) and swayback (Δ) lambs were obtained from Liverpool, normal (●) and lambs with hypomyelinogenesis (×) from Edinburgh. (By courtesy of Dr. A. N. Davison, and *Research in Veterinary Science*.)

toms were seen at or shortly after birth. The calves were unable to stand or stood with a broad-based stance and were ataxic. Tremors, periods of bilateral spastic rigidity, and opisthotonus were seen.

Pathology

The CNS of the calves appeared to be normal in size, but histologically it was seen that the central white matter of the cerebellum entirely lacked myelin (Fig. 5-6). Partial or complete absence of myelin was also seen in the cerebrum, pons, medulla, and cervical spinal cord, though the emerging cranial nerve trunks were normally myelinated. Axons were normal, no microglial proliferation of gitter cell development was observed, nor were products of myelin degeneration seen. In the cerebrum and cervical spinal cord diffuse areas of astrocytic glia were seen with swollen glial nuclei frequently paired.

TABLE 5-I

Lamb No.	Dam Exposed (Days of Pregnancy)	Single or Twin	Histo-pathology	Clinical Observations
A99	8	S	—	Shaker
A95	15	S	++++	Shaker
A96	25	S	++++	Shaker
A93	35		++++	Died at birth
		T		
A94	35		+++	Shaker
A92	47	S	++++	Shaker
A87	52		—	Right hind leg splayed out
		T		
A88	52		+	Died shortly after birth
A97	78		—	Normal
		T		
A98	78		—	Normal
A91	104	S	—	Normal
A79	123	S	—	Normal
A81	125		—	Normal
		T		
A82	125		—	Died shortly after birth
A83	126		—	Born dead
		T		
A84	126		—	Born dead
	Controls			
A80		S	—	
A85		S	—	
A86		S	—	Normal
A89		S	—	
A90		S	—	
A100		S	—	

—: No observed myelin deficiency.
+: Grade 1   Based on a subjective assessment of the degree and extent of
+++: Grade 3   myelin deficiency in the CNS
++++: Grade 4
Taken from Shaw, Winkler, and Terlecki (1967). A summary of clinical and pathological changes in lambs in relation to conceptual age at time of inoculation of the ewe with a suspension of tissue from lambs with hypomyelinogenesis congenita. (By courtesy of I.G. Shaw and *Veterinary Record (London)*.)

Etiology

Saunders *et al.* (1952) considered etiological factors such as infection, trauma, malnutrition, and heredity and concluded that the disease was probably inherited as an autosomal recessive. The occurrences of ataxic calves ceased when two bulls suspected of carrying the defect were removed from the herd. Hulland (1957) found that the incidence was familial, but in both his and Young's

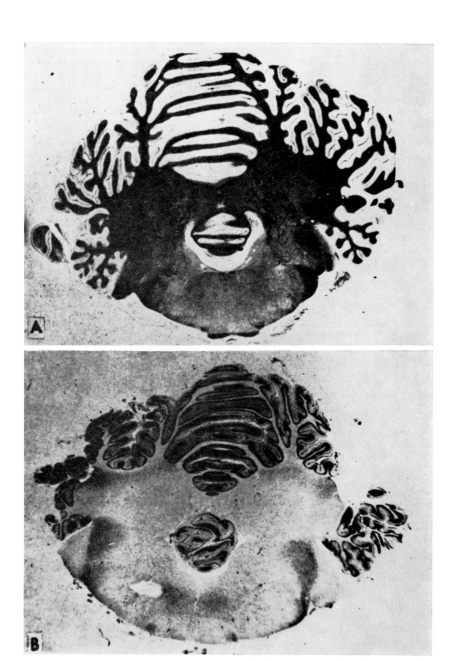

FIGURE 5-6. Sagittal section of a normal three-day-old calf (above) and of a 3-day-old calf with cerebellar ataxia (below). Little myelin is present in the tissue from the ataxic calf. Luxol-fast blue. X4. (By courtesy of Dr. S. Young and *Cornell Veterinarian.*)

(1962) cases the breeding records were inadequate for the establishment of an hereditary basis.

Comment

Hypomyelinogenesis congenita is found in at least three species of domestic animals; the lesion may also be present in some cases of phenylketonuria, and there are many similarities to the quaking mouse syndrome. The basic lesion appears to be a dysfunction of the myelin-forming cells in the CNS. It is of some interest that oligodendroglial cells are damaged and Schwann cells do not appear to be affected. It would be of value to have electron microscope studies of oligodendroglial cells from these cases and to examine the biochemical properties of isolated glial cells from diseased animals in order to more closely define the nature of the defect at the molecular level.

LESIONS ASSOCIATED WITH COPPER DEFICIENCY

Sheep — Swayback

Swayback or enzootic ataxia has a worldwide distribution. It is associated with low levels of copper in the pastures and in the blood and tissues of ewes and affected lambs. The disease can be prevented by giving copper supplements to the ewe during pregnancy (Innes and Saunders, 1962; Underwood, 1962) .

Neuropathology

Changes may be found in the cerebral hemispheres, in large neurons of the brain stem and spinal cord, and in the white matter of the spinal cord (Innes and Shearer, 1940; Barlow, Purves, Butler, and Macintyre, 1960; Howell, Davison, and Oxberry, 1964) . The incidence of cerebral lesions is variable, but lesions in neurons and changes in the white matter of the spinal cord are constantly present. This finding and the nature of the neuronal lesions have been discussed elsewhere and will not be considered here (Howell, 1968; 1970) .

Cerebral white matter. All gradations of change may be observed from small foci of gelatinous softening to complete cavitation of the white matter (Fig. 5-7). The lesions are usually symmetrical, may affect all zones of white matter, and extend to the summits of the convolutions. A thin rim of myelinated fibers and fibrous glia may be present around the large cavities, but the lipid by-products of myelin degeneration are rarely abundant and gitter cells are not common. The gelatinous areas consist of a loose glial network with ill-defined edges through which run a few nerve fibers. The changes have been studied at the ultrastructural level (Cancilla and Barlow, 1966).

White matter of the spinal cord. Changes may be found in the ventrolateral column of white matter close to the median fissure and in the dorsal part of the lateral column immediately below the point of entry of the dorsal nerve root (Fig. 5-8). The lesion is least marked in the lumbar cord and becomes diffuse in the medulla. In the thoracic segments much of the periphery of the lateral columns may be involved and occasionally isolated abnormal fibers are present in the dorsal columns (Barlow *et al.,* 1960; Howell, Davison, and Oxberry, 1969). Ballooned fibers may be seen in sections stained by hematoxylin and eosin, but swollen axons and gitter cells are infrequently present. The lesions are most readily seen in sections stained for myelin where these areas are much paler than the surrounding white matter. They contain Marchi-positive material, but such material may also be found in control lambs and often has a similar distribution (Barlow *et al.,* 1960; Howell *et al.,* 1964, 1969). Using the osmium tetroxide α-naphthylamine technique (Adams, 1959), Howell *et al.* (1964, 1969) have shown that in young lambs there is a reduction of myelinated fibers in the specified areas of spinal cord, and products of myelin degeneration are absent; but in older animals evidence of myelin degeneration and gliosis may be found (Barlow, 1963a; Howell *et al.,* 1969).

Biochemistry. Swayback is associated with low levels of copper in the tissues of the ewe and lamb (Underwood, 1962), and the copper content of the CNS of swayback lambs is lower than that of controls (Howell and Davison, 1959; Mills and Williams, 1962; Howell *et al.,* 1964). The syndrome has been produced in lambs born of ewes fed a semipurified diet of low copper content (Lewis,

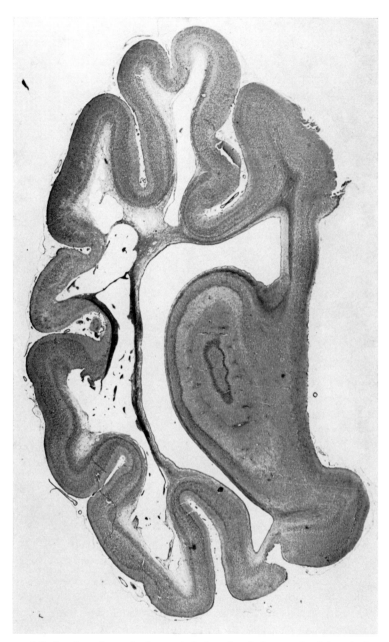

FIGURE 5-7. Section through the occipital pole of the cerebral hemisphere of a one-week-old swayback lamb. Cysts and glial tissue have replaced the white matter. Luxol-fast blue, cresyl violet. X9.

Terlecki, and Allcroft, 1967). Swayback lambs can accumulate copper in their tissues, so in order for the disease to develop, the lambs must be deprived of copper during their period of myelination (Howell, 1968).

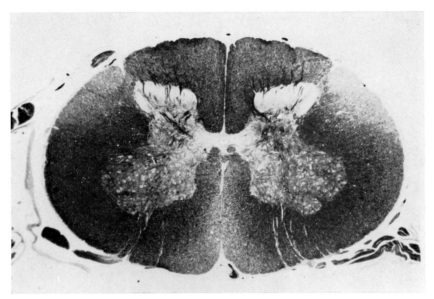

FIGURE 5-8. Cervical spinal cord of an animal with swayback three-and-one-half months old. Pale areas can be seen adjacent to the ventral fissure and below the point of entry of the dorsal nerve root. Loyez. X16. (By courtesy of *Acta Neuropathlogica (Berlin)*.

In copper deficiency, cytochrome oxidase activity and the rate of phospholipid synthesis decrease (Gallagher, Judah, and Rees, 1956a, 1956b), and the relevance of these changes to swayback was discussed by Gallagher (1957, 1964). The cytochrome oxidase activity of the brain of swayback lambs has been found to be significantly lower than for normal lambs (Howell and Davison, 1959; Mills and Williams, 1962; Barlow, 1963b). It has been shown that whereas nucleic acid and protein levels were unaffected in the CNS of swayback lambs, the content of myelin and myelin lipids was reduced (Fig. 5-5). A greater content of cholesterol esters was found in the cerebral tissue of the swayback lambs than in the controls, but this was not so in the white matter of the spinal cord (Howell *et al.,* 1964, 1969).

Pathogenesis

Cerebral lesions. Cavity formation in the cerebral white matter may be a common response to various forms of damage rather than to a specific lesion (Kramer, 1956; Richter, 1957). Changes similar to the cerebral cavitation seen in swayback have been found in lambs born to ewes that were given a living bluetongue virus vaccine during pregnancy (Cordy and Shultz, 1961; Innes and Saunders, 1962; Young and Cordy, 1964) and in lambs that had their CNS experimentally traumatized *in utero* (Howell, unpublished). The lesions resemble the cystic change found in human infantile encephalopathies which may also be caused by anoxia (Courville, 1959; Schwedenberg, 1959; Clarke and Anderson, 1961; Howell *et al.,* 1964). Spais, Palsson, and van Bogaert (1961) described the lesion as a "spongy transformation of the white matter" which was associated with functional vascular disorders. Behrens and Schulz (1959) and Schulz and Behrens (1960) considered the lesion to result from a disturbance in the blood-brain barrier which led to a perivascular cerebral edema and then to a diffuse necrosis. A histological examination of the CNS of fetal and newborn lambs led Barlow *et al.* (1960) to the conclusion that there was a great deal of similarity between the gelatinous cerebral lesions of swayback and the cerebral white matter of normal lambs at an earlier stage of development. They suggested that the primary biochemical lesion inhibited the development of nerve cells, myelin sheaths, and glia and described the lesion as a neurodysgenesis.

Lesions in spinal cord white matter. Innes and Shearer (1940) and Innes and Saunders (1962) were of the opinion that the lesion was a secondary degeneration of spinal cord motor pathways and was dependent upon damage to higher centers. However, it may be independent of such changes (Howell, 1968). Barlow *et al.* (1960) suggested that the lesion was part of an inhibition of development of myelin sheaths, nerve cells, and glia. Howell

et al. (1964, 1969) have suggested that the reduced myelin formation is associated with impaired lipid biosynthesis which can be
directly attributed to copper and cytochrome oxidase deficiencies.
The lesion persists, and if the lamb survives, some of the abnormal
myelin degenerates. Cancilla and Barlow (1968b) have suggested
that in some nerve fibers the axon degenerates before the myelin
sheath.

Pigs

In pigs ataxia associated with low liver copper levels has been
described in Australia and New Zealand (Joyce, 1955; Wilkie,
1959; McGavin, Ranby, and Tammemagi, 1962; O'Hara and
Shortridge, 1966; Munday, 1967). The youngest pigs involved
were two to three weeks old, and ataxia progressed to posterior
paralysis. Lesions were present in the white matter of the spinal
cord and had a similar distribution to those seen in swayback
lambs. It is of some interest that the lesion adjacent to the point
of entry of the dorsal nerve root could be traced through the
posterior cerebellar peduncle into the cerebellum and was therefore taken to be the dorsal spinocerebellar tract (McGavin *et al.*,
1962).

Goats

A condition resembling swayback in sheep has been reported
in the offspring of experimental goats (Barlow, Robertson, Owen,
and Proudfoot, 1962; Owen, Proudfoot, Robertson, Barlow, Butler, and Smith, 1965) and as a naturally occurring disease of kids
in South Africa (Schulz, Merwe, Rensberg, and Swart, 1951) and
Kenya (Hedger, Howard, and Burdin, 1964). Lesions were found
in neurons and spinal cord white matter but not in cerebral white
matter. Owen *et al.* (1965) demonstrated a low activity of cytochrome oxidase in the tissues of the goats.

Comment

The ataxia and defects in myelin in the CNS of swayback
lambs has aroused considerable interest among medical pathologists. The cerebral lesions have been likened to Schilder's disease,

and there was thought to be an association with multiple sclerosis, though this now appears to be unlikely (Campbell, 1963). The cerebral lesions closely resemble cavities found in the brains of some human infants and are probably anoxic in origin. The lesion in the white matter of the spinal cord may have several components. There is a localized lack of myelin as well as evidence of demyelination in older lambs, and it has been suggested that there may be some degree of dysmyelination (Howell, Davison, and Oxberry, 1969). The changes occur in long tracts, and the dorso-lateral component may represent the spinocerebellar tract. Cancilla and Barlow (1968b) have reported a primary axon defect, and in this abnormal biochemical environment long nerve cells may be metabolically unstable. Many interesting facts of abnormal myelination may arise from further study of swayback, and an investigation of the development of the lesion *in utero* would probably be most rewarding.

LIPID DYSTROPHIES

A small number of publications have described syndromes in domestic animals which are similar to the infantile lipodystrophies in man. These syndromes could prove to be a most useful experimental model for the study of disease processes, particularly as it is possible to produce some of the conditions by selective mating (Hirth and Nielsen, 1967; McGrath, personal communication).

Dogs

Globoid Cell Leukodystrophy (Krabbe Type)

Ten cases of a globoid cell leukodystrophy have been reported (Fankhauser, Luginbühl, and Hartley, 1963; Fletcher, Kurtz, and Low, 1966; Hirth and Nielsen, 1967). Lesions were confined to the CNS in which macroscopic examination showed some areas of white matter to be slightly grey. Histologically there was a diffuse demyelination with prominent collections of globoid cells, most of which were in the perivascular spaces. The cells had a vacuolated, finely granular cytoplasm which stained pink with the periodic acid — Schiff (PAS) reaction and was neither sudanophilic nor metachromatic when stained with toluidine blue. The lesions were present throughout the brain and spinal cord, and in the latter the peripheral white matter was most severely involved. Peripheral nerves did not appear to be affected.

Seven of the ten cases were in cairn terriers. In the cases reported by Fletcher *et al.* (1966) the grandsire of one case was the sire of the second case, which was the product of a brother-sister mating. The three cases described by Hirth and Nielsen (1967) were from three litters out of the same dam, with father and son as sires. The pedigree of both parents revealed a common ancestral relationship which was several generations removed. These authors note that the condition in the dog may be a useful experimental model and record that "in our first and only attempt at producing an affected dog by a selected mating, we were successful in obtaining one affected puppy out of a litter of three."

Amaurotic Familial Idiocy

A syndrome of blindness and incoordination has been described in English setters (Hagen, 1953; Koppang, 1960, 1962, 1965, 1966; Diezel, Koppang, and Rossner, 1965; Koppang and Rossner, 1965), in a fox terrier cross cocker spaniel (Ribelin and Kintner, 1956), in two cocker spaniels (Fankhauser, 1965), and in German short-hair pointers (Karbe and Schiefer, 1967; Mc-Grath, Kelly, and Steinberg, 1967). The clinical and pathological pictures in these dogs were similar and resemble the changes seen in amaurotic familial idiocy in man.

Grossly, apart from slight leptomeningeal edema, the CNS appeared to be normal. Histologically changes in nerve cell bodies were conspicuous (Fig. 5-9) and were distributed throughout the brain, spinal cord, and ganglion cells of the retina. The most severe lesions appeared to be in the cerebellum. Deposits of eosinophilic globules of varying size were present in many neurons and some of them were degenerating. The deposit was sudanophilic, PAS positive, stained as for myelin with the Loyez- and Luxol-fast blue stains, and was not birefringent or fluorescent. The enzyme histochemistry and electron microscopy of the lesions have been examined in English setters (Diezel, Koppang, and

Rossner, 1965; Koppang and Rossner, 1965). Ultrastructural
studies of the German short-hair pointers revealed intraneuronal
membranous bodies 0.5μ to 5.0μ in diameter composed of trilami-

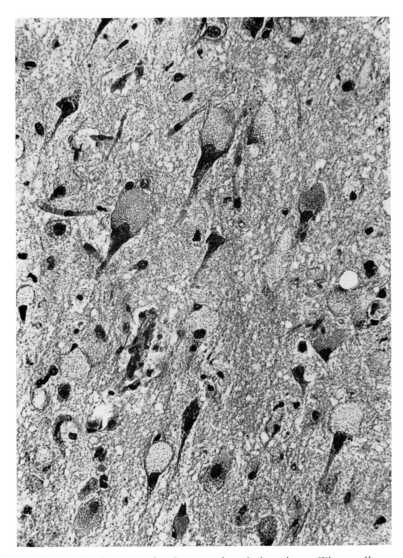

FIGURE 5-9. Cerebral cortex of a German short-hair pointer. The swollen neurons contain a granular material. Stained with cresyl violet. (By courtesy of
Dr. J. T. McGrath.)

nar membranes 50 to 60 Å thick with a periodicity of 48 to 58 Å at points of membrane fusion (Fig. 5-10) (McGrath, Kelly, and Steinberg, 1967). Demyelination does not seem to be a feature of the disease.

Cattle

Pseudolipidosis

Whittem and Walker (1957), Whittem (1962), and Hore (1963) described a neurological syndrome in Aberdeen Angus calves in Australia. The animals showed progressive incoordination and paralysis. Damaged neurons were present throughout the CNS, and in one case they were also seen in the retina. The neurons were swollen and vacuolated. Foamy macrophages were present in lymph nodes. The stored material was not identified and the condition was called pseudolipidosis.

Reticular Histiocytosis

This condition was reported in a bull by Payne, Stevens, and Sautter (1963). The lymph nodes, bone marrow, and spleen were involved, but the CNS was normal. The authors thought the lesions bore some resemblance to Gaucher's disease.

Snorter Dwarf Cattle

An inherited disorder of mucopolysaccharide metabolism has been described in cattle (see Lorinez, 1961). The snorter dwarf cattle have vacuolated cells in brain, liver, and spleen. The condition appears to be similar to Hurler's disease.

Pigs

Tay-Sachs Disease

Read and Bridges (1968) described a cerebrospinal lipodystrophy in two male pigs. Granular, foamy neurons were present throughout the CNS (Fig. 5-11). The stored material was osmiophilic and stained with Luxol-fast blue. Under the electron microscope the interneuronal structures appeared as laminated membranous cytoplasmic bodies which resembled those seen in Tay-Sachs disease (Fig. 5-12).

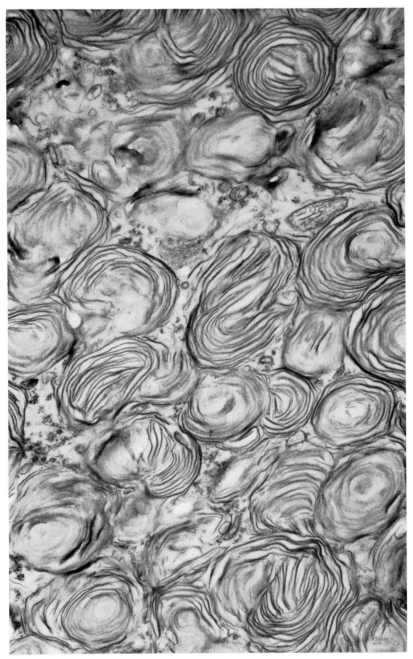

FIGURE 5-10. Electron photomicrograph of the membranous bodies present in the neurons shown in Figure 5-12. X27,500. (By courtesy of Dr. J. T. McGrath.)

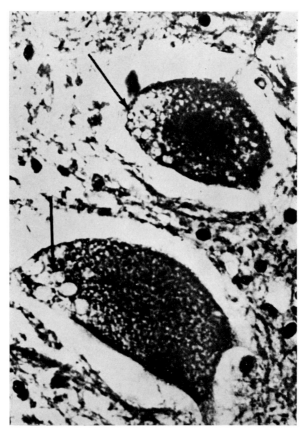

FIGURE 5-11. Neurons from a pig with lipodystrophy. Vacuoles in peripheral cytoplasm (arrow). Hematoxylin and eosin. X1,175. (By courtesy of Dr. W. K. Read and *Pathologia Veterinaria (Basel)*.

Mink

Metachromatic leukodystrophy

A syndrome resembling late infantile, familial, metachromatic leukodystrophy has been described in mink from Denmark (Brander and Palludan, 1965; Christensen and Palludan, 1965; Andersen, 1967; Andersen and Palludan, 1968). Signs of tremor, incoordination, and paralysis were first seen when the kits were between 40 and 120 days old. Degeneration of nerve fibers and oligodendroglial cells was seen throughout the CNS. PAS-positive and metachromatic material was present in the CNS, peripheral nerves, liver, and kidney. There was a marked decrease in cerebrosides and sulphatides in the cerebrum, an apparently normal rate of myelin synthesis, and a destruction of previously formed myelin.

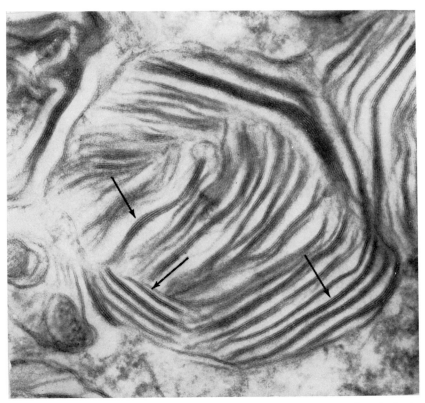

FIGURE 5-12. Electron photomicrograph of a membranous cytoplasmic body showing internal arrangement of individual membranes with a regular parallel periodicity (arrows). Uranyl acetate and lead citrate. X150,000. (By courtesy of Dr. W. K. Read and *Pathologia Veterinaria (Basel)*.

Sheep

Hartley and Kater (1962) reported a lipid-like neuronal degeneration and an idiopathic neuronal degeneration in New Zealand sheep. Only brief details were given, but demyelination did not appear to be a feature of either.

CONCLUSION

The sequence and extent of myelination is affected by certain naturally occurring diseases of domesticated animals, the more important of these diseases having been described in this chapter. The defects in myelination may be the result of abnormal nutrition, and metabolic or genetic factors of the type that have been previously demonstrated in man and experimental animals. The work on hypomyelinogenesis congenita in pigs, however, has demonstrated for the first time that a virus infection of the mother during pregnancy will induce a lesion in the myelin of the off-spring. This is a most exciting development and may be of considerable significance.

The lesions found in swayback lambs have aroused considerable interest among comparative pathologists since they were first described by Innes and Shearer in 1940. Initially the interest was centered on the cerebral lesions, which were compared to those found in children whose brains were damaged before or at birth (Mackay, 1940; Winkelman and Moore, 1942). More recently work has been concentrated upon the spinal cord changes, and the lesion in the white matter of the cord may have amyelinating, demyelinating and dysmyelinating components. Copper deficiency does not readily affect adult myelin, and swayback is a syndrome produced during the vulnerable period of development of the CNS. In the young animal there may be lesions produced before myelination in the brain and during myelination in the cord, so that it can be clearly seen how the stage of development of the animal at the time of insult influences the type of lesion which is produced.

In domestic animals the lipid dystrophies are clearly manifestations of metabolic defects first demonstrated in man. They can be produced under controlled conditions in the laboratory and would be of great value for studies on pathogenesis and therapy. The relationship between lesions in animals and man is most clearly demonstrated by this group.

Until fairly recently there has been little intensive study of neuropathology in the domesticated animals. Much of the work described in this chapter is of recent origin. Much remains to be done, particularly with regard to electron microscopy and biochemistry. The results of these studies would be of great value to veterinary and human pathologists and would greatly increase our understanding of the fundamental aspects of myelination.

REFERENCES

ADAMS, C. W. M.: A histochemical method for the simultaneous demonstration of normal and degenerating myelin. *J Path Bact, 77:*648, 1959.

ANDERSEN, H. A.: Leucodystrophy in mink. A biochemical study. *Acta Neuropath, 7:*297, 1967.

ANDERSEN, H. A., and PALLUDAN, B.: Leucodystrophy in mink. *Acta Neuropath, 11:*347, 1968.

BARLOW, R. M.: Further observations on swayback. I. Transitional pathology. *J Comp Path, 73:*51, 1963,a.

BARLOW, R. M.: Further observations on swayback. II. Histochemical localisation of cytochrome oxidase activity in the central nervous system. *J Comp Path, 73:*61, 1963,b.

BARLOW, R. M., and DICKINSON, A. G.: On the pathology and histochemistry of the central nervous system in Border disease of sheep. *Res Vet Sci, 6:*230, 1965.

BARLOW, R. M.; PURVES, D.; BULTER, E. J., and MacINTYRE, I. J.: Swayback in southeast Scotland. II. Clinical, pathological and biochemical aspects. *J Comp Path, 70:*411, 1960.

BARLOW, R. M.; ROBERTSON, J. M.; OWEN, E. C., and PROUDFOOT, R.: A condition in the goat resembling swayback in lambs. *Vet Rec, 74:*737, 1962.

BARR, M.: Hypomyelinogenesis congenita in lambs. *Vet Rec, 76:* 815, 1964.

BEHRENS, H., and SCHULZ, L. A.: Swayback (enzöotische Ataxie) der Schaflammer. *Deutsch Tieraerztl Wschr, 66:*502, 529, 1959.

BRANDER, N. R., and PALLUDAN, B.: Leucoencephalopathy in mink. *Acta Vet Scand, 6:*41, 1965.

CAMPBELL, A. M. G.: Veterinary workers and disseminated sclerosis. *J Neurol Neurosurg Psychiat, 26:*514, 1963.

CANCILLIA, P. A., and BARLOW, R. M.: Structural changes of central nervous system in swayback (enzootic ataxia) of lambs. III. Electron microscopy of the cerebral lesions. *Acta Neuropath, 6:*260, 1966.

CANCILLA, P. A., and BARLOW, R. M.: An electron microscopic study of the spinal cord in Border disease of lambs. *Res Vet Sci, 9*:88, 1968a.

CANCILLA, P. A., and BARLOW, R. M.: Structural changes in the central nervous system in swayback (enzootic ataxia) of lambs. IV. Electron microscopy of the white matter of the spinal cord. *Acta Neuropath, 11*:294, 1968b.

CHRISTENSEN, E., and CHRISTENSEN, N. O.: Studies on 'Trembling in New-born Pigs'. *Nord Vet Med, 8*:921, 1956.

CHRISTENSEN, E., and PALLUDAN, B.: Late infantile familial metachromatic leucodystrophy in minks. *Acta Neuropath, 4*:640, 1965.

CLARKE, D. B., and ANDERSON, G. W.: Correlation of complications of labour with lesions in the brains of neonates. *J Neuropath Exp Neurol, 20*:265, 1961.

CORDY, D. R., and SHULTZ, G.: Congenital subcortical encephalopathies in lambs. *J Neuropath Exp Neurol, 20*:554, 1961.

COURVILLE, C. B.: Antenatal and paranatal circulatory disorders as a cause of cerebral damage in early life. *J Neuropath Exp Neurol, 18*: 115, 1959.

CROME, L., and PARE, C. M. B.: Phenylketonuria: A review and a report of the pathological findings in four cases. *J Ment Sci, 196*:862, 1960.

DARCEL, C. LE Q.; AVERY, R. J., and BAINBOROUGH, A. R.: Congenital trembling in lambs. *Canad J Comp Med, 25*:132, 1961.

DAVISON, A. N., and OXBERRY, J. M.: A comparison of the composition of white matter lipids in swayback and Border disease of lambs. *Res Vet Sci, 7*:67, 1966.

DICKINSON, A. G., and BARLOW, R. M.: The demonstration of the transmissibility of Border disease of sheep. *Vet Rec, 81*:114, 1967.

DIEZEL, P. B.; KOPPANG, N., and ROSSNER, J. A.: Fermenthistochemische und electronenmikroskopische Untersuchungen an der juvenilen amaurotischen idiotie des Hundes. *Deutsch Z Nervenheilk, 187*:720, 1965.

DONE, J. T.: Congenital nervous diseases of pigs: A review. *Lab Anim, 2*:207, 1968.

DONE, J. T., and HARDING, J. D. J.: Kongenitaler Tremor der Schweine (Zitterkrankheit der Ferkel): Verandergungen und Ursachen. *Deutsch Tieraerztl Wschr, 13*:333, 1967.

EMERSON, J. L., and DELEZ, A. L.: Cerebellar hypoplasia, hypomyelinogenesis, and congenital tremors of pigs, associated with prenatal hog cholera vaccination of sows. *J Amer Vet Med Ass, 147:* 47, 1965.

FANKHAUSER, VON R.: Degenerative, lipoidiotische Erkrankung des Zentralnervensystems bei zwei Hunden. *Schweiz Arch Tierheilk, 107:*73, 1965.

FANKHAUSER, VON R.; LUGINBÜHL, H., and HARTLEY, W. J.: Leukodystrophie vom Typus Krabbe beim Hund. *Schweiz Arch Tierheilk, 105:*198, 1963.

FLETCHER, T. F.; KURTZ, H. J., and LOW, D. G.: Globoid cell leukodystrophy (Krabbe type) in the dog. *J Amer Vet Med Ass, 149:*165, 1966.

FLORIO, R.; FLACHAT, C.; COTTEREAU, P.; FLOCHON, G.; FEDIDA, M., and SAINT-CYR, R.: Sur la 'maladie des tremblements' du porcelet. *Rev Med Vet, 107:*209, 1956.

GALLAGHER, C. H.: The pathology and biochemistry of copper deficiency. *Austr Vet J, 33:*311, 1957.

GALLAGHER, C. H.: *Nutritional Factors and Enzymological Disturbances in Animals.* London, Crosby Lockwood, 1964.

GALLAGHER, C. H.; JUDAH, J. D., and REES, K. R.: The biochemistry of copper deficiency. I. Enzymological disturbances, blood chemistry and excretion of amino acids. *Proc Roy Soc B, 145:*134, 1956.

GALLAGHER, C. H.; JUDAH, J. D., and REES, K. R.: The biochemistry of copper deficiency. II Synthetic processes. *Proc Roy Soc B, 145:* 195, 1956.

GITTER, M., and BOWEN, P. D. G.: Unusual cerebellar conditions in pigs. Part II. Cerebellar hypoplasia in Pigs. *Vet Rec, 74:*1152, 1962.

HAGEN, L. O.: Lipid dystrophic changes in the central nervous system in dogs. *Acta Path Microbiol Scand, 33:*22, 1953.

HARDING, J. D. J.; DONE, J. T., and DARBYSHIRE, J. H.: Congenital tremors in piglets and their relation to swine fever. *Vet Rec, 79:* 388, 1966.

HARTLEY, W. J., and KATER, J. C.: Observations on diseases of the central nervous system of sheep in New Zealand. *New Zealand Vet J, 10:*128, 1962.

HEDGER, R. S.; HOWARD, D. A., and BURDIN, M. L.: The occurrence in goats and sheep in Kenya of a disease closely similar to swayback. *Vet Rec, 76:*493, 1964.

HIRTH, R. S., and NIELSEN, S. W.: A familial canine globoid cell leukodystrophy ('Krabbe type') . *J Small Anim Pract, 8:*569, 1967.

Hore, D. E.: Pseudolipidosis in Aberdeen Angus calves. *Vict Vet Proc, 21:22,* 1963.

Howell, J. McC.: Observations on the histology and possible pathogenesis of lesions in the central nervous system of sheep with swayback. *Proc Nutr Soc, 27:85,* 1968.

Howell, J. McC.: Nutrition and the nervous system in farm animals. *Wld Rev Nutr Diet, 17,* 1970.

Howell, J. McC., and Davison, A. N.: The copper content and cytochrome oxidase activity of tissues from normal and swayback lambs. *Biochem J, 72:365,* 1959.

Howell, J. McC.; Davison, A. N., and Oxberry, J.: Biochemical and neuropathological changes in swayback. *Res Vet Sci, 5:376,* 1964.

Howell, J. McC.; Davison, A. N., and Oxberry, J.: Observations on the lesions in the white matter of the spinal cord of swayback sheep. *Acta Neuropath, 12:33,* 1969.

Hughes, L. E.; Kershaw, G. F., and Shaw, I. G.: 'B' or Border disease. *Vet Rec, 71:313,* 1959.

Hulland, T. J.: Cerebellar ataxia in calves. *Canad J Comp Med, 21:* 72, 1957.

Hupka, E., and Horn, M.: Beitrag zur Ätiologie des Zitterkrampfer der Saugferkel. *Deutsch Tieraerztl Wschr, 63:422,* 1956.

Innes, J. R. M., and Saunders, L. Z.: *Comparative Neuropathology.* London, Academic, 1962.

Innes, J. R. M., and Shearer, G. D.: Swayback, a demyelinating disease of lambs with affinities to Schilder's encephalitis in man. *J Comp Path, 53:1,* 1940.

Jervis, G. A.: In Lyman, F. L. (Ed.) : *Phenylketonuria.* Springfield, Thomas, 1963, p. 96.

Joyce, J. M.: Posterior paralysis in pigs. *New Zeald Vet J, 3:157,* 1955.

Karbe, E., and Schiefer, B.: Familial amaurotic idiocy in male German short-hair pointers. *Path Vet, 4:223,* 1967.

Kinsley, A. T.: Dancing pigs? *Vet Med, 17:123,* 1922.

Koppang, N.: Lipodystrofi i sentralnervesystemet hos hund (Tay-Sachs-lignende sykdom) . *Nord Med, 63:821,* 1960.

Koppang, N.: Lipodystrophia cerebri hos engelsksettere. *Proc 9 Nordic Vet Congr (Copenhagen), 2:862,* 1962.

Koppang, N.: Juvenile amaurotic idiocy by English Setter in Norway. *Acta Path Microbiol Scand, 64:158,* 1965.

Koppang, N.: Familiäre Glykosphingolipoidoses des Hundes (juvenile amaurotische Idiotie) . *Ergebn All Path, 47:1,* 1966.

KOPPANG, N., and ROSSNER, J. A.: Histochemische und electronenmikroskopische untersuchungen an der Juvenilen amaurotischen Idiotie des Hundes. *Fifth Int Congr Neuropath Zürich, 131*:1965.

KRAMER, W.: Multilocular encephalomalacia. *J Neurol Neurosurg Psychiat, 19*:209, 1956.

LEWIS, G.; TERLECKI, S., and ALLCROFT, R.: The occurrence of swayback in the lambs of ewes fed a semi-purified diet of low copper content. *Vet Rec, 81*:415, 1967.

LORINEZ, A. E.: Heritable disorders of acid mucopolysaccharide metabolism in human and in snorter dwarf cattle. *Ann NY Acad Sci, 91*:644, 1961.

MACKAY, R. P.: Congenital demyelinating encephalopathy. *Arch Neurol Psychiat, 43*:111, 1940.

MARKSON, L. M.; TERLECKI, S.; SHAND, A.; SELLERS, K. C., and WOODS, A. J.: Hypomyelinogenesis congenita in sheep. *Vet Rec, 71*:269, 1959.

McGAVIN, M. D.; RANBY, P. D., and TAMMEMAGI, L.: Demyelination associated with low liver copper levels in pigs. *Austr Vet J, 38*:8, 1962.

McGRATH, J. T.; KELLY, A. M., and STEINBERG, S. A.: Cerebral lipidosis in the dog. *Forty-third Annual Meeting of Amer Ass Neuropath,* 1967.

MILLS, C. F., and WILLIAMS, R. B.: Copper concentration and cytochrome oxidase and ribonuclease activities in the brains of copper-deficient lambs. *Biochem J, 85*:629, 1962.

MUNDAY, B. L.: Diseases of the central nervous system of pigs in Tasmania. *Austr Vet J, 43*:374, 1967.

NOTT, J. A., and SHAW, I. G.: Border disease in sheep — its effect on fertility, viability and wool. *Vet Rec, 80*:534, 1967.

O'HARA, P. J., and SHORTRIDGE, E. H.: Some diseases of the porcine central nervous system. *New Zeald Vet J, 14*:1, 1966.

OWEN, E. C.; PROUDFOOT, R.; ROBERTSON, J. M.; BARLOW, R. M.; BUTLER, E. J., and SMITH, B. W. S.: Pathological and biochemical studies of an outbreak of swayback in goats. *J Comp Path, 75*:241, 1965.

PAYNE, B. J.; STEVENS, J. B., and SAUTTER, J. H.: Reticular histiocytosis in a bull. *J Amer Vet Med Ass, 143*:734, 1963.

POBISCH, A.: Beitrag zur Ätiologie der 'Zitterkrankheit.' *Wien Tieraerztl Wschr, 48*:162, 1961.

READ, W. K., and BRIDGES, C. H.: Cerebrospinal lipodystrophy in

Swine. A new disease model in comparative pathology. *Path Vet, 5:* 67, 1968.

RIBELIN, W. E., and KINTNER, L. D.: Lipodystrophy of the central nervous system in a dog. A disease with similarities to Tay-Sachs disease of man. *Cornell Vet, 46:*532, 1956.

RICHTER, R. B.: Infantile subacute necrotizing encephalopathy with predilection for the brain stem. *J Neuropath, 16:*281, 1957.

SAUNDERS, L. Z.; SWEET, J. D.; MARTIN, S. M.; FOX, F. H., and FINCHET, M. G.: Hereditary congenital ataxia in Jersey calves. *Cornell Vet, 42:*559, 1952.

SCHULZ, K. C. A.; MERWE VAN DER P. K.; RENSBURG, VAN P. J. J., and SWART, J. S.: Studies in demyelinating disease of sheep associated with copper deficiency. *Onderstepoort J Vet Res, 25:*35, 1951.

SCHULZ, L. A., and BEHRENS, H.: Beitrag zur Pathogenese der Kupfer-mangelencephalopathie des Schalflammes (swayback). *Beitr Path Anat, 122:*282, 1960.

SCHWEDENBERG, T. H.: Leukoencephalopathy following carbon monoxide asphyxia. *J Neuropath Exp Neurol, 18:*597, 1959.

SHAW, I. G.; WINKLER, C. E., and TERLECKI, S.: Experimental reproduction of hypomyelinogenesis congenita of lambs. *Vet Rec, 81:* 115, 1967.

SPAIS, A.; PALSSON, P. A., and BOGAERT, VAN L.: Pathology of enzootic ataxia of lambs. *Acta Neuropath, 1:*56, 1961.

STROMBERG, M. W., and KITCHELL, R. L.: Studies on Myoclonia congenita. 1. Review of literature and field investigations; *Amer J Vet Res, 19:*377, 1958.

UNDERWOOD, E. J.: *Trace Elements in Animal Nutrition.* London, Academic, 1962.

WHITTEM, J. H.: Pseudolipidosis in calves. *Acta Neuropath (Suppl), 1:* 94, 1962.

WHITTEM, J. H., and WALKER, D.: 'Neuronopathy' and 'pseudolipidosis' in Aberdeen Angus calves. *J Path Bact, 74:*281, 1957.

WILKIE, W. J.: Mineral deficiencies in pigs. *Austr Vet J, 35:*209, 1959.

WINKELMAN, N. W., and MOORE, M. T.: Progressive degenerative encephalopathy. Occurrence in infancy with antenatal onset simulating swayback in lambs. *Arch Neurol Psychiat, 48:*54, 1942.

YOUNG, S.: Hypomyelinogenesis congenita (cerebellar ataxia) in Angus-shorthorn calves. *Cornell Vet, 52:*84, 1962.

YOUNG, S., and CORDY, D. R.: An ovine foetal encephalopathy caused by bluetongue vaccine virus. *J Neuropath Exp Neurol, 23:*635, 1964.

POSTSCRIPT

NEUROANATOMISTS HAVE LONG been interested in myelination and have studied aspects such as the chronological order of myelin formation in different tracts of the brain and spinal cord as well as the manner in which myelin is formed. To the earlier investigators it must have seemed that myelination was an inexplicable process by which a fatty sheath was deposited around certain axons, but electron microscopy has revealed that the process is an exquisitely organized one in which layers of the plasma membrane of the myelin-forming cell are spiraled around an axon. At present, however, we know almost nothing about how this spiral is formed. It clearly involves a very active elaboration of plasma membrane, and for peripheral nerves there is a general concensus of opinion that the spiral is produced through a rotation of the Schwann cell around the axis of the enclosed axon. It should be noted, however, that the concept is based on little solid evidence beyond observations of movements of Schwann cell nuclei in tissue cultures. The mechanics leading to the formation of the spiral of lamellae in central myelin sheaths is a complete mystery. In the central nervous system the oligodendrocytes seem capable of forming more than one length of myelin, so that even the production of a spiral wrapping by rotation of the perikaryon seems to be precluded. Perhaps the answer to this fundamental aspect of how myelin forms is just around the corner, but at present morphologists have either not seen the critical electron microscope section or have failed to properly interpret the clues presented to them.

From the evidence which is accumulating, it seems likely that the early myelin is different from that of the adult. This is reflected not only by the difference in the packing of the lamellae observed in electron micrographs but also by their different compositions. It has been suggested that early central myelin is composed of unchanged neuroglial plasma membrane which is

229

converted to mature myelin by the incorporation of cerebroside. If this is so, then such a transition in the composition of myelin might be expected to be sensitive to the metabolism of the animal. For example, it might be affected by and sensitive to malnutrition and amino acid or hormonal imbalance. Quantitative studies on the response of early myelin composition to various experimental alterations in metabolic conditions would be of great interest in shedding light upon this point.

Recent work on laboratory animals and children has demonstrated that myelination can be inhibited by a variety of conditions. Among these are phenylketonuria, hypothyroidism, and malnutrition. In each of these conditions a marked intellectual deficiency is also frequently present. It does not seem likely that the amyelination in these conditions is the direct cause of the intellectual deficiency, but it may be a contributing factor and also a readily recognizable facet of a general response of the brain. Something of this may be reflected by work such as that of Bornstein (1969), who has been able to isolate two factors from the blood of patients with multiple sclerosis. One factor causes slow demyelination of the axons in tissue cultures, and the other factor causes an immediate blocking of the transmission of nervous impulses. Another example is found in the work of Balazs and his colleagues (1968). They have studied the biochemistry of the hypothyroid brain, and in addition to finding a reduced deposition of myelin, they have evidence for the retardation of various other biochemical systems. For example, the pathway for the conversion of glusose to dicarboxylic amino acid develops more slowly in the cretinous rat, and the formation of synapses also appears to be delayed.

It is hoped that this short book on myelin and its development may serve both as a basis and a stimulus for further investigations of this fascinating substance. We need to know much more about myelin and perhaps most particularly about its pathology, both from a biochemical and a morphological standpoint. Much of the information might be sought by using domestic animals as experimental models for neurological conditions in man. This readily accessible reservoir of material has hardly yet been tapped.

REFERENCES

BALÁZS, R.; KOVÁCS, S.; TEICHGRABER, P.; COCKS, W. A., and EAYRS, J. T.: Biochemical effects of thyroid deficiency on the developing brain. *J Neurochem, 15:*1335, 1968.

BORNSTEIN, M. B.: Immunological factors in experimental allergic encephalomyelitis and multiple sclerosis as revealed by cultures of mammalian nerve tissue. *J Neurol Neurosurg Psychiat,* 1969, In press.

INDEX

A

α-Oxidation, of branched-chain fatty acids, 165
Amaurotic familial idiocy, 216
Amino acids, in bovine myelin, 94
Amyelination, and disease processes, 169, 194, 200, 203
  in leucinosis, 191
  in phenylketonuria, 187
Anoxia, 213, 215
Astrocytes, role in myelination, 51, 120
Ataxia, 207, 214
Autoradiography, 142
Axolemma, 30, 32, 66
Axon, 7, 9
  expansion of, 65
  hillocks, 36
  size of, 25
  size and myelination of, 26

B

Basic protein, 93, 94
  myelin-type, 115
Bipolar neuron, 37
Blood-brain barrier, 126
Bluetongue virus vaccine, 213
Border disease, 169, 203
Brain, development, 184, see also Developing brain
  dry weight of in phenylketonuria, 187
  growth of in different species, 98
  lipids of, 187, see also Brain lipid
  subcellular fractionation, 80
  wet weight, increment of, 99
Brain lipid, increments of, 97, 100, 106
  chemistry of, 85, 88
  composition of in multiple sclerosis, 174
  composition of in phenylketonuria, 187
  composition of in swayback, 210
  histology of in phenylketonuria, 184

heterogeneity of, 80
histology of in phenylketonuria, 188
increment of, 10, 102 et. seq. 186, 206
myelin of, 111

C

Calves, diseases of, 205
Cardiolipin, 91
Cattle, diseases of, 205
Cationic protein, 115
Cavitation, 213
Central nervous system
  fixation of, 38
  structure of, 38
Cerebellum, hypoplasia of, 200
Cerebrum, white matter of, 203
Cerebroside sulfotransferease, 166
Cerebrosides
  accumulation of, 106 et. seq.
  biosynthesis of, 121
  in leucinosis, 191
  long chain fatty acids of, 164
  metabolism of, 132
  myelin content, 90, 97, 101, 106, 113, 185, 192, 193
  sulfate, 166
Chain elongation, 164
Cholesterol, 80, 84, 101, 106, 113, 125, 185
  accumulation, 106 et. seq.
  biosynthesis of, 121
  esters of, 101, 187, 189, 204
  in grey and white matter of, 127
  metabolism, 125
  stability of, 126, 128
Copper deficiency, 169, 209, 222
Corpus callosum, 39, 142
Cyclic nucleotidase, 97, see also Cyclic phosphohydrolase
Cyclic phosphohydrolase (Adenosine 2'3' nucleotide phosphohydrolase),

97, 122
Cytochrome oxidase, 212

D

Dark matrix, 66
7-dehydrocholesterol, 85
Demyelinating diseases, 163
Demyelination, 175, 176, 187
Desmosomes, 30
Desmosterol   (24-dehydrocholesterol) ,
    101
Developing brain, 101
    enzymes in, 116
    glycolipids of in human, 104
    in human, 103
    lipids in, 101, 102, 106
    proteins in, 116
Developing myelin, 7 *et. seq.*, 107, 108
    compositions of, 111, 114
    fatty acids, 108
    low density fraction, 113
    second fraction in, 110
Developing nervous tissue, 97
Developing peripheral nerves, 7
Differential centrifugation, 80
Diphosphoinositides, 89
Dogs, neuropathology of, 216
Domestic   animals,   neuropathology   of,
    199, 228
Dorsal spinocerebellar tract, 209
Dysmyelination, 163

E

EAE, 173, 174, *see also* Experimental
    allergic encephalitis
EEG, 184, 190, 195
Electrophoresis, 95
Encephalopathy, 213
Eng-Smith ratio, 37
Enzyme activity in myelin, 96, 97
Enzootic ataxia, 209
Epliepsy, 190
Ethanolamine   phospholipid,   80,   132,
    see also Phosphatidylethanolamine
Experimental allergic encephalitis, 173
Experimental allergic neuritis, 177
External mesaxon, 17, 41
External tongue process, 41, 59, 64

F

Fatty acid
    chain elongation of, 104
    effects of radiation on, 173
    in developing CNS, 103, 105
    in leucinosis, 191
    long chain, 91, 189
    myelin in, 108, 163
    of optic nerve phosphoglycerides,
        103
    phospholipids, 106
    saturated, 188
    unsaturated in myelin, 163, 188
Fatty acid synthetase, 104
Fibre diameter, 25, 56
Freeze-etched preparations, 61

G

Galactolipids, 80, 84, 85, 86
    precursors of, 104
    see also individual lipids
Galactosyldiglyceride, 101
Gangliosides, 101, 111
    determination of, 85, 87
    in developing brain, 111
Gangliosidoses, 183
Gaucher's disease, infantile, 164
Gelatinous softening, 209
Genetic factors, 203
Gitter cell, 203, 206, 210
Glia, connections, 48
    morphological character, 48
    myelin segments, 53
    role of, 172
Glia to myelin
    connections in adult, 48, 50
    connections in young, 39, 46, 50, 51
Glial cells, 100, 115
    nuceli of, 54
    plasma membrane of, 113, 134
Glial lipids, 114
Glial proliferation, radiation effects, 172
Glioblasts, 119, 120
Gliosis, 200
Globoid cell leucodystrophy, 164, 215
Globoid cells, 215
Glycolipids, in human developing brain,
    104

in leucinosis, 193
in phenylketonuria, 185
Goats, neuropathology of, 214
Grey matter, metabolism of, 123, 127

H
Histones, 117
Hurler's disease, 218
Hyperphenylalaninaemia, 184
Hypomyelinogenesis congenita, 199, 203, 205, 206
Hypothroidism, 166

I
Inborn errors in metabolism, 164, 165, 170, 183
Incoordination, 203
Inositol phospholipids, 131
Inositol plasmalogen, 101
Internodal length, 25
in different species, 25
in young rabbits, 65
Internal mesaxon, 17, 64
Internodes, 3, 53, 56, 57
Intraperiod line, 5, 17, 36, 37, 57
absence in immature sheath, 22, 41
Irradiation, 172

K
Ketoacid, decarboxylation of, 190
Kwashiorkor, 170

L
Lecithin, 80, *see also* Phosphatidylcholine
Leucinosis, 183, 190
brain chemistry of, 191
morphology of, 191
Leucodystrophy, 164, 174
Lipids, analysis of, 84, 86
biosynthesis of, 106, 125
cellular metabolism of, 125, 140
droplets of, 100
dystrophy, 215
in peripheral nerve, 91
separation of, 86
storage of, 84
synthesis of developing, 120
Lipidosis, 165

Lipogensis, in PNS, 123
Liver plasma membrane, composition of, 90
lipids of, 90
Low phenylalanine diet, 189
Loyez stain, 212, 216
Luxol fast blue stain, 216, 218

M
Macrophage, 218
Major dense line, 17, 41, 57
Maple syrup urine disease, 190, *see also* leucinosis
Marchi positive, 210
Marker enzymes, 112
Melanin, 184
Membrane, of mitochondria, 62
subunit of, 62
ultrastructure of, 62
Mental retardation, *xi*, 170, 183
Mesaxon, 13, 15, 41, *see also* External mesaxon and Internal mesaxon
Metachromatic leucodystrophy, 164, 165, 183, 220
Microtubules, 30, 34, 69
Mink, neuropathology of, 220
Mitochondria, 62, 82, 90
Monosialoganglioside, 110
Morphology of the myelin sheath, 3 *et. seq.*
Multiple sclerosis, 164, 173
Myelin
adult composition of, 80, 84
adult in, 163
adult lipids of, 84
aminopeptidases, 96
central, 6
cholesterol, 89, 90, 126
compact, 37
composition of in human, 89
composition of in ox brain, 89
composition of in peripheral nerve, 89
composition of in rat, 89, 90
dark radial lines in, 63
degeneration of, 173, 203
developing, 107
development of, *see* Developing myelin
differences in CNS and PNS, 59

dry weight of, 89
"early," 107, 122, 138
elongation of, 52
emergent fibres of, 13
enzyme activity of, 96, 97
enzymes of, 96, 117
ethanolamine incorporation in, 132
fixation of, 4, 6
formation of in CNS, 39, 43
formation of in PNS, *ix*, 12
forming cells, 46
ganglion cells, 34
gangliosides of, during development, 111
globular structure of, 62
"heavy," 81
in human, 89
in ox, 89
in rat, 89
in species various, *ix*, 57, 89
in squirrel money, 82
instability, 163
isolation in peripheral nerve, 82
isolation of, 80, 82
lanthanum penetration of, 23
leucinosis in, 194
"light," 81
lipid metabolism of, 120, 130
lipids in leucinosis, 193
longtitudonal, 46
"loose," 36, 37, 113
mature, 2, 57
mechanism of formation, 19, 51
metabolic stability of, 125, 166
metabolism of, 125
molecular errors in, 163
molecular structure of, 5, 7, 62
periodicity of, 59
peripheral, 6, 124
physical instability of, 163
protein, 91
protein metabolism of, 138
protein metabolism of, in brain areas, 139
proteinases of, 96
proteins of in brain, 93, 94
proteins of in sciatic nerve, 93
proteolipid increases in, 117
purity of, 83

radial component of, 63
radiation effects of, 172
reticular structure of, 4
role of, 143
segments, lengths of, 65
slippage, 13, 28
staining for electron microscopy, 24
storage of, 81
synthesis of, 7 *et. seq.*, 97
timing, 99
tongue, 41
turnover of lipids in, 137
ultrastructure of, 4, 23
Myelin sheath, redundant, 53
Myelination, 100, 106
    deposition of, 100
    glial, 101
    hormone control of, 115
    lipid changes in, 106
    morphology and development, 3-79
    peripheral nerve, 229

N

Necrosis, 204, 210
Nerve remyelination, 26
Nerve roots, 82, 210
Nervous tissue, storage of, 82
Neural crest, 7
Neurodysgenesis, 213
Neuroglial cells, 4, 46
    perikaryon, 46
Neurokeratin, 4, 91
Neuronal lipids, 114
Neurone, 111, 115
Neuropathology, species various, 199
    et. seq.
Neuropil, 142
Neurotransmitters, 195
Niemann-Pick disease, 164
Nodal axon, 69
Node, identification of, 54
Node of Ranvier, *ix*, 3, 27
    in CNS, 65
    in PNS, 27
Nucleic acid, 83

O

Oligodendrocytes, 46, 120
    and myelin internodes, 56

Oligodendrocytic nucleus, length of 56
Oligodendroglial enzyme activity, 118
Oligodendroglial plasma membrane, 142
Opisthotonos, 190, 206
Optic nerve, in kitten, 103, 118
   in rat, 39, 43
Organophosphorus compounds, 174
Osmic acid, 3
Osmium-staining, 203
Osmophilic lipid, 203
O.T.A.N., 210
Outer loop, 41
Oxidative enzyme activity, 118, 119

P

Paralysis, 214
Paranodal region, 28, 32
Paranodoal cytoplasm, 28
Paranode, 28, 66
Pelizaeus-Merzbacher disease, 164
Pentose phosphate pathway (pentose shunt), 119, 120
Periodic acid schiff (P.A.S.), 216, 220
Peripheral nerve, development of, 7 *et. seq.*
   fatty acids in, 105
   growth in, 13
   isolation of myelin in, see Myelin, 82
   lipid metabolism of, 132, 133
   metabolism of, 124, 125
   myelination of, 7, 13, 229,, see also Myelination
   myelination of, in human, 10
   protein metabolism of, 140
Perivascular edema, 213
Phenylketonuria, 199
   brain composition in, 166, 170, 183, 186
   brain histology, 187
Phosphatidic acid, 89, 101, 131
Phosphatidylcholine (Lecithin), 80, 89, 91, 101
Phosphatidylethanolamine, 80, 89, 101
Phosphatidylserine, 80, 89, 91
Phospholipids, 84, 106
   biosynthesis of, 121
   metabolism of, 127, 129, 138
   rapid turnover of, 131
   synthesis of, 121

Phrenic nerve, in rat, 10
Phytanic acid, 164
Pigs, neuropathology of, 200, 218
Plasma membrane, 6, 15, 24, 36, 90
Polyphosphoinositides, 91, 101, *see also* Triphosphoinositides
Pregnancy, 203, 205, 213, 222
Protein, acidic, 116
   basic myelin-type, 93, 95
   cationic, 115
   encephalitogenic, 117
   in malnutrition, 166
   in myelin, 91
   in rat brain, 138 ,139
   in rat sciatic nerve, 141
   S-100 localization of, 116
   synthesis of in development, 120
Proteolipid, 80, 92, 97, 117
   biosynthesis of, 122
   distribution of, 92, 93
   in leucinosis, 193
   metabolism of, 138
   separation of, 92
Pseudolipidosis, 218
Puncta adhaerentia, 34

Q

Quaking mouse syndrome, 170

R

Radial components, 63, 64
Refsum's syndrome, 164
Remyelination, 39, 50
Reticular histiocytosis, 218
Retina, 216
RNA
   in axons, 122
   in myelin, 122
   redundant myelin sheaths, 53

S

Saltatory conduction, 32
Satellite cell, 115
Sciatic nerve, of mice, 25
   proteins of, 89, 140
Schilder's disease, 189
Schmidt-Lantermann clefts, 17, 33, 64
Schwann cell, *ix,* 37, 229
   cytoplasm of, 23

division of, 8
membrane subunit, 115
migration of, 7
mitosis of, 10
movement of, 19
nuceli of, 4, 17
rotation of, 21, 51
Seizures, 190
Serine phospholipid, 80, *see also* Phosphatidylserine
Shaker lamb, 203
Sheep, diseases of, 203, 221
Silver impregnation, 3
Smith-Eng ratio, 136
Snorter dwarf cattle, diseases of, 218
Sphingolipids, fatty acids, 91
Sphingomyelin, 80, 91, 101, 185, 193
  metabolism of, 129
Spinal cord, 206
Spinal nerve roots, 200
Spiny bracelet, 33
Stable lipids, 136
Sterols, 84
Subcellular fractionation, 80
Sudanophilic lipid, 203
Sulfatase A, deficiency of, 166
Sulfatides, 86, 101, 166, 185, 193
  biosynthesis of, 121
  in leucinosis, 192
  in metachromatic leucodystrophy, 166
  long chain fatty acids of, 164
  metabolism of, 132

metabolism of, in developing brain, 133, 135
metabolism of, in subcellular brain fractions, 134, 135
Swayback, 169, 204, 206, 209
Swine fever, 201, 203
Synaptic membranes, 111

T

Tay-Sach's disease, 183, 218
Tibial nerve, 25
Trembling, 200
Tremor, 200
Triphosphoinositides, 91, 101
Tyrosinase, 184

U

Undernutrition, effect on brain, 169
Unit membrane structure, 62

V

Vagus nerve, 25
Virus infections, 203
Vulnerable period in developing brain, 166, 168

W

White matter, metabolism of in spinal cord, 213

X

X-ray diffraction, 4